FIELD GUIDE TO

# SNAKES

## AND OTHER REPTILES
### OF SOUTHERN AFRICA

To my sons, Robbie, Matthew and Tom, with love.
May we continue to have as much fun in the field.

# FIELD GUIDE TO

# SNAKES

## AND OTHER REPTILES
### OF SOUTHERN AFRICA

BILL BRANCH

RALPH
CURTIS
BOOKS

COVER PHOTOGRAPHS: **Front, left** (top to bottom): Cape cobra/Leonard Hoffmann; Armadillo girdled lizard/Bill Branch; boomslang/Leonard Hoffmann; web-footed gecko/Bill Branch. **Front, centre:** western green snake/Peter Pickford. **Front, right** (top to bottom): shovel-snouted lizard/Leonard Hoffman; striped legless skink/Bill Branch; tent tortoise/Leonard Hoffmann; Nile crocodile/Nigel Dennis. **Spine:** spotted bush snake/Bill Branch. **Back:** western sandveld lizard/Bill Branch.

Ralph Curtis Books Publishing
P.O.Box 349
Sanibel Island
Florida
33957-0349

Library of Congress Catalog Card Number: 98-70012

First published 1988
Second impression 1990
Third impression 1992
Second edition 1994
Second impression 1996
Third Revised edition 1998

Managing editor: Pippa Parker
Editor: Helena Reid
Designer: Dominic Robson
Cover design: Dean Pollard
Maps: Dean Pollard
Proofreader: Wendy Powell
Reproduction by Hirt & Carter Pty (Ltd), Cape Town
Printed and bound by Kyodo Printing Co (S'pore) Pte Ltd

ISBN 0-88359-042-5

# Contents

# Acknowledgements

**First Edition**

It is difficult to acknowledge fully the many friends and colleagues who have made this book possible. First and foremost I extend my tremendous gratitude to Don Broadley (Natural History Museum of Zimbabwe, Bulawayo) and Wulf Haacke (Transvaal Museum, Pretoria), who have patiently nurtured my herpetological education over the last 15 years.

To Rod, Richard and Harold, who have shared fatigue and crushed fingers for the ludicrous pleasure of exposing some small, insignificant 'gem', my thanks for their comradeship. May we share a campfire and a beer, and go frogging again.

More specifically for this book, I thank John Akester, Graham Alexander, Tony Bannister, Hartwig Berger-Dell'mour, Richard Boycott, Don Broadley, John Coates-Palgrave, Atherton de Villiers, Mike Griffin, Wulf Haacke, Leonard Hoffman, George Hughes, Niels Jacobsen, Johan Marais, Chris Mattison, Chris McCartney, Geoff McLachlan, Le Fras Mouton, National Parks Board, C. Schlettwein, Steve Spawls, Chris Stuart and Colin Tilbury, for letting me use their photographs of rare and interesting species (specifically credited on page 389).

Unpublished observations, which helped in many ways to improve the scope and accuracy of the guide, were freely given by Ron Auerbach, Ernst Baard Hartwig Berger-Dell'mour, Don Broadley, Richard Boycott, Atherton de Villiers, Mike Griffin, Wulf Haacke, Niels Jacobsen, Geoff McLachlan, Le Fras Mouton, Steve Spawls and Colin Tilbury. I am greatly in their debt.

Most of the lizard distribution maps in this guide are a result of the diligence and labour of Geoff McLachlan (South African Museum), whose atlas of lizard distributions in southern Africa is as yet unpublished. Similarly, most of the species boundaries for the thick-toed geckos (*Pachydactylus*), a notoriously complicated group, follow those determined by Geoff in his revision (as yet unpublished) of the genus; oversights or unusual interpretations remain my own. Ron Auerbach, Hartwig Berger-Dell'mour, Mike Griffin, Don Broadley and Niels Jacobsen allowed me to incorporate new information from unpublished manuscripts.

Graham Alexander, Orty Bourquin, Harold Braack, Gerald Haagner, Johan Hurter, and all of my colleagues noted above, plus many others I have overlooked, have helped me in obtaining live specimens of rare and wondrous 'beasties' for my chromosomal and hemipenial studies. Forgive me if I also took the opportunity to capture their beauty on film.

I thank the Director and Board of the Port Elizabeth Museum, and my fellows at that enjoyable institution, for making my work so pleasant and worthwhile. Shantal Koch ably prepared most of the illustrations.

To Tracey Hawthorne at Struik, my warm thanks for editing the text. My family has tolerated, and perhaps at times even enjoyed, the endless stream of herpetological oddities (human and otherwise) that have crossed our doorstep. They have also accepted the financial sacrifices of a museum scientist.

Finally, to all my herpetological colleagues, both in South Africa and overseas, I offer this first guide. Darts need dartboards, and I am aware of its limitations. I know their studies will necessitate many changes in future editions.

Bill Branch
Port Elizabeth, 1988

## Second Edition

$\mathcal{T}$he sheer pace of herpetological discovery in southern Africa means that it is impossible for any single worker to keep abreast of the field without the close co-operation of his colleagues. For sharing with me their research findings, often before they have been formally published, I thank Aaron Bauer, Orty Bourquin, Don and Sheila Broadley, Mike Griffin, Wulf Haacke, Niels Jacobsen, Le Fras Mouton, Colin Tilbury, Van Wallach, and Martin Whiting.

Numerous wardens have given me shelter and assistance whilst surveying the protected areas under their charge. Foremost among them I thank Scotty Kyle and family from Kosi Bay, and Harold and Tony Braack, previously in the Richtersveld and now back home in the Kruger National Park. They are models of enthusiasm and stewardship, and my gratitude to Harold, in particular, dwarfs the small gecko now named in his honour.

One joy of herpetology is the goodwill and comradeship that characterize the discipline. It is pleasantly free of the rancour and competition that pervade so many other biological fields. Since 1988 I have been fortunate to collaborate with many fine herpetologists. My abilities as a naturalist and scientist have vastly improved under their guidance, and all have become valued friends.

For letting me use their photographs in the extra plates in this edition, I thank Wulf Haacke, Marius Burger, Greg Rasmussen, Mike Griffin, and Le Fras Mouton.

During my field work I have been fortunate to explore much of the wilderness that covers this beautiful subcontinent. It is the generosity and humour of its people that have ensured my safety and comfort. During these trips I have had many companions, most recently Gerald Haagner, Aaron Bauer, Marias Burger, Craig Weatherby, Alan Channing, Dave Good, Nick Arnold, Rick Shine, Martin Whiting and my sons Robbie, Matthew and Tom. It is their camaraderie and varying skills, that have made these trips so memorable and often successful.

A book is more than text and pictures, it also requires efficient editorial and design teams. With this new edition Pippa Parker, Helena Reid and their colleagues at Struik maintain the high standard set in the earlier editions.

Last, but first, I thank my new wife, Donvé. It is to her nest that my heart and body return for love and nurture after long field trips, and it is her many sacrifices that allow me to indulge this passion. I need, and thank her for her 'potter's touch'.

Bill Branch
Port Elizabeth, 1998

8

# PREFACE TO SECOND EDITION

## EX AFRICA SEMPER ALIQUID NOVI

*I*t is a decade since I prepared the first edition of this field guide, after which I believed, optimistically, that southern African reptile and amphibian 'alpha taxonomy' – the phase of study during which scientists discover new species and the biodiversity of a region is described – was basically complete. The first field guide was published more than 150 years after the inaugural monograph on South Africa's reptiles and amphibians saw the light, and my colleagues and I could therefore be forgiven for thinking that there was little left to be said. The guide covered 397 species. I was cautious, however, and also included photographs of a few 'novelties' that I was aware had still to be described. Now I find my early naivety chastening, for little did I envisage then that those few new taxa comprised just one year's discoveries, and that, ten years later, I would include 83 new species in this revision!

I write having just read a glossy magazine dedicated to birds. It contains a review listing the 46 new bird species discovered in Africa since 1946 – less than one species a year for a whole continent, and only seven species since 1988. Compare this to the discovery of a new reptile species every 44 days in southern Africa alone! Is it any wonder then that one gets frustrated with the lack of attention paid to this treasure trove by provincial conservation bodies, university researchers, and national funding agencies?

This revised edition contains more than just new species accounts. The whole of the text has been reviewed and re-set in order to include new insights, taxonomic changes, and additions to our knowledge of the distributions, biology and breeding of southern African reptiles. Among the taxonomic changes is the separation of the plated lizards (Gerrhosauridae) from the girdled lizards (Cordylidae), and the return of harlequin snakes to the Elapidae.

The many new species included in this revised guide have arisen in different ways. The first group consist of newly discovered species. Most of these have been found in poorly explored regions, such as the Richtersveld or Drakensberg mountains. Some, however, were discovered close to major metropolitan areas – the Cape fold mountains, for instance, and the coastal regions of KwaZulu-Natal. The 14 completely new species include two new snakes, four new skinks, three new girdled lizards, and five new geckos.

The second group comprise what are often termed 'cryptic species', reptiles that were known to scientists but were not recognized for what they were. Many of them were treated as subspecies, or considered synonyms (the same name) of existing species. This group include: two new tortoises, 11 new snakes, five new worm lizards, six new skinks, six new lacertids, 13 new girdled lizards, two new agamas, three new chameleons, and 19 new geckos.

The remaining group of new additions embrace tropical species that are now known to extend into the northern regions of the subcontinent, both in the west into the Kaokoveld of northern Namibia, and in the east along the Mozambique plain. The names of a number of species have changed due to taxonomic revisions in other parts of Africa. Usually these were reptiles whose distribution only just extended to the subcontinent. They are now considered to comprise of a number of 'sibling' species whose southern form required a new name. For example, the Egyptian cobra (*Naja haje*) is now restricted to East and North Africa, and is replaced by the snouted cobra (*N. annulifera*) in the south.

In some cases a species' name remains unchanged, but it does not extend as far north as previously believed. For example, Bibron's gecko (*Pachydactylus bibronii*) is restricted mainly to the Cape and replaced further north by Turner's gecko (*P. turneri*).

Other species have changed their names because they have been reassigned to different genera. Some monotypic genera (for example *Cryptolycus*, *Aporosaura* and *Kaokogecko*) are no longer recognized, while other large genera have been split into a number of smaller ones (for example *Phyllodactylus* into *Afrogecko*, *Goggia* and *Cryptactites*; *Lacerta* into *Australolacerta*; and *Typhlops* into *Rhinotyphlops*).

9

One very rare species, only tentatively included in the first edition and described as a herpetological mystery, has been rediscovered. This reptile, Peringuey's leaf-footed gecko, lives in a few salt marshes on the Eastern Cape coast. It is so unique that it is now placed in its own genus (*Cryptactites peringueyi*).

Four species, known from single type specimens and which have never been rediscovered, have been excluded. All were probably based on specimens from other regions, and their possible true identity is noted in brackets: *Rhoptropus braconnieri* (*R. afer*), *Scelotes bicolor* (*S. arenicolus*), *Melanoseps schebeni* (*M. occidentalis*), and *Latastia kidwelli* (*L. johnstoni*).

The text has been completely reworked and, in addition to the taxonomic changes and updates, includes new information on, for example, range extensions and biology. I have made a note in the Subspecies category when the status of a race has changed. Amendments to provincial boundaries within South Africa (the four provinces became nine after 1994) have necessitated the extensive redescription of species' ranges, and these now place emphasis on geographic regions rather than arbitrary political constructs. The maps have all been reassessed with the inclusion of numerous range extensions (and corrections). To save costs, the original colour plates have been retained but with names amended where necessary. Scientific names have been added – something that will please my scientific colleagues! Sixteen new colour plates have been added to illustrate the new species. Unfortunately, the original formula of displaying similarly coloured species together in order to make identification easier is compromised and users will now have to scan through both colour sections.

Southern Africa is considered to have perhaps the highest reptile diversity in Africa. The lizard fauna is certainly the richest, particularly among geckos, skinks and girdled lizards. The latter may even have evolved originally within the subcontinent. Of the 83 additional species included in this revision, the great majority (61, or 73,5%) are endemic to the subcontinent, and some have known ranges of just a few square kilometres. Their protection becomes an increasingly critical issue, as conservation authorities adjust to new paradigms governing wildlife utilization and general access to conserved areas. In an atmosphere of changing perceptions and priorities, improved education about the region's reptilian riches is vital. Without it these small, mostly harmless yet essential animals will disappear unnoticed. I hope this revision will help, in part, to halt this slow descent into ignorance and neglect.

## PREFACE TO FIRST EDITION

*W*hile this field guide is long overdue, it is also in many ways, premature.

Until now, no book has existed that deals with all the reptiles of southern Africa; a number of texts have dealt with the region's snakes, the most notable being Vivian FitzSimons' monograph (1962), and its scholarly revision by Don Broadley (1983). In addition, a few smaller, popular books have dealt with the more common snakes. The only treatment of our lizards also by Vivian FitzSimons, appeared in the Memoirs of the Transvaal Museum (1943); it has long been out of print, and was always difficult to obtain. Although it remains the scientific base for studies in the region, such have been the advances in our understanding of the subcontinent's lizards that it is now extremely out of date. By 1981, no less than 59% of the lizards of the Cape Province alone had been affected by some form of taxonomic change since FitzSimons' monograph; since then, a further two lizards have been described from the Cape, and others have been discovered or have new names. Changes in the taxonomy of lizards from other parts of the subcontinent are just as extensive. As a result, it became obvious that some form of updated checklist was needed.

Now more than ever before, people are becoming interested in all forms of wildlife, not just large mammals, colourful birds and pretty flowers. If ungainly vultures and thick-skinned rhinos can become conservation 'stars', then surely there is hope that people will begin to take reptiles as seriously. To this end, the public needs an introductory text that will display reptiles in all their diversity and beauty. In southern Africa we have nearly 400 species of reptiles, including the world's richest diversity of land tortoises. More than half of the species are endemic to the subcontinent, while many others occupy most of their range here; if guides for other parts of Africa existed (which they don't), they would still deal with only a fraction of the fauna of southern Africa.

The reason I describe this guide as premature is that we are at present undergoing a renaissance in herpetological studies in southern Africa, and more herpetologists are active in the field and laboratory than ever before. New species, new distributions and new insights have become almost commonplace. I am aware of two new species of leaf-toed gecko (*Phyllodactylus*), four new dwarf chamaeleons (*Bradypodion*), a new Western legless skink (*Typhlacontias*), several new flat lizards (*Platysaurus*), and three new frogs. (A few of these 'novelties' are illustrated on Plate 3.) All are being described at present, and the publication of these descriptions will date this field guide. In addition, Niels Jacobsen's work in the Transvaal, previously thought to be herpetologically well covered, has led to the discovery of numerous new lizard populations that do not fit easily into the current taxonomy. Eventually, this will lead to a greater understanding, but for the moment there is 'chaos' in numerous groups, including the dwarf geckos (*Lygodactylus*), the flat geckos (*Afroedura*), the flat lizards (*Platysaurus*), the crag lizards (*Pseudocordylus*), and Warren's girdled lizard and its relatives (*Cordylus warreni* complex). Anyone collecting specimens in these groups from the Northern Province and Mpumalanga should regard the species accounts in this book as temporary arrangements. However, despite these numerous proposed name changes, the taxonomy of the region's herpetofauna is in a healthy state, particularly when compared with that of the rest of Africa.

Unfortunately, the state of ecological research on reptiles in southern Africa is pitiful; many South African scientists, and Nature Conservation Departments in particular, have had an anti-quated preoccupation with large mammal research, to the neglect of the other groups. Although there are signs that this is changing, there remains an almost total lack of natural history data for our reptiles. Only a handful of detailed lizard ecological studies, plus a couple on tortoises, are available. Nearly all of these have been done by visiting American scientists, who appreciate better the value of small reptiles as models for ecological research. No local snake has ever been studied, although many are venomous and responsible for large numbers of bites (for example the Mozambique spitting cobra, in northern KwaZulu-Natal) while others are endangered and yet acknowledged to be useful in the control of agricultural pests (for example the rock python, in KwaZulu-Natal). The crocodile is the only reptile for which we have more than a superficial knowledge of reproduction, growth, behaviour and habitat.

The following changes, adopted in this guide, have yet to be described in the formal literature:

1. The following, all previously treated as races of more widespread species, are now treated as full species: *Pachydactylus gaiasensis, Pachydactylus labialis, Pachydactylus oculatus, Pachydactylus sansteyni, Scelotes sexlineatus, Cordylus tasmani, Cordylus minor, Cordylus jordani* and *Bitis inornata*.

2. *Homopus bergeri* and *Atractaspis duerdeni* were previously considered to be unusual specimens of more common species, but are now recognized as full species.

3. The following species have recently been discovered in northern Namibia, and are additions to the region's herpetofauna: *Pachydactylus caraculicus, Mabuya chimbana, Cordylus vittifer machadoi* and *Prosymna visseri*. (A few other species are also known to enter the region.)

A similar case could be argued for excluding *Phyllodactylus peringueyi*; this small gecko is generally not considered to be African, but as yet has no other suitable identity. It has eluded all attempts to rediscover its habitat. Until it can be assigned to another species, it must remain provisionally placed in our herpetofauna.

It is my hope that this guide will stimulate naturalists to look more closely at the common and small reptiles that live, largely unnoticed, all around us.

# HOW TO USE THIS BOOK

𝒯his guide provides an easy method of identifying the reptiles found in southern Africa. It is primarily a photographic guide, designed for quick identification by comparison of the reptile with its illustration in the colour plates. The plates do not follow the systematic arrangement of the text, but have instead been arranged according to the reptile's appearance. Note, however, that the revised edition includes an additional 16 colour plates which are not integrated into the main section and must be viewed separately.

All the legless squamates (snakes, amphisbaenians and some lizards) have been placed together, and have been arranged by colour pattern so that all the species that appear similar (for example striped, blotched, green, etc.) are grouped together. The lizard plates (excluding the legless forms) have been grouped by general body shape. For economic and practical reasons it has not been possible to illustrate every reptile species occurring in southern Africa. For some, no photograph exists. A representative of every genus occurring on the subcontinent has been included, and where a species is not illustrated, the reader is referred to a similar species where possible. Although many species have very little colour variation, others occur in such a bewildering array of colour patterns that it is not possible to illustrate all phases. Colour poly-morphism may be linked to sex (adult males are usually more brightly coloured than females), season (some males develop bright colours in the breeding season), age (juveniles may have a different colour and/or pattern from adults), or locality.

When identifying a wild reptile for the first time, take careful note of its general shape. (Does it have legs or a long, smooth tail? Is the body fat and covered with spines? Is there an obvious neck?) Note whether the head, body and tail differ in colour and pattern. Record the habitat in which it is living (Is it on a granite rock face high in mountain grassland, or crawling on a sand dune in the desert?), and the behaviour of the animal. (Did it run up a tree or into a hole in the ground?) Now scan through the photographic plates in the guide. When you find an illustration that is similar to your unknown species, check whether it occurs in the region. If there is a big difference between where you have found it and where it should be, try another picture. If there seems to be no better alternative, match the body shape of the specimen as closely as possible to an illustration in the guide, and read the descriptions of species in the same genus that do occur in the area. You may simply have a colour variant of a common species, such as a striped puff adder (Plate 3), a xanthic brown house snake (Plate 3), or a yellow-throated plated lizard with a blue throat; other unusual specimens may be hybrids, such as a puff adder/Gaboon adder hybrid (Plate 3). Check also that your habitat and biology notes match those of the species. For example, if you think you have found an Austen's gecko, but it was hiding under a rock flake high on a granite outcrop, the chances are that you have misidentified it; Austen's geckos live on the ground in coastal sand dunes. If you cannot match the specimen with anything in the guide, you may have found something new, such as a new species of dwarf chameleon, or at least a new distribution record. Either way, it should be brought to the attention of a herpetologist (see page 388) or a game ranger or teacher, etc. If it is permitted, the specimen may be collected; if not, try to get a good photograph.

The terminology used in the guide has been kept simple. Common words are used rather than their more specific, but often obscure, scientific equivalents, for example 'burrowing' instead of 'fossorial', and 'overlapping' rather than 'imbricate'. However, it is not always possible, or even desirable, to avoid scientific terms, particularly for descriptions of the head scales. The illustrations provided include the scientific terms. The glossary gives simple definitions of technical and scientific terms.

Keys are provided to families and genera. They are designed for local use and may not work elsewhere in Africa. A scientific key is a branching sequence of decisions, presented as alter-natives. Those who are unfamiliar with their use may find the following simple example helpful:

| | |
|---|---|
| 1 - With legs: | go to 2 |
| - Without legs: | go to 3 |

Does the reptile have legs? If so, then go to number 2; if not, then go to number 3. The key is read in this way until the name of a family or genus is reached. Page references are provided for each family or genus.

To avoid repetition, general information common to a number of related species is covered in the introductions to the families and genera. These discuss wider aspects of the distribution and biology of the group, to give a better understanding of the significance and relationships of our local species.

Each species account emphasizes those features that distinguish species within the same genus. However, identifying closely related species may require a good microscope and a working knowledge of scale counting.

There exists no standardized list of common names for the subcontinent's reptiles. Some names have been used regularly in the popular literature and most of these have been maintained. One major change is the use of the more descriptive and traditionally derived name 'burrowing asps' for mole vipers (sometimes also called stiletto snakes).

The following classification of the southern rock python, *Python sebae natalensis*, illustrates the hierarchy of scientific names:

CLASS: Reptilia (Reptiles)
    ORDER: Squamata (Scaled reptiles)
        SUBORDER: Serpentes (Snakes)
            FAMILY: Boidae (Boas and Pythons)
                SUBFAMILY: Pythoninae (Pythons)
                    GENUS: *Python* (Typical pythons)
                        SPECIES: *sebae* (African rock python)
                            SUBSPECIES: *natalensis* (Southern rock python)

For each species, the average and maximum size is given. The latter is the length of the largest specimen recorded locally, and where the sexes differ significantly in maximum size, these are listed separately. Snakes, lizards, amphisbaenians and crocodiles are measured in a straight line along the belly, from the tip of the snout to the lip of the cloacal opening (the snout to vent length, SVL). Where the length of the tail is included, this is the total length (TL) and includes the original tail (untruncated and not regenerated). Only the shells of chelonians are measured. In tortoises and terrapins, the length is taken straight along the midline of the carapace, while sea turtles are measured along the curve of the midline.

The distribution map opposite each species account gives the known range of that particular species in southern Africa. However, these serve only as rough guides; all animals prefer specific habitats to which they are usually restricted within a given geographical area. In addition, our knowledge of species' distributions is very poor, and new range extensions are commonplace. Some maps include isolated records, away from the species' main distribution. Occasionally these have been inadvertently introduced by man. Some are relict populations, survivors of a formerly widespread species, whose range has contracted due to climatic changes or for other reasons. Most, however, probably reflect our ignorance of the intervening gaps, as many regions have been poorly collected.

As much information as possible is given about the biology of a species. Too often field guides simply identify a species without giving any insight into its natural history. Unfortunately, few southern African species have been properly studied and for many only scanty information is available. Where no details are given in a species account, the general information in the generic introduction may help.

'SA RDB' refers to the South African Red Data Book (1988), a national publication that lists those reptiles and amphibians in South Africa that are threatened with extinction. Most seriously threatened are 'endangered' species; these are likely to become extinct within the near future unless urgent steps are taken to protect them and their habitats. 'Vulnerable' species are those that are declining in numbers due to various threats (pollution, habitat destruction, collecting for food or the pet trade, etc.), and will soon become endangered unless action is taken. Species that are classified 'Rare', 'Restricted' or 'Peripheral' may become threatened with extinction because of low population numbers or restricted ranges. To protect threatened species many countries are signatories of CITES (the Convention for International Trade in Endangered Species). This legislation prohibits the movement of endangered species unless special export and import permits are obtained.

The need for and acceptance of subspecies is a controversial concept. Subspecies (races) are populations of a species that are different and geographically restricted. They usually differ in appearance, but other criteria such as their behaviour or their chromosomes, may be used in identification. Where subspecies have been described, they are listed for each species. However, the criteria used to distinguish some of them are both minor and variable, and these poorly defined races may not have general acceptance. They are included only for completeness.

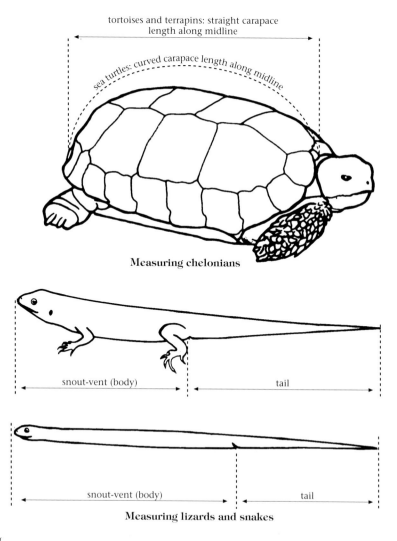

Measuring chelonians

Measuring lizards and snakes

# OBSERVING AND COLLECTING REPTILES

*It* must be stressed at the outset that most reptiles are protected by legislation throughout the subcontinent, and permission must be obtained to collect, transport and possess them. In addition, there is no reason why reptiles cannot be enjoyed in the field as much as birds or mammals; there is no need to collect every specimen. For this reason the index is presented in the form of a checklist, allowing naturalists for the first time to compile a life list. However, it is sometimes necessary to collect specimens, such as for regional surveys or education purposes. The following notes give a few hints.

## HOW TO FIND REPTILES

Since most reptiles are shy, and scurry to safety at the first sign of danger, it takes patience to find them. Knowledge of a species' preferred habitat will save fruitless searching – but search you must, even in prime habitat. The traditional methods are to look under boulders, rotting logs, grass piles, etc. Conservationists are occasionally embarrassed to discover that suburban wasteland with its associated rubbish, is often 'prime habitat' for snakes and lizards; old sheets of corrugated iron make ideal basking sites as they conduct heat, allowing reptiles to warm themselves without being exposed to danger.

Burrowing reptiles can be found by digging in loose soil under boulders and rotting logs, or wind-blown sand at the base of grass tussocks. Many are exposed by farm ploughs or during the construction of new roads. They are often washed downstream when rivers flood. Holes in the ground may act as pit-fall traps and should be investigated closely. Man-made holes are bigger and better than anything found in nature and many interesting specimens, including the first specimens of the dwarf wolf snake, *Lycophidion nanum* (page 78), were found trapped in the trench dug for the Beira-Mutare pipeline. Thousands of reptiles and other animals have been trapped in the new Eastern National Water Carrier in Namibia. Stormwater culverts in most towns also act as traps and should be investigated.

In the cool regions of southern Africa, snakes and lizards often hibernate during winter in old termite nests. Rock-living snakes may also gather in deep rock cracks to avoid winter snows. Many specimens have been collected by smashing open termite nests or dismantling rock out-crops with crowbars. Unfortunately, once flattened, these retreats cannot be used again, and no true conservationist willingly resorts to such destruction.

Do not limit your search to daylight. Nocturnal reptiles often crawl on to tarred roads at night, to absorb the residual heat from the sun-warmed surface. They can be collected by slowly driving on quiet roads on warm evenings (however, the results in southern Africa never seem to approach the success achieved in America). Geckos can be collected around night lights, where they feed on moths and other insects. Chameleons are easier to find at night as they sit in a prominent position and stand out against the dark foliage in the torchlight.

Early in the morning, before the wind blows and obliterates the evidence, the trails of snakes and burrowing legless lizards can be followed in loose sand. This is best done in spring when males are very active, searching for mates. The homes of some lizards can be located by looking for their droppings around rock cracks.

## COLLECTING HINTS

When disturbed, snakes and lizards usually retreat to safety, climbing into trees, deep cracks or holes. A mechanical noose or 'grab-stick' may be used to catch venomous species such as mambas and cobras, which are too alert and dangerous to be grabbed with the unprotected hand. Most lizards are too small and fragile to be collected with grab-sticks, and a noose is more useful. This can be made from thin nylon or cotton, attached to a hollow-fibreglass fishing rod or an extending radio aerial. Many agamas and skinks will let you stalk to within a few metres of them and the noose can be lowered over their head and pulled tight. (Agamas are easy to catch as they have thin necks, but skinks do not, and the noose may slip.) Rock-living lizards, particular-ly cordylids, often retreat into a crack, but can be urged out with wire or, better still, by working a strong nylon noose over their head. A one-metre section of 8-mm copper tubing (for example fuel pipe or old refrigerator cooling tube), threaded with 20-kg fishing line, is ideal. After noosing the lizard, the crack can be gently expanded with a crowbar and the lizard pulled out. There is no need to demolish the whole rock outcrop.

Reptiles in inaccessible spots can sometimes be 'encouraged' to move within range by squirting them with unpleasant fluids, for example chloroform or alcohol (do not use petrol or any other liquid that can cause permanent damage to the reptile's lungs). A water-pistol, loaded with water, can be used to knock geckos from walls and rock faces. Lizards can be stunned with a large elastic band. A range of different sizes can easily be carried and matched to the target. They are hooked on the tip of the thumb, stretched and shot off, just as all schoolboys have done since elastic bands were invented. A variation is to cut long strips from a car inner tube and to 'twang' a strip at a small lizard, while holding one end of the strip. The effective range is reduced to about one metre, but it is more accurate and can be used with more control to stun the victim. Practise on a matchbox first, or you may squash and kill your specimen.

The use of guns and traps is illegal unless special permits are obtained; they should always be used with care and restraint. If specimens are not required alive, they can be killed with 0.22 dust shot. A six- or eight-chamber revolver is best as it is lighter than a rifle. Dust shot is not suitable for a pistol as it does not have sufficient back pressure to eject the spent case. The shot pattern groups at about 30 cm at seven metres (depending on the barrel length) and is sufficient to kill even small lizards without obliterating them in the process.

Reptiles may be collected in pit-fall and funnel traps. An empty five-litre paint tin sunk level with the soil surface acts as an efficient pit-fall trap, and small snakes and lizards (but not most geckos) that fall in cannot crawl out. Pit-fall traps are particularly effective when used with drift fences. Long planks or lengths of thick polythene sheeting or shade cloth fixed on edge flush with the ground will shepherd small reptiles into the mouth of a pit-fall or funnel trap. These traps should always be protected from the sun as the captives may rapidly overheat and die. Pit-fall traps should be attended daily, and should never be discarded in the field.

Reptiles are often found dead on the road, ploughed up during farming or road construction, or drowned in the swimming pool. They can be preserved in formalin (10%) or methylated spirits. Specimens that are thicker than one centimetre should be injected with a preservative or the belly slit open to prevent them rotting in the centre. A label, written in soft pencil, should list the date, time, locality and circumstances in which the specimen was killed or found, and can be tied to or placed with the specimen; if desired, the specimen may be sent to a suitable institution for identification (for a list of addresses, see page 388).

Finally, I would like to emphasize that collecting is rarely necessary. It is usually far preferable to sit and enjoy the reptile, and then both go in peace.

# The southern African environment

_The_ geographical scope of this guide covers the area south of a line connecting the Cunene and Zambezi rivers. This region (over 3,5 million square kilometres in extent) covers the habitats of 480 reptile species, more than a third of all those occurring in Africa. This diversity is a reflection of the varied climates and habitats of the region and exceeds that of both the USA (approximately 300 species in 9,3 million square kilometres) and Europe (excluding the former USSR) and SW Asia (nearly 400 species in 11,25 million square kilometres).

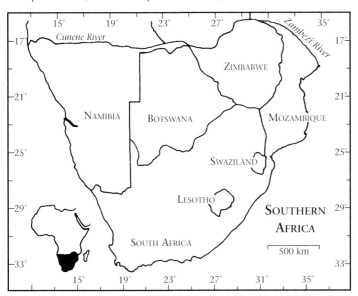

## Climate

Southern Africa has a mainly temperate climate, with wide seasonal contrasts in rainfall and temperature.

The rainfall is strongly influenced by the cold Atlantic Ocean (Benguela) and warm Indian Ocean (Agulhas) currents that sweep up and down the west and east coasts, respectively. The annual rainfall increases considerably in the north and east, whereas the west coast and adjacent regions are the driest parts. Rainfall is largely dependent on the prevailing winds, which in summer sweep anticlockwise across the continent, carrying moist air in the form of thunderstorms from the Indian Ocean across the eastern regions. Because of the high altitude of the interior, little rain remains to fall in the west. In winter, the winds bring rain to the west coast, whereas the rest of the country is dry.

The temperature is affected by both the position (between 17°S and nearly 35°S) and the high altitude (1 000-2 000 m) of much of the interior. The cold Benguela sea current sweeping up the west coast keeps the air temperatures cool, and causes local fogs that sweep across the Namib Desert, and on which many of the region's reptiles depend for their water. Summer temperatures are highest in the Kalahari and surrounding regions, becoming less intense with altitude on the highveld

ANNUAL RAINFALL

■ _more than 500 mm p.a._

☐ _125-500 mm p.a._

▨ _less than 125 mm p.a._

90%

80%

20%   60%

40%

*% falling in October–March*

*Fynbos*

*Forest*

*Desert*

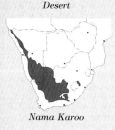

*Nama Karoo*

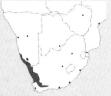

*Succulent Karoo Shrubland*

of the northern provinces and Free State, and the Zimbabwean and Namibian plateaus. Coolest areas at this time are the high mountains of the eastern escarpment and the south-western Cape. Winters are mild along the east coast (the Mozambique Plain and adjacent lowveld of Mpumalanga, and the Limpopo and Zambezi river valleys). The coldest winter regions are the highveld and the mountains of the Great Escarpment, which regularly have night frosts and where (with the exception of the Namibian escarpment) heavy snowfalls are frequent. The rest of the region has warm, sometimes pleasantly sunny, winter days with cool, occasionally cold, nights.

## HABITATS

Ecologically, southern Africa is made up of a complex mosaic of different vegetation types. Eight major categories, called biomes, are recognized, and these have numerous subdivisions.

**Fynbos** is the local name for the Mediterranean-like heathland that covers the south-western and southern Cape, from the Cedarberg to Port Elizabeth. It is composed of an amazing diversity of plant species, dominated by heathers, proteas and restios, that grow on poor, rocky soils. Receiving mainly winter rain (300-2 500 mm per annum), they form a low (1-3 m), woody scrubland that has adapted to frequent fire. There are various subdivisions of fynbos, including renosterbosveld, which has more grass and fewer heathers and proteas. Less than one per cent of renosterbosveld remains, the rest having been ploughed under for wheat and grape farming.

**Forest** vegetation is restricted to high rainfall regions and constitutes less than one per cent of southern Africa. It consists of tall, thick, cool forest (yellowwoods, stinkwoods, etc.) that grows down to sea level in the southern Cape (the Tsitsikamma Coastal Forest). To the north, this vegetation type exists as a scattered 'archipelago' of isolated forests (too small to show on the map) associated with the Great Escarpment. These isolated pockets were abutting and more extensive during cooler glacial periods, but have contracted over the last 16 000 years as the climate has warmed, and have suffered further in the last 200 years as the remaining vestiges have been felled for timber and replaced with pine plantation.

**Desert** occurs as a narrow strip along the west coast. The Namib is an ancient desert, composed of shifting sand dunes along the coastal strip, and hard, gravel plains inland. Plant cover is sparse, with scattered grass and specialized succulent plants on the sand and gravel plains, and stunted acacia trees in the river courses. It is not unusual for less than 10 mm of rain to fall in a year, and droughts lasting 4-5 years may occur. The offshore Benguela Current is responsible for the cold, moisture-laden fogs that may extend up to 50 km inland.

**Nama Karoo** covers the central and western Cape, extending through Namibia, inland of the Namib Desert. In the north, it merges into the arid savannah of the Kalahari. Rainfall (occurring mainly in winter in the west, and in summer in the east) rarely exceeds 250 mm. The soils are poor, shallow and rocky, and support a sparse, dwarf, woody scrub.

**Succulent Karoo shrubland** occurs on the sandy coastal plain of Namaqualand, extending to the rain shadow valleys behind the Cedarberg (the Tanquwa Karoo) and to the Cape fold mountains (the Little Karoo). It is a winter rainfall area, with many succulent plants adapted to the hot, dry summers.

Grassland occurs on the interior plateau from 1 200 to 2 100 m, covering the highveld of Gauteng, Free State and northern Eastern Cape. The growth of trees is inhibited by dry, extremely frosty winters and possibly by the regular winter fires. Rainfall ranges from 250 to 500 mm per year and occurs mainly in summer. Grassland merges into the next biome in the north-east, via the hardveld of eastern Botswana (the Kalahari-Highveld transitional zone).

*Grassland*

Arid savannah is open grassy savannah, adapted to low rainfall and cold, dry winters. As flat, open, acacia woodland it covers the Kalahari sands of southern and central Botswana, extending into northern Namibia (sandveld). As dry mopane woodland it extends along the Limpopo Valley, Mpumalanga lowveld and adjacent Mozambique.

*Arid savannah*

Moist savannah covers the eastern regions of higher rainfall and warmer winters. As the Indian Ocean belt, it extends as a narrow strip along the east coast as far south as East London. Here, the warm Mozambique Current causes high moisture and warm weather; mean annual temperatures range from 26°C in the Zambezi Valley to 17°C at East London, and frost is absent. In the north the belt extends 240 km inland across the sandy soil of the Mozambique Plain, and comprises rich *Brachystegia* woodland (now largely replaced with secondary wooded grassland and cultivation), with patches of mangrove and swamp forest along the coast. From KwaZulu-Natal southwards, the terrain is more rugged and the belt may narrow to as little as eight kilometres. Here, complex soil types occur, and rainfall is moderately high; although it falls mainly in summer, there is no obvious dry season. The vegetation is a mosaic of succulent and moist thicket, which may be dense and impenetrable. A secondary belt of more open *Brachystegia* woodland covers much of the Zimbabwe plateau, the Caprivi Strip and northern Botswana.

*Moist savannah*

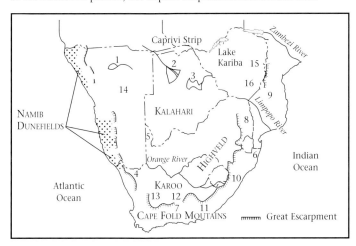

**AREAS OF SPECIAL INTEREST**

1. Etosha Pan
2. Okavango Delta
3. Makgadikgadi Pan
4. Richtersveld
5. Kalahari Gemsbok National Park
6. Maputaland
7. Little Karoo
8. Kruger National Park
9. Mozambique Plain
10. Natal Drakensberg
11. Amatola Mountains
12. Sneeuberg
13. Nuweveldberg
14. Auas Highlands
15. Inyanga
16. Chimanimani Moutains

The Escarpment forms the boundary of the interior plateau, and rises from a minimum of 900 m in the Kalahari depression to over 3 482 m in the Lesotho mountains. It is composed of a number of distinct and imposing mountain ranges. As the Drakensberg of KwaZulu-Natal and Mpumalanga, it forms a sheer and continuous edge, but elsewhere it is broken into a chain of isolated highlands. To the north, it extends as the

**19**

Zimbabwe Eastern Highlands, including Inyanga and the Chimanimani range. In the Cape provinces, it forms the isolated mountains of the Amatolas, Sneeuberg, Nuweveldberg and Roggeveldberg, and in Namibia it exists as the Auas highlands. In the east, it receives high rainfall and is covered with afromontane vegetation. Numerous endemic species are found on the isolated ranges, including the berg adder, the plain mountain adder, and some crag and mountain lizards. Recent discoveries include the cream-spotted mountain snake in the KwaZulu-Natal Drakensberg.

**The Great Karoo** is an area of low rainfall, but flash floods can occur, and with devastating effect. The soils are poor, shallow and stony, with a stunted, woody, scrub vegetation. Most of the Karoo lies above the Great Escarpment but the southern plain falls below it, in the rain shadow of the Cape fold mountains, within which the Little Karoo lies as an isolated pocket. Among the few characteristic species found here are the golden spotted gecko and the tent tortoise. Recent discoveries include the thin-skinned gecko and Braack's dwarf leaf-toed gecko.

**The Kalahari** is a huge, inland drainage basin with a deep cover of old sand which has extended much further east in past dry periods. Although it is sometimes called a desert, no part of the Kalahari receives less than 100 mm of rain a year. The southern region is dry and cold in winter, and covered with arid acacia scrub and grass. The south-western part, including the Kalahari Gemsbok National Park, is very dry, and consists of ancient, long sand dunes. The central Kalahari is flat, and has a number of shallow basins that may periodically flood, including the extensive pans of the Etosha and Makarikari depressions. Both areas are the home of endemic lizard species. Between these pans run the Okavango and Chobe rivers, which bring waters from the Angolan highlands. These never reach the sea, but drain into the deep sands, forming the lush wetlands of the Okavango Delta and Chobe. Among the numerous endemic species found here are the Okavango hinged terrapin, the Barotse water snake, and the striped swamp snake.

**The Namib Desert** runs along the whole coast of Namibia, just entering southern Angola. Over most of its length it is approximately 100 km wide; shifting sands are restricted mainly to the coastal region, with two main dunefields lying north and south of Swakopmund. Much of the inner Namib consists of hard gravel plain, broken by rugged, barren mountains. Annual rainfall in the coastal region is only 10 mm, but for 100-200 days each year, the fog on which many reptiles depend for their water rolls in from the sea. Here, many unique species can be found. The web-footed gecko, Péringuey's adder, the shovel-snouted lizard, and the desert plated lizard, have all adapted to the shifting sands. The Namib day geckos and many thick-toed geckos, desert lizards and sand lizards, are restricted to the Namib gravel plains and rock outcrops. Recent discoveries include the Namibian wolf snake, Johnson's burrowing skink, and Garedes' desert lizard.

**Namaqualand** straddles the lower Orange River. It includes the Richtersveld, a small area of dry, rugged mountains that nestles between Great and Little Namaqualand (which sit north and south of the Orange River, respectively). It is dry (sometimes devastatingly so), but occasionally experiences good winter rains (up to 250 mm). This area is justly famous for the beauty of its spring flowers, and its many unusual reptiles make it a herpetological paradise. Among these are Austen's gecko, Schneider's adder, the speckled padloper, and the Namaqua day gecko. Recent discoveries include Haacke's thick-toed gecko, the Richtersveld dwarf leaf-toed gecko, Imkae's girdled lizard, and Broadley's flat lizard.

**The Highveld** of the Free State and southern Gauteng is an area of high altitude grassland on deep soils. It experiences irregular and often violent summer rains, and cold, dry winters. There has been extensive agricultural and urban development in this region. One of the few endemic reptiles found here is the giant girdled lizard or sungazer.

**The Cape fold mountains** run parallel to the south-western and southern Cape coast, and are responsible for the region's high winter rainfall, as well as its scenic grandeur. Most of the mountains in the range have altitudes of between 1 000 and 1 500 m, with the highest rising to more than 2 000 m. The sandstone has weathered to form rugged gorges and spectacular rock forms. The soils are poor and rocky, and sparsely covered with fynbos vegetation. Unusual endemics found here include the southern rock lizard, the small-scaled leaf-toed gecko, the Cape mountain lizard, and the graceful crag lizard. Recent discoveries include the Swartberg and Hewitt's dwarf leaf-toed geckos, Oelofsen's girdled lizard, the dwarf crag lizard and the red adder.

**Maputaland** and the **Mozambique Plain** of the east coast are composed of Cretaceous and Tertiary sandstones and limestones, extensively covered with sand. The vegetation is varied, with dry mopane woodland occurring in areas of seasonal rainfall and good drainage. In the low-lying coastal strip, swamp and mangrove forest occur. The climate is mild, and the region forms an important corridor for tropical east African species such as the green mamba, the Gaboon adder, and Moreau's tropical house gecko. Recent discoveries include the pygmy wolf snake, Bourquin's and FitzSimons' dwarf burrowing skinks, and numerous endemic species on the Bazaruto Archipelago.

# REPTILES
## CLASS REPTILIA

*P*ublic knowledge of reptiles is full of misconceptions. They are considered to be slimy, cold, slow or cumbersome, and most are thought to be highly venomous. Even among many scientists and naturalists, who perhaps should know better, reptiles are perceived as being inherently inefficient. This is quite untrue. Reptiles are as successful, in terms of their diversity and the varied habitats in which they live, as their furred and feathered descendants. In fact, in southern Africa there are more reptile species than there are mammals, and in the western deserts they exceed birds in number if not diversity. There are more endemic reptiles in southern Africa than any other vertebrates, and new species are being discovered regularly (one every 44 days from 1988-1998!).

In addition to the living forms, there is a bewildering array of extinct reptiles, including creatures as diverse as the giant saurischian and ornithischian dinosaurs, the aquatic plesiosaurs and dolphin-like ichthyosaurs, and the flying pterodactyls. Given this diversity, it is not easy to list simple features that distinguish all reptiles. In many ways they are easier to describe by what they lack rather than by what they possess, and they could be defined as tetrapods (four-legged, at least in their ancestors) – vertebrates that lack fur, feathers, and a tadpole stage in their development.

Perhaps the most obvious characteristic of reptiles is their dry, horny skin that is usually modified into scales or plates. This prevents rapid water loss and has allowed them to move on to dry land, whereas amphibians are still restricted to moist habitats. They are also amniotes (like birds and mammals), having foetal membranes that surround the developing embryo. These contain the embryo in its own 'pond'; amniotes do not have a free tadpole stage like amphibians. In addition, many reptiles lay eggs that have thick shells and yolk stores, and which undergo development independent of water or parents. Such self-contained, sealed eggs are called cleiodic eggs.

A primitive feature of the skull of all reptiles is the single occipital condyle, the knob on the back of the skull that articulates with the backbone. Mammals and birds have paired condyles. Like primitive amphibians and birds, reptiles have only a single bone in the ear, and each half of the lower jaw is composed of several bones.

The relationships of living and extinct reptiles is a complex problem and involves much controversy. The details are beyond the scope of this book, and it is sufficient to note that much of the major grouping is based on skull anatomy, particularly the nature of the openings in the side of the skull. Primitive reptiles and chelonians have a solid skull with no large openings in the side (an anapsid skull), although there is now some controversy as to whether this is secondarily derived in chelonians. All other living reptiles have two openings in the sides of the skull (a diapsid condition), as did the dinosaurs.

All reptiles are cold-blooded, although this is a confusing term, as most are active at body temperatures that exceed those of mammals. The subtle difference between the warm blood of reptiles and that of mammals and birds is that reptiles obtain their heat externally, usually from the sun. All reptiles bask, absorbing warmth from the environment. Many simply sit in the sun until their body reaches the correct temperature, and subsequently shuttle between sun and shade, maintaining a constant optimal temperature. Burrowing species crawl beneath a sun-warmed rock or into the surface layers of the soil to gain heat. Reptiles, therefore, do not generate heat internally by metabolizing food as do mammals and birds; reptiles can more correctly be called ectotherms (meaning 'outer warmth') rather than endotherms ('inner warmth'). The advantage of ectothermy is fuel efficiency. Mammals and birds convert 90% of the food they eat into heat in order to maintain muscle and biochemical efficiency at all times. This allows them to operate at times (late night and winter) and in climates (Arctic tundra and cold seas) that reptiles cannot. However, this requires a constant supply of food. Reptiles, on the other hand, become temporarily dormant in cold weather, and provided they are protected from danger, they need not waste energy. As an extreme example, many snakes survive, and indeed grow, on perhaps 10 meals a year.

Reptiles have internal fertilization. Sperm is transferred to the female via a single penis in crocodilians and chelonians, and paired hemipenes in squamates (although only one hemipenis is used at a time). Tuataras lack intromittent organs and suffice with close contact, rather as birds do. The majority of reptiles lay eggs, and these may be either soft- or hard-shelled. They are laid in a warm, moist, hidden spot and left to incubate on their own. Only crocodiles, and a few lizards and snakes stay with their eggs and protect them during development. In all crocodiles, most chelonians, and some lizards, the sex of the embryo is determined by the incubation temperature. In crocodiles, males develop in eggs at high temperatures, while the same temperatures in chelonians produce females. Lizards vary, depending upon the group.

Various degrees of viviparity have been achieved by squamates, but by no other living reptile. The eggs may be retained in the body for most, or all, of their development, and hatch within weeks, days or even minutes of being laid. Some lizards and snakes have developed a placenta, similar to that of mammals, that allows the mother to transfer food to the foetus. Live-bearing reptiles are usually found in cool climates, or are venomous.

Reptiles arose from amphibians during the Carboniferous period, and the earliest reptile fossils (small, lizard-like creatures, found inside fossil tree stumps) are about 315 million years old. During the subsequent aeons, reptiles evolved a truly bewildering array of forms, including many giant species, and for over 150 million years the dinosaurs and their relatives dominated the earth.

Living reptiles are either remnants of this period, or a recent flowering that has taken place, for the most part, since the dinosaurs became extinct. They are divided into four orders, including the crocodilians (order Crocodylia), tortoises, terrapins and turtles (order Chelonia), snakes, lizards and amphisbaenians (order Squamata), and the tuataras (order Rhynchocephalia). These orders arose as separate evolutionary lineages 200-300 million years ago, very early in the radiation of reptiles; lizards, crocodiles and chelonians can all be distinguished as distinct groups from before the great radiation of dinosaurs. Their fossils can be found intermingled with those of the giant dinosaurs.

With the exception of the lizard-like tuataras, which are restricted to a few islands on the north coast of New Zealand, the other orders are well represented in southern Africa. In total, the world contains more than 6 550 species of reptiles that are arranged in about 900 genera in 48 families. Southern Africa is blessed with 480 species; these are described in the following species accounts.

# CHELONIANS
## ORDER TESTUDINES

𝒯he shield reptiles – tortoises, terrapins and turtles – are all instantly recognizable by virtue of their characteristic shell. This may be soft, leathery, hard, flat, knobbled or hinged, but is unlike anything else, and chelonians can be mistaken for no other reptiles. Chelonians (the correct scientific term) are characterized by a number of features, notably an anapsid skull and a bony protective shell which is divided into an upper carapace and lower plastron. There is sometimes confusion about the common names; the terms 'tortoise', 'turtle' and 'terrapin' have no strict scientific meaning, and are simply used here to differentiate those species that live on land, in the sea, and in fresh water, respectively.

The first fossil chelonians date from Late Triassic rocks in Germany – 210 million years ago. Similar fossils, from the Early Triassic, have recently been discovered in South Africa in the Elliot Formation, at Clocolan in the Free State. It is difficult to appreciate the immensity of such a long period; the chelonians have seen the rise and fall of the dinosaurs, the explosive success of mammals and birds, and man's brief but devastating reign.

The chelonian shell is a complex structure, composed of an outer horny layer covering a bone case which is fused to the rib cage. This entails some radical rearrangements in tortoise anatomy, not the least of which is the placing of the shoulder blades and hips inside the rib cage. Early tortoises had teeth, but these are absent in all living forms. Instead they have a horny beak, similar in appearance and function to that of a parrot. In aquatic habitats the feet may be webbed or modified into flippers, and the bony shell may be reduced. The weight of the protective shell limits locomotion and chelonians are not famed for their speed. Food is therefore usually sedentary, and most chelonians are herbivorous. Some aquatic species with lighter shells capture prey such as fish, but this is usually accompanied by concealment and ambush; others feed on invertebrates such as sponges, molluscs and jellyfish.

All chelonians lay eggs, which are usually soft-shelled in aquatic forms (sea turtles and side-necked terrapins), but hard-shelled in tortoises and soft-shelled terrapins. The female takes great care in finding a suitable, moist yet sunny spot in which to lay her eggs. Sea turtles come ashore to lay their eggs. A small vertical pit is dug with the hind legs, and after the eggs are laid they are covered and left to incubate. This is the extent of maternal care, and after hatching the young must fend for themselves. The time from laying to hatching can vary from four to 15 months, and is in part dependent on the season, as eggs laid in autumn undergo very little development during winter, and do not hatch much earlier than those laid in the following spring. Clutch size varies with the species, the greatest numbers being laid by sea turtles. In many species the sex is determined by the egg incubation temperature, females being produced at higher temperatures (31-34°C).

Chelonians are found in almost every environment – aquatic, oceanic and terrestrial – throughout the tropical and temperate zones. Four sub-orders containing 25 families are recognized, and half of this number is extinct. Living forms are placed in 90 genera, with some 273 species. The southern African subregion has a very rich chelonian fauna, with five sea turtles in coastal waters, nine terrapins in freshwater rivers and vleis, and 14 land tortoises.

1 - Head withdrawn into shell sideways:
    Pelomedusidae (Side-necked terrapins, page 44)
  - Head withdrawn straight back or cannot be withdrawn:    go to 2
2 - Limbs not modified as flippers, with 3-5 claws:    go to 3
  - Limbs modified as flippers, with 0-2 claws:    go to 4
3 - Carapace with horny shields; feet with 4-5 claws:    go to 5
  - Carapace soft, without horny shields; feet with 3 claws:
    Trionychidae (Soft-shelled terrapins, page 42)
4 - Carapace with horny shields; flippers with 1-2 claws:
    Cheloniidae (Modern sea turtles, page 38)
  - Carapace leathery, no horny shields; flippers clawless:
    Dermochelyidae (Leatherback turtles, page 37)
5 - Skin of head divided into large and small shields; toes not webbed;
    terrestrial:    Testudinidae (Land tortoises, page 25)
  - Skin of head smooth and undivided; toes webbed; aquatic:
    Emydidae (Pond terrapins (introduced), page 35)

# MODERN CHELONIANS
## SUBORDER CRYPTODIRA

This suborder comprises the majority of living forms. 'Cryptodira' means 'hidden neck' and refers to the way the head is withdrawn, by a vertical, S-shaped flexure of the neck. In terrestrial forms, this is usually accompanied by retraction of the front legs so that the head is completely hidden and thus protected. All sea turtles and land tortoises, and many terrapins, are cryptodirans.

# Land Tortoises
## FAMILY TESTUDINIDAE

These chelonians are highly modified for terrestrial life. Most have domed, thick shells (except for the pancake tortoise, *Malocochersus tornieri*, from East Africa, and to a lesser degree the Nama padloper, *Homopus* sp. from S. Namibia, which have reduced and very thin shells). The top of the head is covered with several distinct shields. The hind feet are webless and elephant-like; they walk on the tips of their heavily armoured and clawed forefeet. Buttock tubercles are often present. They are found in the temperate and tropical regions of all continents except Australia, as well as on Madagascar and other Indian Ocean islands and the Galapagos Islands. There are 43 species in 14 genera. The world's greatest diversity of land tortoises occurs on the subcontinent. Of the five genera and 14 species occurring in the region, three genera and 12 species are endemic.

KEY TO THE SOUTHERN AFRICAN GENERA IN THE TESTUDINIDAE
1 - Rear of carapace hinged (in adults); outer edge of 4th costal wider
    than that of 3rd costal (all ages):    *Kinixys* (Hinged tortoises, page 33)
  - Rear of carapace not hinged; outer edge of 4th costal equal to or
    smaller than that of 3rd costal:    go to 2
2 - Gular single and protruding:    *Chersina* (Angulate tortoise, page 30)
  - Gulars paired:    go to 3
3 - Nuchal shield absent:    *Geochelone* (Giant land tortoises, page 28)
  - Nuchal shield present:    go to 4

4   Shell usually flat and vertebral shields never conical; each gular
    usually broader than long:                    *Homopus* (Padlopers, page 26)
-   Shell usually domed, often with conical vertebral shields (knobs);
    gulars usually as long as or longer than broad:
                        *Psammobates* (Geometric and Tent tortoises, page 31)

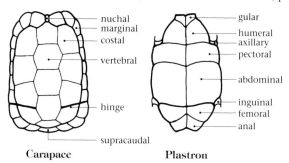

Carapace                    Plastron

**The shields of a tortoise shell**

# Padlopers   *Homopus*

This is a group of small to very small tortoises that includes the world's
smallest species. The carapace is not hinged and is relatively flat, with the
scutes never raised into knobs, and often with depressed centres. The
plastron has paired, thickened gulars that are wider than they are long.
A nuchal is present. Shell abnormalities (extra and misshapen scutes, etc.)
are relatively common. The generic name means 'same foot' as both front
and hind feet of two species have four claws (all other tortoises, including
three padlopers, have five claws on the front feet).

Padlopers are endemic to the southern African subregion and restricted
mainly to the Cape, with two species occurring in adjacent regions. There
are five living species, with one fossil form (*H. fenestratus*) from Carlisle
Bridge near Grahamstown.

### Greater Padloper                    *Homopus femoralis* **(Pl. 6)**

*(Endemic) TL 100-130 mm; max. TL 168 mm, female.*

A small tortoise that weighs only 200-300 g, but is, nonetheless, the
largest padloper. It lacks a hinge, but has a nuchal and paired gulars,
and usually 11 marginals. The beak is not hooked, is tricuspid, and has a
serrated edge. The nostrils are below the level of the eye. The forelimbs
are covered with large, overlapping scales and have four claws. Buttock
tubercles are present, but may be small or absent in juveniles. The
tail does not have a terminal spine. The carapace is olive or reddish-
brown; the individual scutes of juveniles often having black margins.
The plastron is uniform dirty yellow-green in adults, often with darker
areas restricted to the anterior edge of the scutes in juveniles. The skin of
the body is yellow-brown, and sometimes orange-pink. Males do not have
concave plastrons, but have longer tails. Females grow larger than males.
**Biology and breeding:** These chelonians are common in suitable
habitat, where they may be found sheltering under rock slabs or in old,
hollowed-out termitaria. They hibernate deep in burrows when winter
snows blanket the peaks. Enemies include crows and birds of prey, jackals
and the rock leguaan. The female lays 1-3 oval, hard-shelled eggs (29-35 x

25-27 mm) in summer. Hatchlings measure 25-30 mm and weigh 6-8 g.
**Habitat:** Grasslands of mountain plateaus, particularly of the old escarpment. **Range:** Inland mountains of E. Cape, extending into S. and central Free State, N. Cape around Kimberley, and mountains of SE Lesotho. Relict populations occur along the old escarpment edge in the Karoo, from Murraysburg to Sutherland, possibly even into the NW Little Karoo.

### Parrot-beaked Tortoise  *Homopus areolatus* (Pl. 5)

*(Endemic) TL 70-90 mm; max. TL 114 mm, female.*
A small tortoise that lacks a hinge, but does have a nuchal and paired gulars. The carapace is often attractively sculptured, with the scute margins deeply etched and the centres indented. There are usually 11 marginals. The beak is strongly hooked (hence the common name), tricuspid, and has a weakly-serrated edge. The nostrils are situated high on the snout. The forelimbs, which are covered with very large, overlapping scales, each have four claws. Buttock tubercles are absent or very small. The tail does not have a terminal spine. Mature males have flat plastrons and long tails. Females grow slightly larger than males. The carapace is yellowish-olive to green, usually with red-brown areolae and dark brown to black margins in juveniles and adult females; males remain uniform orange-brown, except for a greenish tinge to the edges of the vertebral and costal scutes, and develop orange nasal scales in the breeding season. The plastron is yellowish with a brown centre. **Biology and breeding:** Because of their small size these tortoises rarely forage in the open, favouring sunny spots around the edge of thick cover. They often shelter under rocks or in disused animal burrows. They can climb well up steep slopes. They struggle when restrained and will readily eject the contents of their cloacal water reservoir. They are eaten by crows and even secretary birds. They have lived for longer than 28 years in captivity. The female lays 2-3 eggs (rarely up to four) in a small nest hole dug in sandy soil. Elongate and oval (27-33 x 20-23 mm), the eggs take 150-300 days to hatch. The young weigh 7-8 g and measure 30 mm. **Habitat:** Varied; coastal fynbos, karroid broken veld and open mesic thicket. **Range:** Cape coastal region from East London to Klawer, extending inland to Pearston in the east and Middelpos in the Roggeveldberge. Occurs below 600 m, but extends inland to higher altitudes via the moist corridor of the Cradock gap.

### Karoo or Boulenger's Padloper  *Homopus boulengeri* (Pl. 6)

*(Endemic) TL 100-130 mm; max. TL 160 mm, female.*
A small tortoise that lacks a hinge, but has a nuchal and paired gulars. The flattened shell has a rounded bridge, and usually 12 marginals. The beak is weakly hooked or not hooked at all, is tricuspid, and has a weakly serrated edge. The forelimbs are covered with very large, overlapping scales; each forelimb has five claws. Buttock tubercles are absent. The tail does not have a terminal spine. Males have long tails and a deep concavity in the plastron. The carapace varies in colour from dark red to yellow-brown, and sometimes olive. The plastron is similar but lighter in colour. The skin of the neck and limbs is dull yellow, and sometimes bright yellow with orange scales. **Biology and breeding:** This very secretive species shelters under rock slabs on rocky outcrops, plateaus and dolerite ridges. It is active on cool summer days, particularly when thunderstorms threaten (hence the common name 'donderweerskilpad'; it is also known as the 'klipskilpad' and the 'rooiskilpadjie'). They are killed and eaten by

crows, which break their shells by dropping them on to rocks. Breeding is poorly known; a female laid one egg (32-39 x 22-23 mm, 10 g) in January. **Habitat:** Rocky karroid regions. **Range:** Great Karoo, from Pearston and Wolwefontein in the east, to Sutherland and Carnarvon in the west, extending also into the western Little Karoo.

### Speckled Padloper                    *Homopus signatus* (Pl. 6)
*(Endemic) TL 60-80 mm; max. TL 96 mm, female.*
The world's smallest tortoise. It lacks a hinge, but has a nuchal and paired gulars. The flattened shell has a rounded bridge, and usually 12 marginals that may be serrated (see Subspecies). The beak is weakly hooked or not hooked at all. The forelimbs are covered with large, overlapping scales; each forelimb has five claws. Buttock tubercles are present. Males have a well-developed concavity in the plastron, and a long tail. Coloration is varied (see Subspecies). **Biology and breeding:** Active in the early morning in rocky areas, foraging for small succulent plants among granite slabs. Common in suitable habitat, and several may be found sheltering together under a rock slab. Mating takes place throughout spring and autumn, with head bobbing between the sexes preceding copulation. The female lays a number of single-egg clutches during spring and summer, selecting moist soil under rock overhangs. They take 100-120 days to hatch (at 30°C); the small hatchlings (30 mm CL, weight 7 g) have already absorbed their yolk sacs and start to feed immediately. **Habitat:** Varied; mainly western succulent karoo, but extending into fynbos in the south. **Range:** W. Cape to Namaqualand. **Subspecies:** Two races: *H.s. signatus* has serrated marginals, the nuchal is wider than it is long, and the carapace shields are raised with sunken centres; the carapace is light brown with extensive black splashes. It occurs in Namaqualand with a few Richtersveld specimens. *H.s. cafer* has marginals that are not serrated, the nuchal is narrower than it is long, and the carapace shields are smooth; the carapace is orange-red to salmon-pink, with fine black spots and stippling. It occurs in W. Cape from Piketberg to Klawer and Calvinia.

■ *H.s. signatus*

□ *H.s. cafer*

### Nama Padloper                         *Homopus sp.* (Pl. 6)
*(Endemic) TL 100-150 mm; max. TL 165 mm, female.*
A small tortoise that lacks a hinge, but has a nuchal and paired gulars. The flattened shell has a rounded bridge, and usually 12 smooth marginals. The beak is weakly hooked or not hooked at all. The forelimbs are covered with very large, overlapping scales; each forelimb has five claws. Buttock tubercles are absent. The carapace scutes are chestnut to red-brown, with pale centres and black edges. The plastron is uniform light yellow, sometimes with a greenish tinge. **Biology and breeding:** Not much is known as this species has only recently been rediscovered. It climbs well, and shelters in rock cracks and beneath boulders. **Habitat:** Rocky semi-desert. **Range:** S. Namibia, from Lüderitz to Aus and south to Hunsberg.

## Typical Tortoises    *Geochelone*
This is a large and ancient genus, with numerous living and fossil species. The taxonomy is very confused, and the group has now been divided into six living genera that are distinguished by subtle internal and skeletal characteristics. Previously included the largest living tortoises, *Dipsochelys elephantina* (measuring 1,4 m and weighing 250 kg), from Aldabra Island in the Indian Ocean, and *Chelonoidis nigra* from the Galapagos Islands in

the eastern Pacific. Even these giants are surpassed by the fossil species
*G. gigas* that lived in the East Indies two million years ago; it measured
2,4 m and weighed more than 850 kg. The genus *Geochelone* now contains
only four living species, with two African species, one of which is
widespread and reaches the subcontinent.

## Leopard Tortoise *Geochelone pardalis* (Pl. 4)

*TL 300-450 mm; max. TL 750 mm, female.*
This tortoise weighs between eight and 12 kg, but grows much larger in
E. Cape, where adults average 15-20 kg and may exceptionally exceed
700 mm in length and 40 kg in weight. The carapace is domed and not
hinged, with the scutes only faintly raised (smooth in juveniles and very
old adults). The gulars are paired and are as long as they are wide. The
nuchal is absent. There are 10-12 marginals, with those on the rear edge
usually serrated and often upturned. The beak is sometimes hooked, is
unicuspid and often serrated. Each of the front feet has five claws. There
are 2-3 buttock tubercles on each side. The tail does not have a terminal
spine. The carapace of hatchlings is yellow, with central paired or single
black spots, the ground colour becoming darker and heavily blotched and
streaked in black with age; old adults are often uniform dark grey-brown.
The plastron is yellowish, often with black radiating streaks and spots.
Males have a longer tail than females, and a well-developed plastral
concavity. **Biology and breeding:** Growth in the first years of life is
relatively slow, but increases rapidly as the young tortoise gets too large
for small carnivores to kill, and can feed further from cover. It weighs
about 1 kg by 7-8 years, and thereafter body mass may double every 2-3
years. Sexual maturity is probably reached in 15 years, by which time
growth has slowed considerably. These tortoises may live in captivity for
at least 30, and possibly up to 75 years. They eat a wide variety of plants,
including grasses, annuals and succulents. They also gnaw bones, and
even hyaena faeces, to obtain calcium for shell growth and egg shell
development. Many predators, including rock monitors, storks, crows and
small carnivores, feed on hatchlings and juveniles, whilst ants may attack
the eggs. Adults are relatively immune to predation, except by man. Many
adults have cracked shells from falls in rocky areas, while others are killed
in veld fires. They are usually well infested with ticks in the soft groin
skin. During cold rain and in winter they shelter deep in thick bush. They
occupy a large home range (1-3 sq. km), and have been known to undertake long return journeys (5-10 km) when translocated from their
territories. Two males meeting, particularly in the breeding season, will
engage in combat (pushing, butting and sometimes overturning one
another). Mating is similarly robust, the male pursuing and butting the
female into submission. Copulation is a noisy affair, often accompanied
by much straining and 'asthmatic' wheezing by the male. The gravid
female selects a sunny, well-drained site and excavates a flaskshaped pit
(up to 250 mm across and deep) with her hind feet; she urinates copiously
to soften hard soil. She usually lays 6-15 (exceptionally up to 30) large,
almost spherical, hard-shelled eggs (32-41 x 35-44 mm, similar in size and
shape to pingpong balls). The hole is refilled and the female may tamp
down the soil by lifting and dropping her shell regularly on the spot.
A large female may lay 3-6 similar-sized clutches at monthly intervals
during the summer. Incubation takes 10-15 months, depending on the
temperature (in captivity, eggs incubated at 28°C hatch in eight months);

eggs laid late in the season take longer to develop as they lie dormant during the winter. During the long development, the ground may become very hard; hatchlings may then have to wait for days, even weeks, for rain to soften the soil, before they can burrow to freedom. Hatchlings weigh 23-50 g and measure 40-50 mm TL. **Habitat:** Varied; not restricted to montane grassland, also occurring in fynbos, mesic thicket, and arid and mesic savannah. **Range:** Found throughout the savannahs of Africa, from Sudan to S. Cape. Historically absent from SW Cape and from former Transkei, adjacent KwaZulu-Natal, and Lesotho, but now introduced in some areas. **Subspecies:** Two races are recognized by some; both occur on the subcontinent. The typical race, *G.p. pardalis*, is defined only by a larger plastral concavity in males, and larger size; it is restricted to E. and S. Cape, with a relict population in S. Namibia. *G.p. babcocki* occurs throughout the rest of the range, and is smaller, the plastral concavity covers only the posterior third of males, and it usually has a more contrasting coloration.

# Angulate Tortoise  *Chersina*

This tortoise is endemic to the tip of southern Africa, extending just into S. Namibia. It is unique among African tortoises in having an undivided gular at the front of the plastron. Various aspects of its biology are also unusual. Known from a single living species, and an unnamed fossil species from Miocene deposits on the W. Cape coast.

### Angulate Tortoise                                  *Chersina angulata* (Pl. 4)
*(Endemic) TL 150-250 mm; max. TL 300 mm, male.*

A medium-sized tortoise that grows larger in the western regions. In the east males rarely exceed 220 mm (1 kg), while on Dassen Island and the adjacent west coast mainland even females may exceed 240 mm (1,5 kg). The carapace is never hinged; it is elongate and flared at the front and behind in mature males. The scutes are slightly raised. There are 10-12 (usually 11) marginals. A nuchal is present. The gular is single and protrudes beneath the head in mature males. The beak is weakly hooked, bi- or tricuspid, and is rarely serrated. There are five claws on each of the forefeet. Buttock tubercles are absent. The tail does not have a terminal spine. The carapace is light straw-yellow in colour. The top scutes have dark brown areolae and black edges. The marginals have a black triangle on the posterior edges. The plastron has a dark, irregular centre, often with white sutures in old animals, and the abdominals are light orange to bright red (particularly in W. Cape 'rooipens' form). Old adults become smoothshelled and a uniform dirty straw colour. Unlike most other tortoises, males grow larger than females; the males have a 'peanut' shape, an elongate gular and deep concavity in the plastron. **Biology and breeding:** The diet includes grasses, annuals and succulents. Angulate tortoises drink through the nose from rock pools; on sandy soils they raise the rear legs and extend the neck, pushing the snout into the soil, and filtering water from that which runs off the shell and puddles around the head. They are active during the early morning, and retreat to cover when the sun becomes too hot. They can withstand high body temperatures (higher than 40°C), but prefer to be cooler (around 30°C). This tortoise has lived for 32 years in captivity. It readily ejects the liquid contents of its bowels when handled, often spraying them up to one metre, and this with surprising accuracy. Enemies include small carnivores, rock monitors, secretary birds, sea gulls and crows. Hatchlings have even been found skewered on tree thorns by fiscal shrikes. Juvenile angulate tortoises wander slowly from place to place, and select a suitable territory only when they reach maturity. Males and females have similar size home ranges (up to 2 ha, but often less in moister habitats). The males do not defend territories, but dominant males prevent other males from mating with the females. Combat involves butting and using the enlarged gular to overturn one another. A single 'fall' usually resolves the dispute, but the opponent may right himself and re-enter the fray. After rain, when the soil is soft and moist, the female digs a shallow depression about 100 mm wide, with a small chamber 40 mm wide and deep at its bottom. The claws of the hind foot are used to break up the soil, which is then pushed away with the side of the lower leg. Only a single (very rarely two) hard-shelled, spherical egg (30-35 x 37-42 mm, 20-25 g) is laid, and this may occur 4-6 times a year. After laying, the soil is tamped down by the female with her shell. The whole procedure may take 2-3 hours. Although the area is carefully camouflaged, a large number of eggs are excavated and eaten by mongooses. Incubation takes 90-200 days, depending on the season. Eggs may crack 6-10 days before young emerge. Hatchlings weigh 8-12 g and are 32-35 mm long. Growth is rapid in the first 8-10 years, slowing thereafter; there is little growth after 20 years. Sexual maturity is reached in 9-12 years. **Habitat:** Varied; sandy coastal regions, including mesic thicket and coastal fynbos; scarcer in the arid hinterland. **Range:** Found in Cape coastal regions, from East London to the Sperrgebeit, extending inland as far as Cradock in association with Karoo Broken Veld. There are isolated records in S. Namibia, and relict populations in moister regions of the Karoo.

# Geometric and Tent Tortoises   *Psammobates*

These small, attractive tortoises usually have their carapace scutes raised into knobs, with beautiful, radially arranged light and dark bands giving a striking geometric pattern. The carapace is domed and is never hinged. A nuchal is present. The paired gulars are longer than they are broad. Buttock tubercles are present in some species. Males are much smaller than females. 'Psammobates' means 'sand-loving', and most of these tortoises inhabit the arid interior of the subcontinent.

They are endemic to southern Africa. At present three species are recognized, of which one is very varied with local races, and another endangered due to habitat destruction. A single fossil species from the early Pleistocene is known.

### Serrated or Kalahari Tent Tortoise
*Psammobates oculiferus* **(Pl. 7)**
*(Endemic) TL 80-120 mm; max. TL 147 mm, female.*
A small tortoise with a low, domed carapace with a strongly serrated edge. It lacks a hinge. The nuchal is broad and often divided, and the paired gulars are longer than they are broad. There are 11 (sometimes 10 or 12) marginals that are strongly serrated at the front and back. The scutes are only slightly raised. There is a single axillary scale. The beak is hooked and tricuspid. The forelimbs each have five claws and a few large, and one extremely large, scales. Buttock tubercles are present. The tail does not have a terminal spine. The carapace is light brown-yellow, with each scute beautifully marked with a radial pattern of 6-10 dark brown to black rays. The plastron is yellowish, with radiating dark rays. Males have a longer

tail and flatter shell than females, and an obvious plastral concavity.
**Biology and breeding:** Poorly known, despite its wide distribution.
May dig into loose soil at the base of scrub, or retreat into mammal
burrows. Common in some areas, for example Khuis. Historically, the shell
was used by Bushmen to make buchu pouches and, despite protection, it
is still killed to supply the tourist trade. Feeds on small succulents and
grasses, and sheep and game droppings. Lays 1-2 eggs (28-31 x 40-42 mm)
in December. Cannot swim. **Habitat:** Arid savannah; scrub desert.
**Range:** Kalahari and adjacent regions; not south of Orange River.

### Geometric Tortoise
*Psammobates geometricus* (Pl. 7)
*(Endemic) TL 80-120 mm; max. TL 143 mm female, 123 mm male.*
A small tortoise with a high, domed carapace that lacks a hinge. A nuchal
is present. The paired gulars are longer than they are broad. There are
11-12 marginals (numbers 4-7 being higher than they are broad) that are
slightly upturned at the back. The scutes are only slightly raised. There is
a single axillary scale. The beak is hooked. The forelimbs each have five
claws and are covered with scattered, large scales that are separated by
smaller ones. Buttock tubercles are absent. The tail does not have a terminal
spine. The carapace is beautifully marked with geometric patterns; the
scutes have yellow centres from which yellow rays (8-15 on the vertebrals,
9-12 on the costals and 2-4 on the marginals) radiate, separated by black.
The plastron is yellow, with radiating faint black rays and bands. Many
juveniles have a single yellow 'X' on each carapace scute and a black
plastron; the radial pattern develops with age. Females are more common
than males, and are slightly larger (males average 106 mm and 207 g;
females average 125 mm and 436 g). **Biology and breeding:** Endangered
(CITES Appendix 1; SA RDB, Endangered), due to destruction of habitat for
urban development and cultivation of wheat and vineyards. Only 3 000-
4 000 specimens remain. Veld fires kill some, but hatchlings emerge soon
after fires to feed on young plants. Feeds on succulent and perennial plants;
however, snails and remains of young parrot-beaked tortoises have been
found in faeces. Active in early morning and afternoon, often in cold
conditions. Enemies include crows and secretary birds, small carnivores
and man. Probably lives for longer than 30 years. Lays 2-5 eggs (32 x
24 mm) in September/November at the base of a grass tussock, usually
on a north-facing slope. These hatch in March-May, after 150-210 days'
incubation; hatchlings (30-40 mm TL; 7 g) emerge with first winter rains.
Growth is relatively rapid, with two growth rings being laid down each
year. Sexual maturity is attained in 7-8 years. **Habitat:** Low-lying coastal
renosterbosveld. **Range:** Previously from Cape Flats to Eendekuil, 160 km
north along W. Cape forelands, with isolated populations around Ceres
and Worcester. Now restricted to a few patches of natural veld (96% of its
habitat has been destroyed). A number of reserves have been proclaimed.

### Tent Tortoise
*Psammobates tentorius* (Pl. 7)
*(Endemic) TL 80-120 mm; max. TL 150 mm, female.*
A small tortoise that comes in a bewildering range of shapes and colours.
This single species has at times been divided into no fewer than six species
with 22 races. The carapace is domed or flat, with or without raised scutes
(see Subspecies), and is not hinged. A nuchal is present, typically broader
than it is long, and is often minute but rarely absent. The paired gulars
are longer than they are broad. There are usually 11 (sometimes 10 or 12)

P.t. *tentorius*

P.t. *verroxii*

P.t. *trimeni*

32

marginals (numbers 4-7 being broader than they are high). Two to three (rarely one) axillaries are present. The beak is usually hooked and bi- or tricuspid. The forelimbs each have five claws and are covered with large, abutting scales. Buttock tubercles are typically present, but may be reduced or absent in the western race. The tail does not have a terminal spine. Coloration is varied; the carapace usually has geometric patterning (see Subspecies). The males are much smaller than the females, rarely exceeding 100 mm, and they have longer tails and a shallow plastral concavity. **Biology and breeding:** Despite its wide range, this species is not easily found and often occurs in low densities. During droughts they burrow into sandy soil at the base of low shrub, emerging after the onset of rains. They are active in the cool of early morning and evening, when they feed on small succulents. Their geometric patterning provides very effective camouflage in broken shade at the base of bush. They drink by raising the rear legs and sipping the water that drains along the shell grooves to the forelimbs. They rarely do well out of their natural range, and have lived for only 7-8 years in captivity. Enemies include small carnivores, rock monitors, eagles, goshawks, crows, and even ostriches. Very few details are known about their breeding. The female lays a few eggs: only 1-2 (24 x 35 mm) in the western races, and 2-3 in the typical race (21-24 x 27-31 mm). These are laid in summer (September-January) and hatch after about 220 days. Hatchlings (25-30 mm) are more circular in shape than adults. **Habitat:** Varied; usually arid karroid areas or rocky sandveld. **Range:** Throughout Great and Little Karoo, to succulent Karoo of Cape west coast and into S. Namibia. **Subspecies:** Only three races are recognized at present; the species is very variable and intermediate conditions occur. *P.t. tentorius* is a large race. Its carapace scutes are strongly raised into knobs, with a well-marked pattern of yellow to orange radiating stripes on a black background. The plastron has solid mahogany markings in the centre and a yellow to orange edge. It occurs in SE Cape, from Grahamstown to Matjiesfontein, intergrading with the next race in central Karoo. *P.t. verroxii* has a carapace with smooth or faintly raised scutes, and is a drab colour, sometimes uniform brown, but usually with dull orange stripes on a dark brown background. The plastron has diffuse or indistinct dark brown patterning. It occurs in N. and central Karoo, intergrading with the next race in Bushmanland and S. Namibia. *P.t. trimeni* is the most attractive and smallest race, its carapace having small knobs and being well-marked with rich orange-yellow stripes (shading to red around the marginals) on a black background. The dark brown centre of the plastron is broken by lighter patches. It occurs in Namaqualand and S. Namibia, intergrading with the previous race in the east.

# Hinged Tortoises   *Kinixys*

These unusual tortoises have a unique hinge in the carapace (in adults) that allows the rear of the shell to close, protecting the hind feet and tail region. Juveniles in which the hinge has not developed can be distinguished from the padlopers, *Homopus* (page 26), as the outer edge of the third costal is longer than that of the fourth (these two genera are rarely sympatric, so this feature is academic in the field). The hinge develops first at the edge between the seventh and eighth marginals and then spreads inwards, separating the second and third costals, the sutures being replaced with fibrous cartilage. In some adults the hinge fails to develop. Nuchal and submarginal scutes are present. The paired gulars are very thickened at the front; they are sometimes longer than they are broad. There are usually five claws on each of the forefeet.

Six species are recognized. Two of these (*K. homeana* and *K. erosa*) have spiny and upturned marginals, and are restricted to the rain forests of W. and central Africa. The other four species inhabit savannah; all occur on the subcontinent, and two are endemic.

### Bell's Hinged Tortoise                         *Kinixys belliana* (Pl. 5)

*TL 150-200 mm; max. TL 211 mm, female.*

A medium-sized tortoise with a smooth, convex carapace and a prominent hinge. A nuchal is present. The gulars (together) are less than twice as wide as they are long, not forked, and with a flat or convex lip. There are 11 marginals that are not serrated or upturned. The supracaudal is undivided with a smooth underside. There are 2-3 axillaries. The beak is unicuspid. The forefeet each have five claws (but four in *K.b. nogueyi* from W. Africa) and are covered with large, overlapping, sometimes pointed scales. Buttock tubercles are absent. The tail has a terminal spine, which is large in males. Coloration consists of a yellow and black radial pattern (4-6 rays) on the vertebrals and costals. The plastron is varied in colour, but is largely black in juveniles, except for a broad yellow band. The patterning may fade in adults, particularly in males. Males are easily distinguished by this fading, the plastral concavity and the very large tail. **Biology and breeding:** This species lives for up to 22 years in captivity. It prefers humid conditions. Some specimens struggle when captured, and may empty the bowels before retreating into their shells and closing the hinge. Breeding is poorly known locally. The female lays 2-7 (sometimes 10) elongate eggs (39-48 x 32-36 mm, 23-32 g) throughout summer (November-April); she may lay clutches at 40-day intervals. Incubation takes 90-110 days; hatchlings (38-40 mm) have been found in September-October and March-April. **Habitat:** In south restricted to coastal plain and dune forest, entering thornveld and savannah in north. **Range:** Mozambique coastal plain as far south as Zululand, into E. Zimbabwe and north through East Africa to Somalia, Sudan and Central African Republic. Also on Madagascar, but probably introduced. **Subspecies:** Two recognized; only the typical race occurring in southern Africa. *K.b. nogueyi* has four claws on each of its forefeet, and occurs in W. Africa to Cameroon.

*K.b. belliana*

### Speke's Hinged Tortoise                        *Kinixys spekii* (Pl. 5)

*TL 140-160 mm; max. TL 183 mm.*

A medium-sized tortoise with a smooth, depressed carapace with a well-developed hinge. The beak is unicuspid, and the supracaudal undivided with a smooth underside. Mature males have a concave plastron. The shell of juveniles has a zonary pattern, each shield having a dark brown centre with concentric light and dark zones. These may persist in males (which may also be uniform olive-brown to buff), whilst the dark zones break up into ragged rays in adult females. The belly is a uniform dirty yellow in males, with vague zonary patterning in females and juveniles. **Biology and breeding:** These tortoises are active in the wet summer months, aestivating underground during the cold dry season (April-September) in old termitaria or small burrows which they scrape into earth embankments. They have large home ranges and occur in low densities (2-3 per ha). The diet is very varied, and includes *Syzygium* and other fruit, mushrooms, giant land snails (*Achatina*), beetles and pill

millipedes. Clutch size varies from 2-6, and eggs measure 33-47 x
28-34 mm and weigh 19-31 g. Females move out of their normal ranges
to locate suitable egg laying sites, usually in shade beneath large trees.
**Habitat:** Savannah, coastal plain and dune forest, entering thornveld.
**Range:** Savannahs of central and E. Africa, through Zimbabwe to NW
and N. provinces of South Africa, and along the lowveld and Mozambique
coastal plain as far south as Swaziland.

### Lobatse Hinged Tortoise    *Kinixys lobatsiana* (Pls. 97 and 112)
*TL 150-180 mm; max. TL 200 mm, female.*

Medium-sized with a smooth, moderately convex to depressed carapace
with a well-developed hinge. The beak is unicuspid. The supracaudal is
undivided, with a longitudinal groove on the underside. The posterior
marginals are serrated and curve upwards. Mature males have a concave
plastron. Juveniles and females have a broken radiate pattern on each
carapace shield, and each shield has a red-brown centre. Males are usually
uniform brown. The plastron is uniform dirty yellow in adult males, but
with sparce, dark, radiating streaks in females and juveniles. **Biology and
breeding:** Varied diet; includes mainly leaves and fruit, but also mushrooms, beetles, snails and millipedes. A female laid six eggs in mid-April
that hatched after 313 days. **Habitat:** Bushveld, thornveld, and *Burkea*
savannah. **Range:** NW and N. provinces in South Africa; SE Botswana.

### Natal Hinged Tortoise      *Kinixys natalensis* (Pl. 5)
*(Endemic) TL 80-120 mm; max. TL 155 mm.*

A small tortoise with a slightly convex carapace and a poorly-developed
hinge. A nuchal is present. Combined, the gulars are more than twice as
wide as they are long. There are 12-13 marginals on each side; they are
not serrated or upturned. The supracaudal is usually divided. There are
2-3 axillaries. The beak is tricuspid. The forefeet each have five claws and
are covered with large, overlapping, sometimes pointed scales. Buttock
tubercles are absent. The tail has a terminal spine which is large in males.
The carapace shield displays concentric patterning, with the areolae light
to dark brown with concentric rings of orange-yellow and black-brown;
there is a similar ringed pattern on the plastron shield that may fade in
adults. Males lack a concave plastron and are smaller than females.
**Biology and breeding:** This tortoise inhabits dry, rocky areas in an
altitude range of 300-1 000 m. Copulation in captivity has been observed
in February. **Habitat:** It prefers tropical lowveld, entering mesic thicket
in the south. **Range:** Found in the KwaZulu-Natal lowlands, through
the Lebombo range to Mpumalanga.

# Pond Terrapins
FAMILY EMYDIDAE

These are the characteristic terrapins of N. and central America and SE
Asia. The shell is hard, with some species having hinges in the plastron.
The feet usually have some webbing between the toes. Although mainly
aquatic, some species are terrestrial (for example the American box turtles,
*Terrapene*), and the family is closely related to land tortoises.

    There are two European genera (*Emys* and *Mauremys*) which are
normally found in N. Africa. One N. American species, *Trachemys scripta*,
has escaped from captivity and become established in South Africa.

# Pond Terrapins  *Trachemys*

These terrapins have a hard carapace that is notched and serrated on the rear margin, and is usually keeled. The plastron lacks a hinge. The head is withdrawn backwards.

Five species are distributed throughout the swamps and slow-flowing rivers of central America, with some extending into the USA. One species is bred commercially, and is distributed as a pet throughout the world. Escapees have been discovered in Europe, Israel and South Africa.

### American Red-eared Terrapin  *Trachemys scripta* (Pl. 10)

*(Introduced) TL 150-250 mm; max. TL 280 mm, female.*
A medium-sized terrapin with a hard shell that lacks a hinge. The head is withdrawn straight back. The hind feet usually have slight webbing. The carapace is green, with irregular patterning that is darker and duller in adults. The plastron is yellow with scattered patterning. The head has pale stripes and a red ear spot in juveniles. **Biology and breeding:** Omnivorous, this terrapin feeds on water insects, snails, frogs, water weed, etc. It hibernates under water or in hollow logs during winter (when the water temperature drops below 10°C). Although not well established in South Africa, this species has the potential to become a pest and it should not be released into the wild. Sexually mature males develop long claws on the front feet, with which they stroke the females in an elaborate courtship. Females lay 8-15 (up to 23) eggs in damp soil. Two or three clutches may be laid between August and February. The brightly coloured young hatch in 2-3 months. **Habitat:** Quiet backwaters and ponds. **Range:** N. and central America; babies, imported with tropical fish, were released when they outgrew their homes and have been found in vleis and streams near Pretoria, Johannesburg, Silverton and Durban. Similar introductions are known in Europe and Israel. **Subspecies:** Numerous races exist. Commercially farmed specimens are usually of the Texas race, *T.s. elegans.*

## SEA TURTLES
### SUPERFAMILY CHELONIOIDEA

The first chelonians lived in swamps, but by the Cretaceous period at least four families had moved into the oceans. Many of these early sea turtles were large, the largest being the giant *Archelon* which was over 3 m long. Sea turtles are now less diverse than in those times, and are represented by only eight species in two families, one of which (the leatherback turtle) is highly aberrant. They retain certain primitive features, such as being unable to retract the head or limbs, and they have a robust skull and a row of inframarginals across the bridge. Other unusual features which are adaptations to marine life include the excretion of excess salt via the tear ducts and the modification of the limbs into flippers, which retain only one or two claws and are 'rowed' in unison rather than used alternately as do the terrapins.

All sea turtles are tied to land for reproduction and must brave dangers as they haul themselves ashore to lay their eggs. Clumsy and almost helpless on land, the breeding females are easy to kill. Their numbers have been decimated and all are now endangered. All breed in a similar fashion, crawling ashore onto sheltered, sandy beaches, often on moonless nights. They dig a deep pit and lay large numbers of spherical, soft-shelled eggs. They emerge from the water one to five times at 10- to 15-day intervals, and may lay up to 1 000 eggs during a breeding season. Most females breed at three- to four-year intervals, but this varies with the species and the individual. Hatchling sex is determined by incubation temperature; the critical period is the third week of incubation, and higher temperatures (32-34°C) produce females.

Two of the five species found in southern African waters lay their eggs in the sandy beaches of Maputaland. Protected by the KwaZulu-Natal Parks Board (SA RDB, Vulnerable), their numbers are slowly increasing. Small numbers of another species nest on Bazaruto Island, Mozambique.

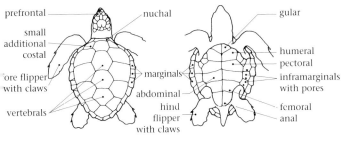

The shields of a sea turtle

# Leatherback Turtles
## FAMILY DERMOCHELYIDAE

This group of large to giant sea turtles is characterized by various skull features (including the lack of nasal bones), extreme reduction of the bones of the carapace and plastron, and a unique internal shell that is composed of small, polygonal bones.

Four fossil genera are known, dating back to the Eocene epoch. Only a single living representative survives.

## Leatherback Turtle  *Dermochelys*

There is a single species in the genus, and it is peculiar in both anatomy and behaviour. It is undergoing dangerous population declines and over two-thirds of the world population have been lost during the last 15 years (from 115 000 in 1980 to 35 000 in 1995). Although the southern African population appears to be growing, elsewhere the species seems to be heading for extinction.

### Leatherback Turtle  *Dermochelys coriacea* (Pl. 9)
*TL 1 300-1 700 mm; max. TL 1 780 mm, female.*

A giant turtle (it can weigh over 800 kg) with a deep, narrow, barrel-shaped shell that lacks horny scutes, being covered instead with thick, smooth skin that resembles vulcanized rubber. The skin has 12 long ridges (five each on the carapace and the plastron, and one on each side). The shells of hatchlings are covered with small, bead-like scales. The flippers are long and lack claws, although these may be present for a short time in some hatchlings. The neck is short and thick. The beak is bicuspid, sharp-edged and hooked. In adults, the carapace and flippers are black, usually with scattered white spots. The plastron and lower surfaces of the head and flippers are white, suffused with pink and grey-black. The carapace and flippers of juveniles are blue-grey when dry and blackish when wet,

LAND TORTOISES & SEA TURTLES          37

with white ridges on the shell and the trailing edges of the flippers.
**Biology and breeding:** Leatherback turtles undertake long journeys and often temporarily enter cold currents to feed. They have many internal adaptations to conserve heat in cold waters, and can even metabolize fat to generate heat. They are therefore the only living reptile that is regularly endothermic. The average dive is 60 m deep and lasts approximately 10 minutes. Leatherback turtles can, however, stay underwater for up to 37 minutes and reach depths of over 350 m, possibly as much as 1000 m. Adults feed exclusively on jellyfish, but hatchlings may take other floating organisms. The throat is coated with long, backwardly projecting spines that prevent slippery food from escaping. Some leatherbacks have died after ingesting large sheets of clear plastic, presuming them to be edible. Nesting is restricted to tropical beaches, the most southerly of which is the small rookery on the Maputaland beaches in northern KwaZulu-Natal. In recent years a few females have even nested as far south as Algoa Bay. Gravid females haul themselves ashore at night in summer (November-January), favouring moonless nights with high tide around midnight. Each digs a deep, flask-shaped nest hole above the high-water mark. A thousand billiard ball-sized eggs are laid in batches of 100-120 at nine- to 11-day intervals. Eggs have a high fertility (normally 70-75%, and up to 90%), and hatch in about 70 days. Females may return to nest every one to five years. Hatchlings emerge at night to avoid heavy predation by ghost crabs, sea gulls and fish. Growth is very rapid; the carapace grows about one centimetre a week, and weight increases a hundredfold in 29 weeks. Sexual maturity is reached in 3-5 years at approximately 1 400-mm carapace length. **Habitat:** The leatherback turtle usually prefers the surface waters of the temperate and tropical oceans. **Range:** It is found worldwide. **Subspecies:** Indo-Pacific leatherbacks are sometimes referred to as a separate race (*D.c. schlegeli*), but this is questionable.

# Modern Sea Turtles
FAMILY CHELONIIDAE

These are advanced sea turtles that retain a hard shell and have strengthened limbs to increase their swimming efficiency.

Known from the Cretaceous period, there are 33 genera, 27 of these extinct and five living. Four genera are represented in the southern African subregion.

KEY TO THE SOUTHERN AFRICAN GENERA IN THE CHELONIIDAE
1 - Carapace with 4 pairs of costals, the first pair separated from the nuchal and never the smallest:                                    go to 2
  - Carapace with 5 pairs of costals, the first being small and usually touching the nuchal:                                             go to 3
2 - Snout not compressed; 2 prefrontals on head; shields not overlapping; 1 claw on each flipper:          *Chelonia* (Green sea turtles, page 39)
  - Snout hooked 4 prefrontals on head; shields strongly overlapping; 2 claws on each flipper:         *Eretmochelys* (Hawksbill turtle, page 40)
3 - 5 pairs of costals; 3 inframarginals (without pores) across bridge; reddish colour:                   *Caretta* (Loggerhead sea turtle, page 41)
  - 6-9 pairs of costals; 4 inframarginals (often with pores) across bridge; olive colour:                 *Lepidochelys* (Ridley sea turtles, page 40)

# Green Sea Turtles   *Chelonia*

Widely distributed, two species are recognized at present. Extralimitally, the Pacifc green turtle (*C. agassizi*) occurs in the eastern Pacific, and is a small, dark turtle with a high, narrow carapace. The flatback sea turtle, previously placed within *Chelonia*, is now placed in a separate genus (*Nator depressa*). It occurs in Australasian waters, and is characterized by its flat shell and carnivorous habits; it lays only a few, large eggs. Only the green turtle (*C. mydas*) occurs in southern African coastal waters.

## Green Turtle                                  *Chelonia mydas* **(Pl. 8)**

*TL 980-1 200 mm; max. TL 1 400 mm, female.*

A very large, hard-shelled turtle; nesting females on the Mozambique islands weighed 124-208 kg, and those from the Atlantic up to 300 kg. The shell is smooth, with thin, non-overlapping scutes, and a median keel in juveniles which disappears in adults. There are 12 pairs of marginals, the posterior ones being serrated in juveniles and smooth in adults. Four pairs of costals are present. The plastron is relatively large, with two long ridges in the young. The bridge is wide, with four inframarginals that lack pores. The head is compact and relatively small. The prefrontal scales on the nose are undivided and elongate. The front flippers each have a single claw (two in juveniles); there is only one claw on each of the hind flippers. Males have longer tails than females. Coloration is varied. Hatchlings have a black-brown carapace with bronze highlights on the vertebrals, and a white border and plastron. Juveniles have a carapace that is dark grey when approximately 200 mm long, and thereafter may have varied ground colour (pale red-brown to dark brown), streaked with dark brown, red-brown and yellow. The adult's carapace varies from greenish-brown to black; streaking may persist, break into spots or fade completely. The plastron is dirty white to yellow. The head shields are black to red-brown, and often white-edged. Females are usually darker than males. **Biology and breeding:** During the first year of life, green turtles feed on jellyfish and other floating organisms, but then become predominantly herbivorous, grazing on sea grasses (for example *Zostera* beds) in estuaries and shallow seas. Subadults and occasional adults are common along the eastern seaboard with a few temporary residents in most open estuaries. It is not known whether these temporary residents return to northern waters to breed, or if they are non-breeding vagrants. In the west, adults come ashore on the Skeleton Coast, but are not known to breed and are probably basking out of cold waters. The green turtle breeds locally only in small numbers on Bazaruto Island, Mozambique. The nearest main rookery is Europa Island in the Mozambique Channel, where 4 000-9 000 turtles nest annually. Other nesting sites occur in N. Tanzania. Nesting occurs throughout the year, with a midsummer peak, and up to 750 females may come ashore each night. Mating takes place in shallow coastal waters in typical chelonian fashion: the males have enlarged claws on their front flippers which they hook over the leading edge of the female's carapace. Females move up the beach by 'humping', moving both forelegs together as if swimming. All other sea turtles move on land by moving alternate limbs. The eggs are spherical (41-47 mm dia., 38-58 g) and 115-197 are laid in each clutch. The female returns 2-3 (and up to six) times at intervals of 10-20 days. Eggs hatch in about 56 days, the young emerging together, usually at night. Carapace length in hatchlings is 45-51 mm, and they weigh 18-29 g. Growth is slow and sexual maturity

is reached in 10-15 years. **Habitat:** Shallow waters with abundant vegetation. **Range:** Tropical and subtropical seas, adults and subadults entering
southern African waters. **Subspecies:** None recognized at present; the
E. Pacific *C. agassizi* is now treated as a full species.

# Hawksbill Turtle   *Eretmochelys*

This is a medium-sized, highly distinctive sea turtle. Only a single species
is recognized. No fossils are known.

### Hawksbill Turtle                     *Eretmochelys imbricata* (Pl. 8)

*TL 600-900 mm; max. TL 1 070 mm.*

A relatively small turtle that rarely weighs more than 50 kg, but has
attained 139 kg. Its shell scales are thick and overlapping, and the head is
narrow and anteriorly pointed, with a long, slightly bird-like beak (hence
its common name). It has two pairs of prefrontals, four pairs of costals
and 12 pairs of marginals, the posterior ones markedly serrated. There are
four poreless inframarginals. The forelimbs have very long digits, and
there are two claws on each limb. Males have long tails and narrower
carapaces than females, and a small plastral concavity. In hatchlings, the
carapace is uniform brown and the plastron dark, each scale having a
large, dark spot. In adults, the carapace shields are translucent amber,
beautifully patterned with irregular, radiating streaks of light red-brown,
black and yellow. The plastron is uniform yellow to orange-yellow, and
the head is yellowish, with black-centred scales. **Biology and breeding:**
Juveniles eat floating vegetation (for example *Sargassum*), but adults are
mainly carnivorous, feeding on hard-bodied bottom-living marine invertebrates, including corals and urchins. They may become poisonous to man
after feeding on toxic corals, and human deaths have been recorded. Wild
populations are endangered, mainly as a result of the curio trade. The
scutes are made into 'tortoiseshell' jewellery and other objets d'art. The
volume of trade is horrendous; Indonesia and Japan imported 260 000 kg
of raw shell in 1978-9, while in Singapore and the Phillipines nearly
100 000 juveniles are sold as curios annually. They do not breed locally;
the nearest rookeries are in NE Madagascar, Tromelin Island, and Primeiras
and St Brandon islands in Mauritius. Females are wary when emerging to
breed, and come out in small groups on irregular nights. Nesting beaches
are usually of coarse sand. Depending on the region and the size of the
female, 70-200 spherical eggs (40-42 mm dia.) are laid in a flask-shaped
nest; 2-4 clutches are laid at 15- to 19-day intervals during the season.
After 58-64 days' incubation, hatchlings measuring 40 mm emerge at
night. Growth is relatively rapid, and sexual maturity is reached in 8-10
years. **Habitat:** Coral reefs of tropical waters. **Range:** Circumtropical;
second most common turtle in Mozambique coastal waters, but a relatively rare vagrant further south, exceptionally reaching the SW Cape Atlantic
coast. **Subspecies:** A number recognized (for example *E.i. imbricata* in
Atlantic, *E.i. bissa* and *E.i. squamata* in Indo-Pacific); none is well defined.

# Ridley Sea Turtles   *Lepidochelys*

These are the smallest of the sea turtles, with unusually broad shells. They
were once famed for breeding in 'arribadas', when massive numbers of
turtles (up to 46 000) emerged to breed on 1 km of beach in a single day.
Although this resulted in a tremendous wastage of turtle eggs, as females
often dug up the eggs laid only minutes earlier by other females, it served

to swamp predators and resulted in overall survival of the young hatchlings. Unfortunately, man is a most efficient predator, and today these unique sights are no longer seen, the breeding females having been decimated for food. Two species are recognized: extralimitally, Kemp's ridley (*L. kempi*) is a critically endangered species restricted to the Gulf of Mexico and northern temperate areas of Atlantic Ocean. *L. olivacea* is a rare vagrant to the coastal waters of the subcontinent.

### Olive Ridley Turtle                              *Lepidochelys olivacea* (Pl. 8)
*TL 500-650 mm; max. TL 750 mm.*

The smallest sea turtle, weighing up to 45 kg. It has a broad, flat-topped, smooth carapace, and numerous costal shields (5-9 on each side). Hatchlings and juveniles have three dorsal keels, and two on the plastron. There are 12-14 marginals, which are slightly serrated at the rear. There are four inframarginals, each with a pore on its posterior edge. The head is triangular, with two pairs of prefrontals. Each limb has two claws. Males have longer tails than females, and narrower, strongly tapered shells, with more intense pigmentation. In hatchlings, the carapace is uniform grey-black with light areas on the plastron, which in a few months become more extensive; adults are dark to light olive-green dorsally, with pale yellow, almost white plastrons. **Biology and breeding:** Sometimes form large aggregations, migrating between nesting beaches and feeding grounds. May sleep floating at the surface in large numbers, unlike other sea turtles, which usually sleep on the sea floor. They feed, sometimes at considerable depths, on bottom-living crustaceans, particularly prawns and shrimps, but also fish and squid. Small turtles even eat dead insects floating on the surface. Perhaps the most common surviving sea turtle, it is still endangered by trade in leather from the neck and limbs, and accidental capture in shrimp trawls. Does not breed locally, although a stray female once nested on Warner Beach in KwaZulu-Natal; the nearest rookery is on the coast of N. Mozambique, where 500-1 000 nests are laid each year. Local 'arribadas' are unknown; the nearest is in Orissa State in India. The female lays 2-3 clutches (at 17- to 29-day intervals) of 105-116 white, soft-shelled, spherical eggs (37-40 mm dia., 31-38 g), and may return to nest at one- to two-year intervals. Nest construction and egg-laying are rapid, and may be completed in one hour; the female tamps down the sand over the eggs with the thickened sides of her plastron. Incubation period is short (only 42-62 days). Hatchlings measure 39-48 mm and weigh 14-18 g. Sexual maturity is possibly reached in 7-9 years. **Habitat:** Mostly found in coastal mainland waters, often in major estuaries. **Range:** Circum-global; present in tropical regions of the Atlantic, Indian and Pacific oceans. Locally very rare, with vagrants entering the coastal waters of KwaZulu-Natal and N. Namibia from time to time. **Subspecies:** None is recognized; the Caribbean *L. kempi* is treated as a separate species.

## Loggerhead Turtle   *Caretta*
This genus contains a single living species, and a number of indeterminate fossil forms dating back to the late Cretaceous period of Europe.

### Loggerhead Turtle                              *Caretta caretta* (Pl. 8)
*TL 700-1 000 mm; max. TL 1 070 mm, female.*
A large turtle, weighing 80-138 kg. Locally, a specimen has been recorded weighing 140 kg, while in the Atlantic, 159 kg has been recorded. (Reports

of gigantic loggerheads weighing up to 400 kg are unconfirmed.) This sea turtle has a big head and an elongate shell that tapers at the rear and is smooth in adults, but has median keels on the costals and vertebrals in juveniles. There are five pairs of costals and 11-12 pairs of marginals which are sometimes bluntly serrated at the rear in juveniles. The plastron of hatchlings has two strong, long keels. There are three inframarginals without pores. The head is very broad (up to 250 mm across), and the jaw has extensive crushing surfaces. There are two pairs of prefrontals. Each limb has two claws. Male loggerheads have longer tails than females, as well as an enlarged, strongly curved claw on each front flipper, more massive heads, and smooth shell margins. In hatchlings, the carapace, plastron and head are uniform brown of varying shades, while the skin of the neck and flippers is darker. In both juveniles and adults, the carapace and the top of the head are uniform red-brown, with white-edged scales. The plastron is uniform yellowish, and the skin is light yellowish-grey.

**Biology and breeding:** After breeding in Maputaland, adult logger-heads move north to feed in the warm waters off Mozambique and E. Africa. Many hatchlings drift south in the Agulhas Current, some 'wrecking' on the E. and S. Cape coasts during onshore winds; others may continue in the southern Indian Ocean gyral, returning to the African coast three years later. For the first three years of life, they drift in surface waters, eating bluebottles, comb jellies, etc. Subsequently, they search for food in shallow coastal waters, becoming carnivorous. The extremely strong jaws are well adapted for feeding on crabs, molluscs and sea urchins, and can even crush giant clams. They nest mainly in sub-tropical waters, including the sandy beaches of Maputaland in KwaZulu-Natal, where 400-500 females breed each year, and smaller numbers on the Bazaruto Archipelago. The largest rookery is on Masirah Island in Oman, where 30 000 females breed annually. Mating takes places at the beginning of the nesting season. Females emerge at night in late spring-summer (November-January in Maputaland) and lay about 500 eggs (40-42 mm dia.) in batches of 100-120 at 15-day intervals. Most return to nest after 2-3 years, but some may exceptionally take up to eight years before breeding again, and others breed more frequently (up to six times in nine years). Incubation takes 47-66 days; hatchlings measure 39-49 mm.

**Habitat:** Coastal waters and reefs. **Range:** Found worldwide in temperate and subtropical waters. More common on the east than on the west coast of the subcontinent. **Subspecies:** A number of subspecies have been proposed, including *C.c. gigas* for Indo-Pacific loggerheads, but none are recognized at present.

# Soft-shelled Terrapins
## FAMILY TRIONYCHIDAE

These are unusual chelonians, surprisingly named not for their very odd, soft shells, but for having only three claws on each foot. Abundant in N. America and SE Asia, there are a few African species. These terrapins are fully aquatic, with the shell flat and disc-like, often with a flexible edge. The horny shell is completely absent, except for a few vestiges, and the underlying bone is also reduced. The neck is usually very long and extendible, with a snorkel-like nose. Many grow to a large size. They are a shy, active omnivorous species. There are three genera containing five species in Africa; two species in separate genera just enter the subcontinent.

1 - Plastron without femoral flaps:
> *Trionyx* (Soft-shelled terrapins, page 43)
- Plastron with femoral flaps that cover retracted hind feet:
> *Cycloderma* (African flapped soft-shelled terrapins, page 43)

# Soft-shelled Terrapins  *Trionyx*

Now a monotypic genus, with the removal of other species to new genera (*Apalone* in N. America, 3 species; *Aspideretes* in India, 4 species; *Dogania* in Malaysia, 1 species; *Nilssonia* in Burma, 1 species; *Palea* in China, 1 species; *Pelochelys* in Asia, 1 species; *Pelodiscus* in China, 1 species; and *Rafetus* in the Near East, 2 species).

### Nile Soft-shelled Terrapin  *Trionyx triunguis* (Pl. 9)
*TL 400-600 mm; max. TL 950 mm, female.*

This terrapin attains a maximum weight of 40 kg. It is a very large soft-shelled terrapin, that lacks flexible flaps over the hind limbs. The head is elongate and flattened, with a snorkel-like snout. The forelimbs have three sharp-edged, crescentic skin folds. The young have indistinct median keels and wavy lines of tubercles on the carapace. The carapace is dark brown or olive, usually covered with small white or yellow spots, that may disappear in adults. The plastron is white, sometimes with dusky infusions at the front. The head and limbs are dark and profusely spotted. **Biology and breeding:** Omnivorous, they eat molluscs, insects, frogs and fish, as well as palm nuts and fruits. The terrapins are eaten in many regions, and the flesh is reported to taste like rich and slightly oily veal. They move fast in water and on land. Usually vicious, they are ever-ready to bite. The very sharp and powerful jaws are efficient amputators of ill-placed fingers. They can survive seawater, and have apparently expanded their range by undertaking short marine excursions between river mouths. Long-lived, they have survived for longer than 42 years in captivity. The female lays 25-60 spherical, hard-shelled eggs (25-30 mm dia.) in nests buried 300-400 mm deep in exposed sand banks along rivers. Incubation is rapid, and the eggs hatch in 76-78 days. **Habitat:** Deepish water in lakes, rivers and estuaries. **Range:** Throughout the Nile and most major river systems of W. and central Africa, but often absent upstream from major waterfalls (for example, absent from Lake Victoria). Just entering the subcontinent, occurring in Cunene River downstream of Ruacana Falls. Possibly also present in Kavango in N. Namibia.

# African Flapped Soft-shelled Terrapins
*Cycloderma* and *Cyclanorbis*

These two genera of African soft-shelled terrapins are distinguished by the flexible flaps that cover the hind limbs when they are withdrawn. Each genus contains two species of medium-sized to large terrapins, distributed through the tropical regions of Africa. All are poorly known. In *Cycloderma*, the eyes are located closer to the snout than in *Cyclanorbis*, and there are other osteological differences. Only one species enters the subregion.

### Zambezi Soft-shelled Terrapin  *Cycloderma frenatum* (Pl. 9)
*TL 350-450 mm; max. TL 560 mm, female.*

This terrapin, attaining a weight of up to 14 kg, is a large soft-shelled species, with flexible flaps that cover the hind limbs. The head is elongate

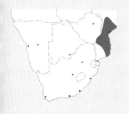

and flattened, with a snorkel-like snout. The forefeet have four or five sharp-edged, crescentic skin-flaps. The young terrapins have indistinct median keels and wavy lines of tubercles on the carapace. In colour, the carapace of adults is uniform pale to dark olive, sometimes faintly blotched; the young have a white edge to the carapace. The plastron is white to flesh-pink, sometimes with grey infusions in adults. The head and neck of the young are grey, with broad white stripes; these fade gradually in adult specimens, in which the head and neck are dark olive. **Biology and breeding:** This terrapin digs with its forelegs in soft mud for snails and freshwater mussels, which it crushes with its strong jaws. It also eats fish, frogs and aquatic insects. Shy, the adults are rarely seen. When disturbed, they burrow into soft mud, and will bite and claw if captured. Enemies include crocodiles, otters and man. The eggs and terrapins are edible. Clutches of 15-25 hard-shelled, almost spherical eggs (30-35 mm dia.) are laid in December-March. Hatchlings (40-48 mm) emerge from nesting banks during the following rainy season. **Habitat:** Found in rivers, lakes and stagnant ponds. **Range:** Occurs in E. Africa, from Tanzania to the Save River on the Mozambique floodplain, and Sabi-Lundi river confluence in Zimbabwe.

## SIDE-NECKED TERRAPINS
### SUBORDER PLEURODIRA

'Pleurodira' means 'side-neck' and refers to the manner of head withdrawal that characterizes side-necked terrapins: it is pulled to one side under the carapace, so that usually one eye can still be seen (some species have developed a hinge in the plastron to further protect the head). The shell is usually flat and hard, and there is an unpaired intergular at the front of the plastron. The hind feet are webbed. Some species have very long necks.

# Side-necked Terrapins
### FAMILY PELOMEDUSIDAE

These are primitive terrapins, that today are restricted to the African continent and Madagascar.

The neck of these terrapins is completely retractable under the carapace edge, and the carapace lacks nuchal and supracaudal scutes. The plastron has an intergular.

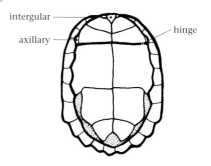

**Plastron of *Pelusios***

1    Plastron not hinged at front:

                              *Pelomedusa* (Marsh or Helmeted terrapin, page 45)

-  Plastron hinged at front:           *Pelusios* (Hinged terrapins, page 46)

# Marsh or Helmeted Terrapin    *Pelomedusa*

This genus contains a single species which is widely distributed in sub-Saharan Africa. The local name 'Cape water terrapin' is too parochial as this terrapin swims in the Nile and also occurs on Madagascar.

### Marsh or Helmeted Terrapin    *Pelomedusa subrufa* (Pl. 10)

*TL 200-300 mm; max. TL 325 mm, male.*

A medium-sized side-necked terrapin with a flat, hard, thin shell with no plastral hinge. This species has a large head with two small tentacles (of unknown function, but possibly used in mating) beneath the chin, and musk glands on the fourth to eighth marginals near the carapace edge. The hind feet have a webbed fringe. Males have longer tails and narrower, flatter shells than females, and grow to a larger size. The shell is uniform olive to dark brown above, sometimes with the shields black-edged and the marginals paler; below, it is either entirely black, pale-coloured, or has a symmetrical, pale-centred pattern. The head is dark on top with vermiculations, and pale below and on the jaws. **Biology and breeding:** This is a very common species, particularly in temporary pans, even in the central Karoo. Because of its thin shell, it is usually absent from permanent waters inhabited by crocodiles. Omnivorous, it eats almost anything, including water weed, insects and frogs. In some regions (for example Etosha Pan) it acts 'crocodile' and ambushes, drowns and devours doves and sand grouse drinking at the water's edge. It basks by either emerging onto the bank or a log, or floats at the surface in warm water. It aestivates during droughts by burrowing into moist soil, often far from its aquatic home. Many are killed on roads while migrating to new vleis after good rains. They have lived for over 16 years in captivity. Few people eat them, as they have an unpleasant, musky smell. They do not make the best pets; they are belligerent, long-necked and ever-willing to bite or to eject their cloacal contents. Mating occurs in water throughout summer. The male pursues the female, touching his snout against her vent and hind quarters. If she is receptive, he grips the edge of her shell with his feet and rubs the two short sensory tentacles which are situated under his chin on the back of her head; he also expels a stream of water from his nostrils over her face. Usually 10-30 (but up to and sometimes more than 40) soft-shelled, elongate eggs (30-40 x 18-28 mm, 10 g) are laid in a flask-shaped pit. The female digs this with her hind feet in soft, moist soil above the high-water mark. If the ground is hard, she urinates to soften it. Young hatch in 90-110 days, emerging after the ground has been softened by rain; they measure 25-38 mm, weigh 8-10 g. **Habitat:** Slow-moving and still water, including temporary pans. **Range:** Wherever water is present, even in central Karoo and Etosha. Elsewhere, throughout most of sub-Saharan Africa; Madagascar. **Subspecies:** A poorly defined southern race is recognized by some; it and the typical race both occur in the region. *P.s. nigra* has dull coloration, a black plastron, and black triangles on the lower sutures of the marginals. Occurs in KwaZulu-Natal, extending into adjacent Free State, and E. Cape. *P.s. subrufa* has large, off-white areas on the plastron, and occurs over the rest of the subcontinent.

# Hinged Terrapins   *Pelusios*

These terrapins are immediately recognizable by the hinge at the front of the plastron, which can be closed, protecting the head and forelimbs. The shell is usually domed and thick and in some species has a serrated top and/or posterior edge, especially in juveniles.

Distributed throughout most of sub-Saharan Africa, it is also present on Madagascar and the islands of the Indian Ocean. The number of species is debatable; possibly as many as 15; five species are present on the sub-continent. The colour pattern of the plastron is an important local distinguishing feature.

### Serrated Hinged Terrapin                    *Pelusios sinuatus* (Pl. 11)
*TL 300-400 mm; max. TL 465 mm, female.*
The largest hinged terrapin. The posterior marginals are enlarged to give a serrated edge, and the vertebrals are keeled, particularly in juveniles. An axillary scale is present at the front junction of the carapace and the plastron. The head is relatively small, with a weakly bicuspid beak and usually two longish tentacles under the chin. Females grow larger than males. The carapace and bridge are uniform black in colour. The plastron is yellow-centred, with a sharply defined, black, angular pattern around the edge. The head is blackish-brown with yellow or brown vermiculations. The skin of the neck and limbs is pale olive-grey. **Biology and breeding:** Common in large water bodies. Often seen basking on logs and rocks during the day. Larger specimens eat mussels, while juveniles take invertebrates, frogs, etc. They scavenge at game killed by crocodiles, to which they in turn regularly fall prey. Engorged ticks are often taken from the legs of large game. May become a nuisance, taking baits set for fish. Retreat into their shell when caught, and rarely bite. Live for longer than 12 years in captivity. The female lays 7-25 eggs (24-26 x 42-45 mm, 18-21 g), up to 500 m from the nearest water, in October-January. In the wild hatchlings appear in March-April. Eggs artificially incubated (32°C) may hatch in 48 days. Hatchlings measure 40-43 mm, weigh 12-15 g. **Habitat:** Perennial rivers and permanent lakes and pans. **Range:** Tropical E. Africa; along Zambezi River to Victoria Falls, and south to N. Zululand.

### Pan Hinged Terrapin                         *Pelusios subniger* (Pl. 11)
*TL 130-180 mm; max. TL 200 mm, female.*
A small hinged terrapin with a rounded, smooth shell and a small plastral hinge. There is no axillary. The head is large, with a blunt snout and smooth beak; there are usually two tentacles under the chin. The carapace is uniform brown, and brown-grey when dry. The bridge is yellow and brown. The shields of the plastron have pale yellow centres. The head is uniform brown, not vermiculated and sometimes has black spots. The skin of the neck and limbs is grey or black. **Biology and breeding:** Similar to the marsh terrapin, *Pelomedusa subrufa* (page 45), this terrapin often aestivates on land during droughts. Many have been found with their shells scarred by fire. They feed on small frogs and invertebrates. In defence, they may discharge their cloacal contents. The females probably nest throughout summer; in captivity, up to eight eggs are laid in February-March. Incubation takes 104-107 days (28°C) and hatchlings measuring 30 mm TL are found in March-April. **Habitat:** Pans and temporary water bodies. **Range:** Madagascar and E. Africa, into Zimbabwe and N. Botswana, reaching Upper Limpopo River, S. Mozambique, the

*P.s. subniger*

Bazaruto Archipelago and N. Kruger National Park. An isolated race occurs on the Seychelles and possibly Mauritius. **Subspecies:** Two races are recognized. The typical race, *P.s. subniger*, occurs on the African mainland and Madagascar, and is replaced on Indian Ocean islands by *P.s. parietalis*.

## Okavango Hinged Terrapin — *Pelusios bechuanicus* (Pl. 11)

*TL 250-300 mm; max. TL 330 mm, female.*
A large terrapin with a heavy, domed, elongate shell with a small plastral hinge. There is no axillary. The vertebrals are slightly keeled in juveniles. The head is very large, with a smooth beak, and usually three tentacles under the chin. The carapace is uniform black. The plastron is largely or entirely black (but sometimes yellowish in the centre). The head is black, with symmetrical black and yellow markings that are prominent in juveniles. Skin of neck and limbs is yellowish. **Biology and breeding:** Lives in deep, clear water and feeds on invertebrates and fish. Large clutches of soft-shelled eggs (35-39 x 21-23 mm) are laid in moist soil in early summer. **Habitat:** Clear waters of Okavango Swamp; Kafue Flats. **Range:** Greater Okavango Basin, Zambezi River above Victoria Falls.

## Mashona Hinged Terrapin — *Pelusios rhodesianus* (Pl. 11)

*TL 180-220 mm; max. TL 250 mm.*
This medium-sized hinged terrapin has a domed, elongate, smooth shell with a small plastral hinge. There is no axillary. The head is small, with a strongly bicuspid beak, and usually two tentacles under the chin. The carapace is uniform black. The plastron is black, with a diffuse yellow centre. The head is dark brown, and yellow on the sides. The skin of the neck and limbs is pale yellow. **Biology and breeding:** This terrapin feeds on aquatic insects, frogs and small fish. The female lays small clutches of small, soft-shelled eggs (33-37 x 20-23 mm). She may lay more than one clutch in a summer (nesting has been recorded in September-April). Hatchlings have been recorded in December-January. **Habitat:** Quiet, weed-choked backwaters on dams and vleis. **Range:** Central and SE Africa, entering Okavango Swamp and central Zimbabwe, and with relict populations in N. Zululand and Durban.

## Yellow-bellied Hinged Terrapin — *Pelusios castanoides* (Pl. 11)

*TL 180-200 mm; max. TL 220 mm.*
This is a medium-sized terrapin, with an elongate, smooth shell with a small plastral hinge. There is no axillary. The head is of moderate size, with a strongly bicuspid beak, and usually two tentacles under the chin. The carapace is olive, blackish-brown or yellowish. The plastron is yellow, usually with faint black markings on the front sutures. The head is blackish-brown, with fine yellow vermiculations. The skin of the neck and limbs is yellow. **Biology and breeding:** This terrapin frequents shallow water, burying itself in mud when the water dries up, and re-emerging with rains. Many specimens have shells scarred from dry-season fires. It feeds on aquatic insects and frogs, and also freshwater snails and floating vegetation. Two females were recorded laying 25 eggs (30-33 x 21-23 mm) each, at the end of September. **Habitat:** Still lakes and swamps at low altitudes. **Range:** E. Africa, through central Mozambique Plain to N. Zululand; isolated populations in Madagascar and the Seychelles. **Subspecies:** Two races are recognized. The typical race, *P.c. castanoides*, occurs in Africa and Madagascar, and is replaced by *P.c. intergularis* on the Seychelles.

*P.c. castanoides*

# SCALED REPTILES
## ORDER SQUAMATA

These reptiles are characterized by a scaly skin that is covered with a thin, dry, horny layer that is periodically shed, either in bits or in one piece. They usually lack osteoderms, although these may be present on the head and body scales in some lizard families. The skull is diapsid, having openings in the upper and lower temporal regions. The bones of the palate do not form a continuous roof to the mouth. There are two nostrils. The cloacal aperture is transverse, and the paired male sexual organs (hemipenes) are stored in the tail base. They evert in use (so that the inner surface becomes the outer, rather like turning a sock inside-out), and are usually adorned with spines and flounces. Only a single hemipenis is used at a time. Most species lay eggs, but viviparity has evolved on numerous occasions.

Squamates arose in the Triassic epoch, from eosuchian stock, although lizards did not become common until the Cretaceous period, and snakes a little later. Amphisbaenians are not known until the Eocene epoch, but must have evolved much earlier, probably from early lizards. The squamates are now at the peak of their radiation and represent the flowering of modern reptiles. They are distributed throughout the world's tropical and temperate regions, in all habitats, but with only one successful marine group (the sea snakes). The squamates constitute the largest group of living reptiles, containing more than 6 200 species, and exceed in number all the world's mammal species. Three suborders are recognized. The lizards and snakes each constitute large suborders, while that of the amphisbaenians is much less diverse, and consist of only about 150 species.

**Snake, amphisbaenian or legless lizard?** Legless lizards are frequently confused with snakes. As a result, many are needlessly killed by people who think they may be poisonous. Amphisbaenians look so like worms that they are often called worm lizards, although they are neither worms nor lizards.

Legs are not always useful, and in some habitats can get in the way. A sinuous movement, like that of fish, is used by some long-bodied reptiles to move in long grass or sandy soils; forward motion is achieved by pressing different parts of the body in waves against the ground or vegetation. Lizards in such habitats have evolved serpentine bodies. Movement in grass requires less strength than in sand, and is achieved by increased tail length; some legless grassland lizards have tails that are three times the length of their body. Even in loose sandy soils, burrowing requires more effort and fossorial reptiles have shorter tails and thicker, more muscular bodies. Snakes probably evolved from burrowing legless lizards. They have a very unusual eye structure. This is most easily explained by assuming that it redeveloped from vestiges left in an ancestral blind legless lizard. Most of the primitive snakes are burrowing. More advanced snakes have radiated back on to the surface and even into trees and the sea.

Amphisbaenians, which live permanently underground, probably evolved from very early lizards. Their bodies are usually pink and are always covered with rings of squarish, non-overlapping scales, and the head is often covered with a thick shield that resembles a thumbnail. While they may sometimes be confused with worms they do not resemble snakes.

It is not always easy to tell snakes and legless lizards apart, particularly when the primitive burrowing snakes are compared with modern fossorial lizards. Most snakes have enlarged belly scales: these are never found in lizards, even in the burrowing species. Snakes' eyes (when present) are always covered with an immovable spectacle so they have an unblinking stare; many legless lizards retain movable eyelids, so you may presume that if it winks, it's safe. Unfortunately, many highly specialized fossorial lizards and primitive burrowing snakes lack external eyes, and all that can be seen are black dots under the head shields. Both groups also have small belly scales, so there really is no simple rule for telling these two groups of reptiles apart. All blind snakes have extremely short tails, with a sharp spine at the tip. In addition, thread snakes and blind snakes have much rounder, blunter heads than any legless lizards. Confusion between these latter groups, however, is academic as no primitive snakes are venomous.

# Snakes
## SUBORDER SERPENTES (OPHIDIA)

Snakes are legless squamates that lack eyelids, external ears and osteoderms. In some primitive families, vestiges of hind limbs are still present. The left lung is reduced or absent. The tongue is retractile into a sheath. Snakes have long backbones (some with more than 440 vertebrae), with many articulated ribs that are used for locomotion and to maintain the shape of the body.

All are carnivorous, and many are specialist feeders on particular prey. This may be engulfed alive, or first subdued, either by constriction or by the injection of venom. Teeth may be enlarged and used to grip prey, or modified for the injection of venom, which is derived from the salivary juices. Prey is swallowed whole, and in many species the lower jaw can be dislocated to allow large items to be engulfed. Some species have very toxic venoms which may be used defensively against predators. The tail can be shed in a few species, but it cannot be regenerated. All regularly shed their skin, usually in one piece, starting at the snout. Most lay soft-shelled eggs, but viviparity has evolved in some species, usually in cold climates.

The earliest fossils are from Spain and date from the Early Cretaceous period, about 135 million years ago, but it is likely that they evolved even earlier. There are approximately 2 600 living species in over 420 genera and at least 18 families, distributed throughout most of the temperate and tropical regions of the earth.

Snakes, like sharks, scare many people. Although most people realize that not all snakes are poisonous, few bother to learn which snakes are dangerous, and even fewer consider that even the venomous species may be beneficial.

Of the 143 species of snakes in southern Africa, 37 have fangs and venom that have caused clinical symptoms; some of these have venoms that are less toxic than those of wasps and bees, and cannot be considered dangerous. Only 15 snakes have killed people on the subcontinent. These include the five species of cobra, the two species of mamba, the rinkhals, the shieldnose snake, Namibian coral snake, the puff adder and gaboon adder, the boomslang, the bird snake, and the rock python (these species are marked with a black skull-and-crossbones on the colour plates). The bites of several others (the garter snakes, and the many-horned adder) can be serious, and may even have been fatal in exceptional circumstances. However, there have been no documented deaths from bites by these species (marked with a red skull-and-crossbones on the colour plates), or from the local burrowing asps, night adders, the small adders (including the berg adder and horned adder), the sea snake, skaapstekers, or any other back-fanged species. Obviously, the numbers and types of snakes differ from region to region, but no part of South Africa is free of snakes, and at least one venomous species occurs in all regions. Even where there are large numbers of snakes, including many venomous species (such as in Zululand), snakebite is rarely a significant risk. The following figures illustrate the point: in South Africa over 10 000 people are killed every year in road accidents; 2 000 die from lung cancer and other diseases related to cigarette smoking; about 200 are struck and killed by lightning; and fewer than 20, perhaps as few as 10, die from snakebite.

While a 'hug-a-snake' campaign is not necessary, greater tolerance and understanding of these efficient and unique predators is certainly called for. The vast majority of our local snakes are completely harmless or clinically unimportant. In fact, they do a tremendous amount of good in controlling agricultural pests. Thailand provides a good example: because many Asian people have a great belief in the healing properties of snake extracts, in 1985 Thailand exported 1,3 million snakes to Hong Kong, Korea, Japan and even the USA. With the crash in the country's snake population, rats proliferated and are estimated to have destroyed 400 000 hectares of valuable rice fields. In southern Africa, snakes are considered as important as birds of prey in controlling dassies and cane-rats in farmlands.

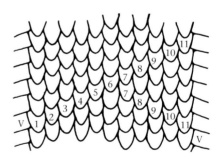

V = Ventral scale

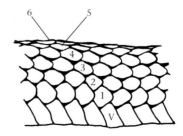

Counting midbody scale rows

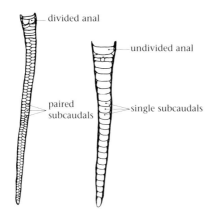

_divided anal_

_undivided anal_

_paired subcaudals_

_single subcaudals_

**The ventral surface of a snake's tail**

### KEY TO THE SNAKE FAMILIES IN SOUTHERN AFRICA

1 - Body worm-like, head hardly distinct from body, tail blunt; back and belly covered with small, similar-sized scales; eyes vestigial, buried under head shields: go to 2
  - Body not worm-like, head distinct from body, tail tapered; belly covered with transversely enlarged scales; eyes well developed and movable, with a transparent spectacle: go to 3
2 - Ocular shield not bordering lip; teeth present only in upper jaw; 20 or more scale rows at midbody; tail slightly longer than broad: Typhlopidae (Blind snakes, page 52)
  - Ocular shield bordering lip; teeth present only in lower jaw; 14 scale rows at midbody; tail at least three times longer than broad: Leptotyphlopidae (Thread snakes, page 55)
3 - More than 70 scale rows at midbody; some labials with deep, heat-sensitive pits; vestigial hind limbs present as a pair of claws bordering the vent: Boidae (Boas and pythons, page 58)
  - Fewer than 50 scale rows at midbody; labials without deep, heat-sensitive pits; vestigial hind limbs absent: go to 4
4 - No enlarged poison fangs at front of upper jaw: go to 5
  - One or more pairs of enlarged, tubular poison fangs at front of upper jaw: go to 6
5 - Loreal absent; grooved back fangs present; burrowing snakes: Atractaspididae (part) (African burrowing snakes, page 60)
  - Loreal present; grooved back fangs present or absent; terrestrial, aquatic or arboreal snakes: Colubridae (Typical snakes, page 69)
6 - Head covered with large, symmetrical shields; loreal absent: go to 7
  - Head usually covered with irregular, small, keeled scales (enlarged head shields in night adders); loreal present; poison fangs large, hinged and enclosed in membranous sheath: Viperidae (Adders and vipers, page 112)
7 - Poison fangs small to moderate, not hinged and not enclosed in membranous sheath: Elapidae (Cobras, mambas and their relatives, page 101)
  - Poison fangs long and straight and partially hinged: Atractaspididae (part) (Burrowing asps, page 60)

# Blind Snakes
## FAMILY TYPHLOPIDAE

These are very primitive snakes, with fossils known from the early Paleocene. They have a toothless lower jaw and internal vestiges of a pelvic girdle. They display many adaptations for burrowing, including having a cylindrical body and an indistinct head; polished, tightly fitting scales with ventrals that are not enlarged on the belly; reduced eyes under the head shields; and an exceptionally short tail with a terminal spine. All blind snakes are very similar in appearance and colour.

They feed mainly on termites but occasionally eat other invertebrates. They are commonly found under stones or in termite nests, and are sometimes forced to the surface by floods or exposed during ploughing. Oviparous and viviparous species are known. During mating the male coils tightly around the rear of the female. The skin is shed in compacted rings.

These snakes are distributed throughout the tropical regions of the world; there are about 160 species in six genera (although even further division is likely). Three genera, none endemic and one introduced, enter the subcontinent.

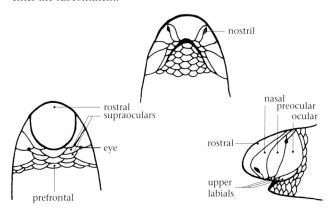

**The head scales of a blind snake**

KEY TO THE GENERA OF SOUTHERN AFRICA TYPHLOPIDAE
1 - Nostril pierced laterally in a divided nasal; rostral narrow; 20 scales around midbody:
    *Ramphotyphlops* (Australasian blind snakes, introduced, page 52)
  - Nostril pierced inferiorly in a semi-divided nasal; rostral wide; 22 or more scales around body:                                          go to 2
2 - Rostral greater than half width of snout at level of nostrils:
    *Rhinotyphlops* (Beaked blind snakes, page 53)
  - Rostral narrower than half width of snout at level of nostrils:
    *Typhlops* (Typical blind snakes, page 54)

## Australasian Blind Snakes    *Ramphotyphlops*
Australasian blind snakes are distinguished by a unique hemipenis that has a solid, non-eversible tip.

There are about 20 species in the genus, all except one being restricted to Australasia; one introduced species occurs on the subcontinent.

**Flower-pot Snake**  *Ramphotyphlops braminus* **(Pl. 40)**
*(Introduced) max. SVL 161 mm.*
This very small, slender snake has 20 scales around its body, 300-350
dorsals, and a rounded snout. It is uniform grey to pale brown in colour,
with a paler belly. The snout, cloacal region and tail tip are cream.
**Biology and breeding:** It feeds on ant and termite larvae. Unique
among snakes in being an all-female species (parthenogenetic). This has
allowed it to colonize many oceanic islands and most continents. It lays
2-6 minute eggs (2 x 6 mm). It is commonly transported in nursery
plants, hence the common name. **Habitat:** Humic soil. **Range:**
Introduced populations in Cape Town, Durban and Beira. Elsewhere,
scattered along E. African coastal regions and throughout Indo-Pacific,
and to Florida in the United States.

# Beaked Blind Snakes  *Rhinotyphlops*

Small to very large typhlopids with beaked snouts, a feature that
distinguishes them from all other local blind snakes. They also have a
very wide rostral and a distinct pattern of lip scale overlap. The body
colour is pale blue or beige, and there is a high number (400-700) of mid-
dorsal scales. The eye is usually inconspicuous (at most a small, pigmented
spot beneath the skin), and the liver large and unsegmented.

The genus contains about 27 species that are restricted mainly to the
African continent, with one Gondwanaland relict from India (*R. actutus*),
and another entering the Near East (*R. simoni*). Twenty-four species are
found in sub-Saharan Africa. Of the four occurring on the subcontinent,
three are endemic.

### Boyle's Beaked Blind Snake  *Rhinotyphlops boylei*
*(Endemic) max. SVL 217 mm.*
This small, slender snake has 26-28 scales around the body, more than 300
dorsals, and an angular snout. The body is olive-brown above, with yellow-
edged scales; the flank scales are pale with dark brown centres. The belly
is pale yellow. **Habitat:** Sandveld. **Range:** Damaraland to W. Botswana.

### Delalande's Beaked Blind Snake  *Rhinotyphlops lalandei* **(Pl. 39)**
*(Endemic) max. SVL 350 mm.*
This slender species has 26-30 scales around the body, more than 300
dorsals, and a prominent horizontal cutting edge to the snout. Coloration
is uniform pinkish-slate to grey-brown above, with each scale pale-edged,
giving a chequered effect. The belly is pale pink-grey. The young are flesh-
coloured. **Biology and breeding:** Widespread in the temperate regions
of southern Africa, with relict populations in moist enclaves in the drier
west. A main predator is the spotted harlequin snake (page 102). Females
lay 2-4 eggs. **Habitat:** Varied; semi-desert, coastal bush, fynbos and
savannah. **Range:** Cape provinces, north to E. Botswana and
S. Zimbabwe. Entering E. Swaziland, but absent from KwaZulu-Natal;
scattered records in central and W. Namibia.

### Schinz's Beaked Blind Snake  *Rhinotyphlops schinzi* **(Pl. 39)**
*(Endemic) max. SVL 278 mm.*
This small, slender blind snake has 22-26 scales around the body,
more than 400 dorsals, and a prominent hooked snout. It is yellowish to
flesh-coloured, with heavy blue-black to reddish-brown blotching that

may form crossbars along the back. **Habitat:** Usually prefers semi-desert and arid savannah regions. **Range:** Found in Namibia and adjacent Botswana, and also south to Calvinia and Kenhardt in the N. Cape province of South Africa.

### Schlegel's Beaked Blind Snake  *Rhinotyphlops schlegelii* (Pl. 39)
*Max. SVL 950 mm.*

The largest typhlopid in the world. It has 30-44 scales around the body (see Subspecies), over 300 (and up to 623) dorsals and a prominent horizontal edge to the snout. The uniform colour phase is brown to black with a straw-yellow belly; the blotched phase has irregular dark brown to black blotches on the back, with the belly and flanks yellow to yellow-green; and in the striped phase, each scale is black-edged, forming dark lines that merge with age. Freshly sloughed snakes are blue-grey, 'tanning' to red-brown with time. **Biology and breeding:** Very large specimens are rarely seen; they live deep underground and lay down large fat stores for long fasts. The female lays 12-40 (up to 60 in very large females) eggs (20-22 x 10-12 mm) in late spring to summer. Embryos are well developed, and the young hatch in only 35-42 days. **Habitat:** Varied; coastal bush to sandveld. **Range:** Found in the northern regions of the subcontinent to Sudan. **Subspecies:** Four races recognized: *R.s. brevis* is extralimital, occurring in NE Africa; *R.s. schlegelii* has 36-44 scale rows; there is a uniform and a blotched phase. It occurs in extreme N. Zululand and S. Mozambique, in an arc through Swaziland, E. Mpumalanga to NW Province and E. Botswana. *R.s. mucruso* has 30-36 scale rows, and both striped and blotched phases occur (in a ratio of 2:1). It is found in E. Botswana, extreme N. Province of South Africa, Zimbabwe and N. Mozambique, through to Kenya. *R.s. petersii* has 34-40 scale rows and occurs as a blotched phase only. It is found in Namibia, and N. Botswana to S. Angola.

■ *R.s. petersii*

□ *R.s. mucruso*

▦ *R.s. schlegelii*

## Typical Blind Snakes  *Typhlops*
The genus contains about 129 species, distributed throughout the tropics (except Australia). Twenty-four species are found in sub-Saharan Africa. Of the three species occurring on the subcontinent, two are endemic.

### Slender Blind Snake  *Typhlops obtusus* (Pls. 39 and 97)
*Max. SVL 370 mm.*

This extremely slender snake has 24-26 scales around the body, more than 300 dorsals, and a smoothly rounded snout. Coloration is dark brown above, each scale paler at its base, and cream to pale brown below. **Habitat:** Loose humic soil in forest. **Range:** Extreme E. Zimbabwe. Elsewhere, in S. Malawi and adjacent Mozambique.

### Fornasini's Blind Snake  *Typhlops fornasinii* (Pl. 40)
*(Endemic) max. SVL 180 mm.*
This very small snake has 22-27 scales around the body, fewer than 300 dorsals (only 236-264 on Bazaruto Archipelago), and a rounded snout. It is uniform greyish to black, with yellow-white blotches on the throat and beneath the tail. **Biology:** A very common species in alluvial sands of the coastal plain, where it burrows in shallow sand beneath leaf litter. **Habitat:** Found in coastal bush and grassland. **Range:** From N. Zululand in South Africa and adjacent Mozambique, to extreme SE Zimbabwe.

## Bibron's Blind Snake

*Typhlops bibronii* **(Pl. 39)**

*(Endemic) max. SVL 296 mm male; 477 female.*
This stout species has 30 scales around the body, more than 300 dorsals and an angular snout. Coloration is uniform brown to dark olive-brown above, with a paler belly; the young are paler than the adults. Rare specimens from Gauteng and N. Province are bicolored, with very pale flanks and bellies. **Biology and breeding:** They search underground for the brood chambers of ants and termites, where they bloat themselves on vast quantities of eggs and larvae. Their shiny, close-fitting scales protect them from the attacks of soldier ants. The female lays 5-14 thin-walled eggs (variable in size, from 42-43 x 9,5-10 mm) in late summer (January-March). Embryos are well developed, and the young (109-129 mm TL) hatch in only 5-6 days. Females may guard their eggs until they hatch. **Habitat:** Highveld and coastal grassland. **Range:** N. provinces and S. KwaZulu-Natal to Albany district of E. Cape. A relict population occurs in E. Zimbabwe.

# Thread Snakes
FAMILY LEPTOTYPHLOPIDAE

These very small, thin, primitive, burrowing snakes have no teeth in the upper jaw, a single lung and oviduct, and internal vestiges of a pelvic girdle (some W. African species also have small external claws). The body is cylindrical, with a blunt head and a short tail. All are blind with the eye reduced to a black spot beneath the head shields. In one recently-discovered E. African species (*L. macrops*) the eye remains very large, although still covered by the head shields. The scales are highly polished and not enlarged on the belly. The skin is shed in compacted rings.

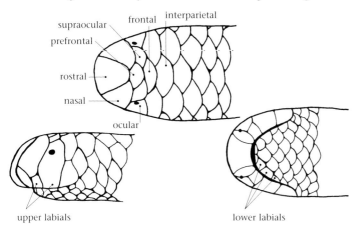

supraocular, frontal, interparietal, prefrontal, rostral, nasal, ocular, upper labials, lower labials

**The head scales of a thread snake**

These snakes are found throughout Africa (except in the Sahara Desert) and in the adjacent Near East, as well as in Amazonia and Middle America. There are 87 species, all in one genus, except *Rhinoleptus*, a species that is restricted to W. Africa. Thread snakes burrow underground, and are active during the night and the day, moving up and down in the soil layers to thermoregulate. They follow the scent trails of ants and termites to their nests. Small prey is swallowed whole, while only the soft abdomens of larger prey are sucked out. They coil and produce pheromones to prevent damage from attacks by soldier ants and termites. They also eat fleas, and have been found in birds' nests, attracted by bird-fleas. Predators include snakes and large invertebrates, for example scorpions and spiders. Female thread snakes lay a few (1-7) elongate eggs that are sometimes strung together like sausages. The Texas thread snake guards its eggs by coiling around them, but this is not known to occur in African species. Colour may change from pink-grey to black, depending on skin dryness.

There are 37 species in Africa, with eleven species occurring on the subcontinent, seven of which are endemic.

### Long-tailed Thread Snake — *Leptotyphlops longicaudus* (Pl. 40)
*Max. SVL 217 mm.*

A small, slender snake with a blunt, rounded head, a relatively long tail (34-58 subcaudals), and a discrete prefrontal. Coloration is uniform lilac to dark grey above, tinged with pink; the belly is flesh-pink. **Breeding:** Two or more eggs (21-23 x 3-4 mm) are laid beneath a rock in summer. **Habitat:** Moist savanna. **Range:** E. Mpumalanga and N. Province, through Zimbabwe and Mozambique Plain to Kenya.

### Black Thread Snake — *Leptotyphlops nigricans*
*(Endemic) max. SVL 196 mm.*

A very small, slender species with a short tail (19-33 subcaudals) and a discrete prefrontal. Coloration is uniform dark brown to black, with the scales sometimes pale-edged. **Biology:** In winter congregate under rubble, etc., where up to 100 individuals may be found in a few square metres. **Habitat:** Varied; fynbos, thicket, grassland and savanna. **Range:** Disjunct, with main centre from Mpumalanga and N. Province, through Zambia to Sudan. Isolated population occurs in south from East London to Cape Town. **Subspecies:** None; northern race now considered full species. Mpumalanga population is also taxonomically distinct.

### Slender Thread Snake — *Leptotyphlops gracilior* (Pl. 40)
*(Endemic) max. SVL 225 mm.*

A very slender snake with 300-350 dorsals, a fused prefrontal-frontal, 14 scale rows at midbody, and 10 scales around the tail. Coloration is uniform brown to black. **Biology:** Common around Nieuwoudtville, where large numbers are exposed in termite nests during ploughing. **Habitat:** Succulent Karoo. **Range:** Inland W. Cape; an isolated record in S. Namibia.

### Cape and Eastern Thread Snakes — *Leptotyphlops conjunctus* (Pl. 97)
*Max. SVL 175 mm.*

L.c. incognitus
L.c. conjunctus

This thread snake has fewer than 300 dorsals, the prefrontal-frontal is fused, and 10 scales around the tail. It has a narrow rostral, and the tail tip tapers gently. It is uniform brown-black above and below; the preanal plate is sometimes white. **Breeding:** The very small eggs (3-4) are similar to large rice grains (10,5-11 x 2,5-3 mm). Hatchlings appear in February-March and are 51-68 mm long. **Habitat:** Varied; grassland, coastal bush, mesic and arid savanna. **Range:** Eastern regions from East London to

Malawi. **Subspecies:** Two races: *L.c. conjunctus* has more than 230 dorsals, and more than 27 subcaudals. Occurs from East London to N. provinces. *L.c. incognitus* has fewer than 230 dorsals, and fewer than 27 subcaudals. Occurs throughout N. provinces; isolated populations in Namibia, Zimbabwe, Mozambique (including Benguera Island) and Malawi. Probably a full species.

### Peters' Thread Snake
*Leptotyphlops scutifrons* **(Pl. 40)**
*Max. SVL 260 mm.*

This species is similar to the Cape thread snake, *L. conjunctus* (above), but grows much larger. It has a wider rostral and a short tail (19-30 subcaudals) that ends abruptly in a spine. It is red-brown to black above, and sometimes paler below, with the scales often pale-edged. **Biology and breeding:** It may sham death when handled roughly. It lays 3-7 elongate eggs (3,5 x 14 mm) in November-December. The eggs may remain attached to each other like a string of sausages. **Habitat:** Varied; grassland, coastal bush and mesic and arid savannah. **Range:** Throughout subcontinent, except most of Cape, S. and coastal Namibia and S. Mozambique Plain. **Subspecies:** Two races recognized. The typical race occurs on the subcontinent and is replaced in N. Tanzania and Kenya by *L.s. merkeri*.

*L.s. scutifrons*

### Tello's Thread Snake
*Leptotyphlops telloi*
*(Endemic) max. SVL 165 mm.*

This rare, small species is similar to Distant's thread snake, *L. distanti* (below). The prefrontal-frontal is fused, and it has 12 scales around the tail. There are more than 300 dorsals, a narrow rostral, and an undivided occipital. Uniform black, with white patches on the head. **Habitat:** Thornveld. **Range:** Restricted to the Lebombo Mountains of Swaziland and Mozambique.

### Distant's Thread Snake
*Leptotyphlops distanti* **(Pl. 40)**
*(Endemic) max. SVL 220 mm.*

This species is similar to Tello's thread snake *L. telloi* (above), except that the rostral is very broad and the occipital is divided. It is grey-black above and paler below, with the scales often pale-edged. **Habitat:** Varied; coastal bush, grass and savannah. **Range:** Found in N. Province and Mpumalanga, with scattered records in KwaZulu-Natal, and extending into S. Mozambique.

### Forest Thread Snake
*Leptotyphlops sylvicolus* **(Pl. 97)**
*(Endemic) Max. SVL 105 mm.*

This small, very short species has only been described recently (1997). It is similar to the Cape thread snake (page 56), except that the body is much shorter (only 171-194 dorsals) and it inhabits forest. There are 14 scale rows at midbody, and ten around the tail. The rostral is elongate and the occipital is undivided. It is black above and paler below, sometimes with white patches near the vent. **Habitat:** Coastal forest. **Range:** Scattered records in coastal KwaZulu-Natal, and Port St John.

### Western Thread Snake
*Leptotyphlops occidentalis* **(Pl. 40)**
*(Endemic) max. SVL 264 mm.*

A very slender, small species that has its prefrontal-frontal fused, and 12 scales around the tail. There are fewer than 300 dorsals, and the anterior upper labial is fused with the supranasal. It is light grey-brown to purple-

brown in colour, with pale-edged scales giving a chequered effect; it is paler below. **Habitat:** Desert and arid savannah. **Range:** Namibia, from Kaokoveld to Little Namaqualand.

### Damara Thread Snake    *Leptotyphlops labialis* **(Pl. 97)**
*Max. SVL 260 mm.*
A large, fairly slender species with 12 scales around the tail. It is locally unique in having the supraoculars fused with the oculars. Coloration is uniform grey-brown to brown above, and paler below, with the scales pale-edged. **Habitat:** Arid savannah. **Range:** N. Namibia to S. Angola.

### Pungwe Thread Snake    *Leptotyphlops pungwensis*
*(Endemic) max. SVL 84 mm.*
Recently described (1997); only a single juvenile specimen is known. It is similar to *L. sylvicolus* (see page 57). The rostral is narrow and wedge-shaped, the interparietal divided lengthways, and the interoccipital is enlarged. The body is covered with 14 rows of scales that reduce to 10 rows on the tail. It is pale brown above and below, with darker patches on the head and scattered white patches on the lower belly and around the cloacal shield. **Habitat:** Coastal forest. **Range:** Known only from a single specimen from the Pungwe Flats, Mozambique.

# Boas and Pythons
FAMILY BOIDAE

This large, ancient family contains some of the largest snakes (e.g. the anaconda and the reticulated python, which grow to about 11 m). Internally, all have minute limb bones and small spurs on either side of the cloaca that are vestiges of the pelvic girdles; these are slightly larger in males.

Fossils are known from the Upper Cretaceous period (100 million years ago). The family is distributed widely, with 65-70 species in 23 genera. It is usually split into three subfamilies: the egg-laying pythons (Pythoninae), and the viviparous sand boas (Erycinae) and typical boas (Boinae). Only pythons are found on the subcontinent.

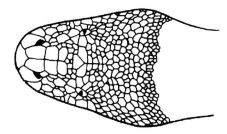

The fragmented head scales of
the African rock python

## Pythons    *Pythoninae*
Pythons are medium to large snakes with small, smooth scales. The head has enlarged scales, but these are not symmetrically arranged or as large as in colubrid snakes. Pelvic spurs (vestiges of the hind limbs) are present on either side of the anal shield.

All pythons lay eggs. The female coils tightly around the eggs, and some species shiver, generating extra body heat to incubate the embryos. The triangular pits on or between the lip scales detect infra-red radiation, enabling the snake to 'see' warm-blooded prey in the dark, or even when blind. All pythons constrict their prey.

Pythons are distributed throughout the African continent and S. Asia to Australia. There are 7-10 species (depending on the generic assignment), and three African species, with two on the subcontinent. The royal python (*P. regius*) from W. Africa is very similar in size and habits to Anchieta's dwarf python.

### Anchieta's Dwarf Python
*Python anchietae* (Pl. 17)

*Max. SVL 1 290 mm male, 1 520 mm female.*
Stoutly built, Anchieta's dwarf python has a broad head and small, tubercular head shields. The upper lip has five heat-sensitive labial pits. The body scales are small, smooth and in 57-61 rows. The head has a large, triangular, reddish-brown mark that is bordered by a white, black-edged band. The body is pale red-brown, with black-edged, white spots and bands. The belly is yellowish, with a few brown spots on the sides. **Biology and breeding:** A poorly known species, this small, gentle python is fully protected in Namibia. It is very rare in captivity. Wild specimens eat birds and gerbils, which they constrict. They are often associated with springs where they ambush prey coming to drink. When captured, they roll into a tight, defensive ball and hide their heads. The female python lays approximately five large eggs (62 x 37 mm) in November; these usually hatch in 60-70 days. The young hatchlings measure 440-500 mm TL. Females are not known to shiver during incubation. **Habitat:** Found in rugged, dry, rocky sandveld and riverine bush. **Range:** S. Angola and N. Namibia.

### African Rock Python
*Python sebae* (Pl. 17)

*Max. size: male 4,25 m TL, 44 kg; female 5,0 m, 55 kg; elsewhere up to 6,0 m (Uganda), debatably 9,8 m (Ivory Coast).*
Africa's largest snake, the African rock python is very solid and stoutly built, with a triangular head with fragmented head shields. There are heat-sensitive pits on two of the upper labials and 4-6 of the lower labials. The body scales are very small, smooth and in 78-95 rows. There is a large, dark spearhead mark on the crown of the head, and dark and light bands radiating from the eye to the lip. The body is grey-green or grey-brown, with dark brown, black-edged bars and blotches on top, irregularly connected with sinuous dark brown bands that may form isolated blotches on the flanks. The belly is white with dark speckles. Juveniles are more brightly marked. **Biology and breeding:** They often bask, especially after feeding or when sloughing, and are fond of water, in which they may lie and hunt. They may dive into deep pools and remain submerged for long periods. Prey is ambushed and constricted, usually at dusk or after dark. Adults take small buck, monkeys, etc. although fish, monitors and crocodiles are also eaten. They can swallow very large prey, but are vulnerable to attack by wild dogs and hyaenas when swollen with food. They may fast for long periods (two-and-a-half years has been recorded in captivity), and live for over 27 years. Although they make good pets, some specimens never tame and the adults may grow too large to handle. They lunge and bite readily in defence. The teeth are very large and can inflict

painful, ripping wounds. This is the only snake large enough to consider humans edible, but attacks on man are exceptionally rare, especially as most large pythons have been exterminated. Fatalities have, however, been recorded. The skins are used for fashion, but pythons are protected in southern Africa (SA RDB, Vulnerable). They are a valuable aid in controlling dassies, and cane-rats in KwaZulu-Natal sugarcane fields. The female lays 30-50 (and more than 100 in very large females) large, almost spherical eggs (130-160 g each, about 100 mm dia., the size of an orange) in disused aardvark burrows, termite nests, caves, etc. The female coils around her clutch to protect the eggs, but does not incubate them by shivering. The young, measuring about 450-600 mm, hatch in 65-80 days. Sexual maturity is reached in 3-5 years, at 2-3 m. **Habitat:** Usually found in open savannah regions, particularly rocky areas and riverine scrub. Absent only from true desert and dense rain forest. **Range:** Restricted mainly to the lowveld, reaching KwaZulu-Natal south coast, and extending along the Limpopo River valley to Lobatse in Botswana and into the N. Cape, with isolated records around the Kalahari Gemsbok National Park. They also occur along the Zambezi and Cunene River valleys, extending into Okavango and N. Namibia. Considered extinct (since 1927) in E. Cape, but recent records suggest that it may still occur in some remote areas. Elsewhere, throughout sub-Saharan Africa. **Subspecies:** Two races recognized. Only the southern race (*P.s. natalensis*) is found on the subcontinent; this subspecies is replaced by the typical race (which has larger head shields and a different colour pattern) in W. Africa, to Uganda.

# African Burrowing Snakes
## FAMILY ATRACTASPIDIDAE

These are unusual African burrowing snakes that show a wide range of fang types and associated glands. Usually back-fanged, one genus has long, hollow fangs that can rotate forwards and inject venom. The head is small and not distinct from the neck. The eyes are small to minute, with round pupils. The snout is usually round, but is very pointed in one genus. The head shields are often fused, and thus reduced in number. The loreal is always absent. The body is cylindrical, and sometimes very long and thin. The scales are smooth and lack apical pits. Many of these snakes are uniform grey to black, but a few species are brightly coloured. They all have similar skulls, vertebrae and hemipenes. Most are harmless, but a few may be clinically dangerous.

These burrowing snakes live underground, some species utilizing rock cracks or insect and mammal tunnels, others pushing through loose sand or leaf litter. Many have very specialized diets. With one exception, all are oviparous.

The taxonomy is confused; at present, there are 11 genera and about 60-65 species divided into two subfamilies. They are distributed throughout the African continent, with one genus (*Micrelaps*) entering the Near East. Six genera (one endemic) occur in the subcontinent.

KEY TO THE GENERA OF ATRACTASPIDIDAE
1 - Pair of elongate, hollow, partly erectile fangs at front of mouth:
                       *Atractaspis* (Burrowing asps, page 61)
  - Grooved fangs present only at back of mouth:          go to 2
2 - Snout strongly projecting, depressed and pointed; rostral very large

with an obtuse to sub-acute horizontal edge:

> *Xenocalamus* (Quill-snouted snakes, page 67)

- Snout rounded, not depressed or pointed:     go to 3
3 - Subcaudals in pairs:     go to 4
  - Subcaudals single:     go to 5
4 - A small preocular present; eye small, diameter being about equal to its distance from lip margin; head and neck black, and three well-marked longitudinal black stripes over back and tail:

> *Chilorhinophis* (Black and yellow burrowing snakes, page 67)

  - Preocular absent; eye minute, its diameter being much less than its distance from the lip margin:

> *Amblyodipsas* (Purple-glossed snakes, page 65)

5 - Scales in 23-27 rows at midbody; no preocular; body moderately large and stout:     *Macrelaps* (Natal black snake, page 64)
  - Scales in 15 rows at midbody; preocular present; body small and moderately slender:     *Aparallactus* (Centipede eaters, page 63)

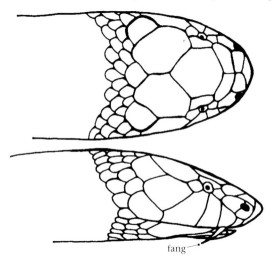

fang

The head scales and fangs
of a burrowing asp

## SUBFAMILY ATRACTASPININAE

# Burrowing Asps   *Atractaspis*

These unusual snakes have a small head that is not distinct from the neck, and is covered with symmetrical head shields. The eyes are very small with round pupils. The body is cylindrical, with smooth, shiny scales in 17-37 rows. The anal is undivided. The tail is short, with paired or single subcaudals. These asps are distinguished by the large, hollow poison fangs that are situated at the front of the mouth on an otherwise toothless maxilla. In colour, they are usually uniform purple-brown to black, with a white, grey or black belly. Two species from the Horn of Africa have white heads. They are confused with some harmless species, for example purple-glossed snakes *Amblyodipsas* (page 65), and wolf snakes, *Lycophidion* (page 76).

Previously called 'mole vipers' or 'burrowing adders' because of their erectile front fangs, these similarities are now known to be due to convergent evolution (similar evolution to meet a similar need). Other common names include 'stiletto snakes' and 'side-stabbing snakes'.

These burrowing snakes may emerge on the surface at night, particularly after rain. They are very common in suitable habitat, feeding on small vertebrates, particularly other burrowing reptiles. Baby rodents, sleeping skinks and lacertids, legless lizards and other snakes are all eaten. They may use the side of the head to excavate a chamber beneath a sun-warmed stone. They have a peculiar 'aromatic' smell, the function of which is unknown. Oviparous, they lay a few (usually 4-7, but up to 11) elongate eggs in leaf litter. The neck is unusually flexed on a hard surface, with the nose pointing down vertically. They bite with a peculiar sideways 'stab', which is why they cannot be safely held behind the head. The fangs have limited rotation and are hooked into the prey without the snake fully opening its mouth; usually only a single fang is injected, but multiple bites may be delivered. The venom glands are large, and in some species extend into the neck. Bites from most species are mild, causing intense pain and local swelling, but deaths have been caused by three W. and N. African species. Polyvalent antivenom is ineffective in the treatment of their bites.

They are distributed throughout most of sub-Saharan Africa, with an isolated species in the Jordan Valley and in Arabia. The taxonomy is confused; there are about 16 species, with only three occurring in our region, one of which is endemic.

### Southern or Bibron's Burrowing Asp
*Atractaspis bibronii* **(Pl. 38)**

*Max. SVL 650 mm male, 610 mm female.*
This short, stocky snake has smooth, close-fitting scales in 21-23 rows (19 on Bazaruto Archipelago). The head shields are symmetrical. It has enlarged, erectile front fangs. Ventrals number 213-256. The anal is undivided. The tail is short (18-28 single subcaudals), with a terminal spine. In colour, the back is uniform purple-brown to black. The belly colour is variable; it is either uniform white to cream, sometimes with scattered dark blotches, or uniform dark grey. **Biology and breeding:** Usually found under cover (in old termitaria, under stones, etc.), these snakes emerge on the surface on warm, wet summer nights. The diet is varied; mainly other burrowing reptiles are taken, but it also eats small mammals and frogs. Irascible and ever-willing to bite, these snakes are best left undisturbed. The glands yield minute amounts of venom (1,3-7,4 mg), which is straw-yellow in colour. The venom causes immediate pain and local swelling; mild neurotoxic symptoms (for example nausea, dry throat and vertigo) may be present in the early stages, but necrosis is rare, and is usually a result of bad treatment. Bites are common in Zulu-land and Mpumalanga lowveld, but no fatalities have been recorded. Polyvalent antivenom is ineffective in the treatment of this snakebite. The female usually lays 3-7 eggs (27-36 x 10-12 mm) in summer. The young measure about 150 mm TL. It has lived over 22 years in captivity. **Habitat:** Varied; ranging from highveld grassland and semi-desert to coastal bush. **Range:** Found throughout the northern regions, to the KwaZulu-Natal south coast, and with scattered inland records. Elsewhere, north to Kenya.

## Eastern Congo Burrowing Asp

*Atractaspis congica*

Max. SVL 481 mm male, 506 mm female.
This short, stocky snake has smooth, close-fitting scales in 19-21 rows. The head shields are symmetrical. It has enlarged, erectile front fangs. Ventrals number 193-208. The anal is undivided. The tail is short (18-25 paired subcaudals), with a terminal spine. The back and belly are uniform purple-brown to black. **Biology and breeding:** This species' venom has not been studied; no bites have been reported. Three to six elongate eggs (62 x 12 mm) have been recorded. **Habitat:** Moist savannah. **Range:** Cameroon, through Democratic Republic of Congo (former Zaïre) to N. Angola and N. Zambia, with a single isolated record from the Caprivi Strip. **Subspecies:** Three poorly-defined races are recognized; the Caprivi specimen appears referable to the eastern race (*A.c. orientalis*).

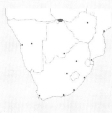

*A.c. orientalis*

## Duerden's or Beaked Burrowing Asp

*Atractaspis duerdeni* (Pl. 38)

*(Endemic) max. SVL 440 mm male, 512 mm female.*
This short, stocky snake's abrupt, rounded snout has a sharp horizontal edge at its tip. The smooth, close-fitting scales are in 23-25 rows. It has symmetrical head shields, and enlarged, erectile front fangs. Ventrals number 193-225. The anal is undivided and the tail is short (19-27 unpaired subcaudals) with a terminal spine. In colour, the body is uni-form blackish-brown or grey above, and uniform white or cream-pink on the belly, extending on to the lower flanks and lips. **Biology:** Thicker bodied and less aggressive than Bibron's burrowing asp, *A. bibronii* (page 62), with shorter fangs. Sleeping lizards and snakes are eaten. **Habitat:** Sandy soil in thornbush savannah. **Range:** Isolated populations in central Namibia and SE Botswana and adjacent NW Province.

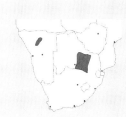

## SUBFAMILY APARALLACTINAE

# Centipede Eaters  *Aparallactus*

These are small, unusual snakes with a small head that is barely distinct from the neck, and very small eyes with round pupils. There are usually two large back fangs (absent in *A. modestus*), which are sometimes grooved, on the maxillary below the eye. The body is cylindrical, with smooth scales in 15 rows. The anal is undivided, and the tail is short to moderately long, with unpaired subcaudals.

Burrowers, these snakes live in loose soil, old termitaria, under rocks or in rotting logs. They feed almost exclusively on centipedes, which they grab and chew; the prey quickly succumbs to the venom, and is swallowed head first. Most are oviparous, but the Kenyan *A. jacksonii* gives birth to a few live young.

Centipede eaters are distributed throughout sub-Saharan Africa, from Ethiopia in the east to Guinea in the west, but are absent from most of the Cape. There are 11 species, with four in the region; one is endemic.

## Reticulated Centipede Eater

*Aparallactus lunulatus* (Pl. 26)

Max. SVL 360 mm male, 430 mm female.
This small snake has its first lower labials in contact behind the mental. It has six lower labials, 144-176 ventrals, and 48-65 subcaudals. The back is pale grey to olive or dark brown, often with the scales dark-edged, giving a reticulated effect; juveniles have a black collar and up to 12 blotches

*A.l. lunulatus*

on the forebody that fade in adults. The belly is greenish-white sometimes suffused with dark grey. **Biology and breeding:** It is found under logs and stones at low altitudes, and eats scorpions as well as centipedes. The female lays 3-4 elongate eggs (30 x 7 mm) in summer. **Habitat:** Sandy lowveld. **Range:** Zimbabwe and adjacent Mozambique, south into Kruger National Park and N. Swaziland. Elsewhere, to Sudan and Democratic Republic of Congo. **Subspecies:** Two races are recognized. The typical race occurs in the region and throughout most of the range; it is replaced in Somalia by *A.l. scortecci.*

### Black Centipede Eater                 *Aparallactus guentheri* (Pl. 26)
*Max. SVL 345 mm male, 380 mm female.*
This small, slender snake has its first lower labials separated by the mental. The nasal is divided. There are five lower labials, 150-173 ventrals, and 49-60 subcaudals. The head and back are blue-grey to black, with two narrow yellow collars on the neck; the chin and belly are off-white. **Biology:** This snake is similar in habits and behaviour to the reticulated centipede eater *A. lunulatus* (above). **Habitat:** Areas of high rainfall supporting evergreen forest. **Range:** E. Zimbabwe, north to Kenya.

### Cape Centipede Eater                 *Aparallactus capensis* (Pl. 26)
*Max. SVL 270 mm male, 324 mm female.*
This small, slender snake has its first lower labials separated by the mental. Each nostril pierces the undivided nasal. There are five lower labials, 126-186 ventrals, and 29-63 subcaudals. The back is red-brown to grey-buff, with a black collar and a brownish head. The belly is grey-white. **Biology and breeding:** They are common in old termitaria which offer shelter, warmth and food. When caught they struggle wildly and may attempt to bite, but their minute teeth are harmless. They lay 2-4 very elongate eggs (32 x 4-5 mm). The young are 90-120 mm TL. Predators include garter snakes and burrowing asps. **Habitat:** Varied; including highveld and montane grassland, savannah and coastal bush. **Range:** Eastern regions, from Port Elizabeth to Zimbabwe, N. Botswana and Caprivi Strip. There is an old record from central Namibia. It is absent from S. Mozambique plain.

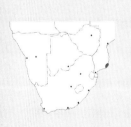

### Mozambique Centipede Eater                 *Aparallactus nigriceps*
*(Endemic) max. SVL 200 mm male, 210 mm female.*
This small snake is similar to the Cape centipede eater, *A. capensis* (above), but it has fewer ventrals (108-123) and subcaudals (20-35). Its coloration is also similar to that of the Cape centipede eater, except that the nape collar is twice as broad. **Biology and breeding:** Nothing is known about this rare and localized snake but it is presumed to have similar habits and behaviour to the Cape centipede eater. **Habitat:** Prefers coastal bush. **Range:** Found in the area around Inhambane in S. Mozambique.

# Natal Black Snake   *Macrelaps*
This unusual genus is endemic to South Africa, and contains a single species. It may be confused with the purple-glossed snakes, *Amblyodipsas* (below), which differ by having paired subcaudals, and the burrowing asps, *Atractaspis* (page 61), which can be distinguished by their erectile front fangs and preocular.

**Natal Black Snake**    *Macrelaps microlepidotus* (Pl. 37)

*(Endemic) max. SVL 640 mm male, 938 mm female.*
A thick-bodied snake with a blunt head that is not distinct from the neck.
The minute eyes have round pupils. There is no loreal or preocular. The
prefrontal enters the eye. The maxillary is short, with four teeth and two
very large, grooved fangs under the eye. The body is cylindrical, with
smooth scales (but feebly keeled in the anal region) in 25-27 rows.
Ventrals number 158-172. The anal is undivided, and the tail is short
(35-50 subcaudals). In colour, the back is ashy-black to jet-black, and
sometimes paler on the belly. **Biology and breeding:** This snake
burrows in moist leaf litter and humic soil, coming to the surface on
warm, damp nights. It feeds on rain frogs (*Breviceps*), small mammals,
legless lizards (particularly the giant legless skink) and other snakes.
The prey is seized, restrained in the body coils and chewed to introduce
venom. It is a good swimmer. Docile, it rarely bites. The venom is poorly
known; bites are reported to cause loss of consciousness and collapse for
up to 30 minutes, but are very rare. Antivenom is ineffective in treating
this snakebite. The female lays 3-10 large eggs (38-56 x 23-31 mm) in
December-January in leaf litter. The young, which hatch in March,
measure 200-290 mm TL. **Habitat:** Coastal bush. **Range:** Eastern coastal
regions from East London to Zululand, with an isolated population
in remnant forest at Stutterheim, E. Cape.

# Purple-glossed Snakes   *Amblyodipsas*

These burrowing snakes are widely distributed through sub-Saharan Africa.
They are very similar in appearance to the Natal black snake, *Macrelaps
microlepidotus* (above), and the burrowing asps, *Atractaspis* (page 61). The
head is small and not distinct from the neck. The eyes are very small, with
round pupils. There is no loreal, preocular or anterior temporal. The maxillary is very short, with 3-5 teeth and two large, grooved fangs under the
eye. The body is cylindrical and solid, with smooth scales in 15-21 rows.
The anal is divided and the tail is very short, with paired subcaudals.

Purple-glossed snakes are found in various habitats, from coastal bush
and moist forest to dry savannah, and in the Kalahari. They burrow in
loose soil and feed on other burrowing reptiles, small mammals and
amphibians. Prey is subdued by venom while it is held in the body coils
(this may take up to four hours). Although rarely seen, they may surface
on warm, damp nights. Docile, they rarely bite. They are usually
oviparous, the exception being *A. concolor*. Males are often much smaller
than females and have longer tails. There are nine species, with four in
the region, two of which are endemic.

### Natal Purple-glossed Snake    *Amblyodipsas concolor* (Pl. 38)

*(Endemic) max. SVL 367 mm male, 749 mm female.*
A thick-bodied snake with a blunt snout. It has seven upper labials,
the fifth of which is the largest. There are two pairs of chin shields. The
scales are smooth, in 17 rows. There are 133-157 ventrals. The tail is short
(28-39 subcaudals), tapering to a point. The back is uniform glossy dark
brown to black with a purple sheen; the belly is paler. **Biology and
breeding:** This rare species burrows in humic soil in forested areas; when
hungry, it may lie just below the surface with its head partially exposed.
Adults readily eat other snakes, while juveniles take small lizards. Very
docile, they rarely bite. There is some confusion about this snake's

breeding habits: 10 hatchlings and two eggs (30 x 18 mm) were found in February in moist soil (in KwaZulu-Natal); 11 eggs (26-32 x 15-17 mm) were laid by a female in December (Gauteng); and a female (N. Province) gave birth to 12 babies in March. **Habitat:** Moist forested areas. **Range:** Kwa-Zulu-Natal lowlands, through Mpumalanga and Gauteng to N. Province.

### Common Purple-glossed Snake *Amblyodipsas polylepis* (Pl. 38)
*Max. SVL 495 mm male, 1 050 mm female.*
This stocky snake has a blunt snout, and six upper labials, the fifth of which is the largest. There are seven lower labials, the first four touching the single pair of chin shields. The internasals are not fused with the pre-frontals. The scales are smooth, in 19-21 rows. Ventrals number 154-215 (fewer than 180 in males, more than 185 in females), and subcaudals 15-31 (more than 24 in females, fewer than 25 in males). The back and belly are glossy dark brown to black, with a purple sheen. **Biology:** Feeds on burrowing reptiles, including blind snakes; captures sleeping lizards in their burrows at night. It is docile, rarely biting. **Habitat:** Savannah, entering dry forest. **Range:** KwaZulu-Natal, through Mpumalanga and N. Province, Caprivi Strip, N. Botswana, Zimbabwe and Mozambique. Elsewhere, to Angola, Democratic Rep. of Congo and Zambia. **Subspecies:** Two races, with only the typical race occurring in the region. Replaced in coastal Kenya and Tanzania by *A.p. hildebrandtii*, which has only 17-19 scale rows.

*A.p. polylepis*

### Eastern Purple-glossed or White-lipped Snake
*Amblyodipsas microphthalma* (Pl. 24)
*(Endemic) max. SVL 320 mm male, 313 mm female.*
This is a small snake with a bluntish snout. There are five upper labials, the fourth of which is the largest, and six lower labials, the first four touching the single pair of chin shields. The internasals are fused with the prefrontals. The scales are smooth, in 15 rows. The back is uniform dark brown to black, with a purple sheen. The upper lip and throat are white or yellow. The belly either has a dark median stripe bordered by white or yellow that extends onto the adjacent body scales, or is uniform black. **Biology:** The typical race burrows in deep sandy soil, while *A.m. nigra* hides under stones in rocky terrain. Legless skinks are eaten. **Habitat:** Deep alluvial soil or rocky thornveld. **Range:** St Lucia in KwaZulu-Natal and adjacent Mozambique Plain, to NE Mpumalanga. **Subspecies:** Two races are recognized, both occurring in the region. *A.m. microphthalma* has a white-yellow belly, and 120-153 ventrals; it is found in KwaZulu-Natal, Mozambique, Bazaruto Archipelago, N. Kruger National Park. *A.m. nigra* has a black belly, and 146-168 ventrals; it is found in N. Province.

*A.m. microphthalma*
*A.m. nigra*

### Kalahari Purple-glossed Snake
*Amblyodipsas ventrimaculata* (Pl. 24)
*Max. SVL 305 mm male, 445 mm female.*
This small snake has a bluntish snout. There are five upper labials, the fourth of which is the largest, and five lower labials, the first three touching the single pair of chin shields. The internasals are not fused with the prefrontals. The scales are smooth, in 15 rows. Ventrals number 172-205. The tail is short (18-29 subcaudals). The back has a broad purple-brown to black dorsal stripe; the scales may be tipped with yellow. The flanks, upper lip and subcaudals are yellow. The belly is uniform white, rarely with scattered black blotches. **Biology and breeding:** Found in sandy soil in

moist regions of the Kalahari, this snake feeds on burrowing reptiles, including amphisbaenids (*Zygaspis*), legless skinks (*Typhlacontias punctatissimus*) and garter snakes. Three eggs have been found in a female.
**Habitat:** Kalahari sand. **Range:** W. Botswana and adjacent Namibia and NW Zimbabwe, north to Zambia.

# Black and Yellow Burrowing Snakes
*Chilorhinophis*

Very small, elongate snakes found in E. and central Africa. The head is small, not distinct from the neck, and has a rounded snout. The eyes are small, with round (sometimes elliptical) pupils. There is no internasal or loreal. The prefrontals are very large, covering the snout. Each nostril pierces a single nasal. The maxillary is short, with 3-4 teeth and two large, grooved fangs. The body is slender and cylindrical, with smooth scales in 15 rows. The anal is divided, and the tail is short, with paired subcaudals.

All these snakes are brightly coloured, with the tail the same shape and colour as the head. In defense, they draw themselves into loose coils, hide the head and raise the tail, waving it slowly to deflect danger away from the vital organs. They are oviparous.

There are three species, one of which just enters the region.

### Gerard's Black and Yellow Burrowing Snake
*Chilorhinophis gerardi* (Pl. 24)

*Max. SVL 400 mm male, 445 mm female.*
This is a very slender, small snake with a rounded snout. The eyes have round pupils. A small preocular is present. There are four upper labials, the third entering the eye, and five lower labials. Ventrals number 244-294, and subcaudals 19-31. The back is chrome to pale greenish-yellow, with three black stripes. The head and tail tip are black above, the head with pink-yellow blotches. The throat and chin are white, the belly bright orange. The anterior of the tail is orange-yellow, followed by a black band, with the rest being light blue. **Biology and breeding:** This snake burrows in loose soil, feeding on small amphisbaenids and snakes. The tail display is a dramatic bluff, and it may even give a mock 'strike'. The female lays six elongate eggs (30 x 6 mm) in summer. **Habitat:** Savannah. **Range:** N. Zimbabwe, north to S. Democratic Rep. of Congo. **Subspecies:** Two races; typical race occurs in the region, and is replaced by *C.g. tanganyikae* in N. Zambia, SE Democratic Republic of Congo and W. Tanzania.

*C.g. gerardi*

# Quill-snouted Snakes
*Xenocalamus*

These unusual African snakes have a small, elongate (quill-shaped) head which is not or is hardly distinct from the neck. The snout is almost hooked, with an underslung mouth. The minute eyes have round pupils. The elongate 'preocular' is actually a displaced prefrontal. The maxillary is short, with 4-6 teeth and two large fangs under the eye. The body is cylindrical, with smooth scales in 17 rows. The anal is divided. The tail is short and blunt, with paired subcaudals.

The very thin body, pointed snout and underslung mouth of these snakes are adaptations for burrowing in sandy soils. They feed almost exclusively on amphisbaenians. They are slow-moving, and struggle when captured, but never bite although the sharp snout may give a painful prick. There are five species, which are distributed through central and southern Africa, with four in the region, two of which are endemic.

## Sabi Quill-snouted Snake
*Xenocalamus sabiensis*

*(Endemic) max. SVL 400 mm male, 470 mm female.*
This small, slender snake has its snout depressed and prominent, but not hooked. There are 5-6 upper labials and six lower labials. The nasal is usually divided. Ventrals number 187-218, and subcaudals 22-33. In colour the back is uniform black, the lower flanks chrome-yellow, and the belly off-white (sometimes with scattered brown blotches). **Biology and breeding:** Rarely seen unless they are forced to the surface by rain. The female lays approximately three large, elongate eggs. **Habitat:** Alluvial sands. **Range:** SE Zimbabwe and adjacent Mozambique.

## Transvaal Quill-snouted Snake
*Xenocalamus transvaalensis* **(Pl. 29)**

*(Endemic) max. SVL 370 mm male, 315 mm female.*
This small, slender snake has its snout depressed and prominent. There are five upper and five lower labials. Each nostril pierces a single large nasal. There are 183-192 ventrals and 23-32 subcaudals. The back is black, sometimes with pale-centred scales, giving a speckled appearance. The belly and lower flanks are white-yellow (sometimes black-blotched). **Biology and breeding:** The diet is probably composed of dwarf burrowing skinks and worm lizards. The female lays two eggs (28 x 6 mm) (SA RDB, Rare). **Habitat:** Kalahari and alluvial sand. **Range:** Vicinity of Kosi Bay and adjacent S. Mozambique, and N. Kruger National Park.

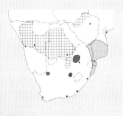

## Bicoloured Quill-snouted Snake
*Xenocalamus bicolor* **(Pls. 18 and 24)**

*Max. SVL 590 mm male, 680 mm female.*
A slender snake with a prominent, depressed and hooked snout. It has 5-6 upper labials and five lower labials. The nasal is divided. There are 186-250 ventrals and 20-37 subcaudals. Coloration is varied, with four basic colour phases. The striped phase is black to purple-brown above, with the lower flanks off-white to chrome-yellow and the belly white (sometimes with dark blotches). The spotted phase is yellow above, with two rows of purple-brown spots, and a white belly. The reticulated phase has the back brown or grey, with each scale pale-edged, and the lower flanks and belly white. The melanistic phase is uniform black above and below. **Biology and breeding:** These snakes live in deep sand. The female snake usually lays 3-4 elongate eggs (40-47 x 15 mm) in December. The young measure about 200 mm TL. **Habitat:** Kalahari and alluvial sands. **Range:** Found in the northern parts of the region, reaching N. Zululand, and with an isolated population in the Free State. Elsewhere, north to Angola and the Democratic Republic of Congo (former Zaïre). **Subspecies:** There are four races, with three occurring in the region. *X.b. bicolor* (the bicoloured quill-snouted snake) occurs in all colour phases, and has six upper labials and high ventral counts; it is found over most of the range. *X.b. lineatus* (the striped quill-snouted snake) is striped, and has six upper labials, a very strongly compressed head, and high ventral counts; it is a small race (max. TL 592 mm) and found in SE Zimbabwe, south to N. Zululand, and also on Bazaruto Archipelago. *X.b. australis* (the Waterberg quill-snouted snake) is striped, and has five upper labials and low ventral counts; it is found in the Waterberg range in N. Province. Extralimitally, *X.b. machadoi* occurs in Angola and the Democratic Republic of Congo (former Zaïre).

■ *X.b. australis*

□ *X.b. lineatus*

▦ *X.b. bicolor*

## Elongate Quill-snouted Snake    *Xenocalamus mechowii* (Pl. 18)

*Max. SVL 580 mm male, 800 mm female.*
This very elongate snake has a prominent, depressed snout. There are
six upper labials and five lower labials. The nasal is divided. The frontal
enters the orbit. The ventral count is 247-296, and subcaudals number
22-32. The back is light purple-brown to lemon-yellow, with two irregular
rows of dark blotches. The belly is white to dirty yellow, and sometimes
faintly blotched. Rare specimens are uniform black. **Biology and breeding:** This secretive species burrows for amphisbaenians in regions of
Kalahari sand. The female lays up to four large eggs. **Habitat:** Kalahari
sand. **Range:** Northern regions, from NE Namibia to NW Zimbabwe.
Elsewhere, to N. Angola and Democratic Republic of Congo. **Subspecies:**
Two races, with only *X.m. inornatus* occurring in the region. The typical
race is found in N. Angola and SW Democratic Republic of Congo.

*X.m. inornatus*

# Typical Snakes
### FAMILY COLUBRIDAE

This very large family contains some of the most successful and most
common snakes. Most are medium sized. None has a functional left
lung or pelvic vestiges. They usually have a 'typical' arrangement of nine,
symmetrical, enlarged head shields. Most species lack fangs, but some
groups have back fangs. The majority are harmless (even many of those
species with enlarged back fangs), but a few have powerful and unusual
venoms that can cause human deaths (for example the boomslang
and twig snakes).

Colubrids occur on all continents (except Antarctica) and most islands.
The family includes more than 1 500 species in about 300 genera. Many
attempts have been made to divide it into smaller groups, but no system
has gained universal acceptance. Some authorities recognize as many as
six separate families, with varying numbers of subfamilies and tribes.
A conservative arrangement has been adopted here, and a number of
problematic local genera (four) have not been assigned to any subfamily.
Four subfamilies occur on the subcontinent. Locally, the family contains
27 genera (only three of which are endemic) and 73 species (26 of which
are endemic).

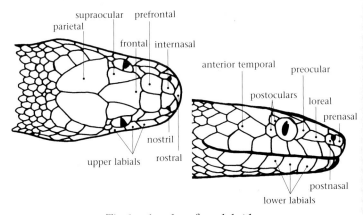

**The head scales of a colubrid**

KEY TO THE SOUTHERN AFRICAN GENERA IN THE COLUBRIDAE

1 - No enlarged grooved poison fangs in the upper jaw:
                  go to 2
 - Pair of enlarged grooved poison fangs in the upper jaw (usually below
  the eye):              go to 14
2 - Scales on back smooth (partly keeled only in *Prosymna janii*):  go to 3
 - Scales on back distinctly keeled:        go to 13
3 - Nostril pierced between two nasal shields; tail moderate to long:
                  go to 4
 - Nostril pierced in a single or semi-divided nasal shield; tail short:
                  go to 11
4 - Anal entire; pupil vertical (occasionally roundish in *Lycodonomorphus*):
                  go to 5
 - Anal divided; pupil round or horizontal:     go to 6
5 - Midbody scale rows numbering 19 or 21; 153-177 ventrals; belly
  usually yellow, orange or pink, often with a dark stripe below the
  tail and sometimes a dark stripe or scattered spots anteriorly;
  semi-aquatic:    *Lycodonomorphus* (Water snakes, page 72)
 - Midbody scale rows usually numbering 23 or more (rarely 17-21);
  165-230 ventrals; belly usually uniform white or dark grey; terrestrial:
           *Lamprophis* (House snakes, page 73)
6 - Snout rather pointed, prominent and with vertical sides; internasal
  shield entering nostril; scales in 25-31 rows at midbody:
          *Pseudaspis* (Mole snake, page 80)
 - Snout more or less rounded; internasal not entering the nostril; scales
  not exceeding 23 rows at midbody:     go to 7
7 - Scales in not more than 15 rows at midbody; eye proportionately
  large; habit slender; tail 25-33% of total length; usually bright green,
  bluish-green or olive-green:
      *Philothamnus* (Green and Bush snakes, page 93)
 - Scales in 17-23 (exceptionally 15) rows at midbody; eye of moderate
  size; body moderately slender; tail 20-33% of total length; never
  bright green:           go to 8
8 - Parietal in contact with or narrowly separated from 6th upper labial;
  tail short, 15-20% of total length; a broad, pale, dorsolateral stripe on
  either side:  *Limnophis* (Striped swamp snake, page 81)
 - Parietal well separated from 6th upper labial by anterior temporals;
  tail moderate to long, 20-33% of total length:   go to 9
9 - Ventrals not exceeding 150; scales in 17-19 (exceptionally 15) rows at
  midbody; mandibular teeth smallest in front:
        *Natriciteres* (Marsh snakes, page 81)
 - Ventrals exceeding 170; scales in 19-23 rows at midbody; mandibular
  teeth largest in front:        go to 10
10 - Scales in 21 rows at midbody; eight upper labials, fourth and fifth
  entering eye; no subocular present:
      *Meizodon* (African smooth snakes, page 93)
 - Scales in 23 rows at midbody; nine upper labials, fifth and sixth
  entering eye; a single anterior subocular present:
         *Coluber* (Racers, page 99)
11 - Pupil vertical (or almost so); loreal shield present:  go to 12
 - Pupil round; loreal shield normally absent (when present much
  reduced in size); nasal shield single; rostral small:
        *Duberria* (Slug eaters, page 79)

70

12 - Nostril pierced in a single nasal shield; snout rounded; rostral small; anterior maxillary teeth longest: *Lycophidion* (Wolf snakes, page 76)
- Nostril pierced in a semi-divided nasal; snout strongly depressed, projecting and with an angular, horizontal edge; rostral proportionately large; maxillary teeth very small, slightly larger posteriorly:
*Prosymna* (Shovel-snout snakes, page 83)
13 - Scales in 15-19 rows at midbody, without apical pits; scales along backbone enlarged and with 2 keels; loreal present; nostril large and pierced between 2 nasal shields; teeth normal and distinct:
*Mehelya* (File snakes, page 78)
- Scales in 21-27 rows at midbody, with apical pits; scales along backbone not enlarged; loreal absent; nostril moderate and pierced in a semi-divided nasal shield; teeth few and rudimentary:
*Dasypeltis* (Egg eaters, page 95)
14 - Subcaudals single; parietals broken up into small scales; pupil vertical:
*Pythonodipsas* (Western keeled snake, page 82)
- Subcaudals paired; parietals entire: go to 15
15 - Pupil vertical; head much broader than neck: go to 16
- Pupil round or horizontal; head not or only moderately broader than neck: go to 18
16 - Anal usually divided (entire only in *T. beetzii*); loreal separated from the eye by a preocular; maxillary teeth smallest in front; body and tail conspicuously banded with black: *Telescopus* (Tiger snakes, page 97)
- Anal entire; body and tail not banded with black: go to 17
17 - Loreal entering the orbit; more than 70 subcaudals:
*Dipsadoboa* (Cat-eyed tree snakes, page 98)
- Loreal separated from orbit by a preocular; less than 70 subcaudals:
*Crotaphopeltis* (Herald snakes, page 96)
18 - Eye large; pupil horizontal when fully dilated normally keyhole- or dumbbell shaped when partly dilated in daylight; habit very slender; scales in 19 rows at midbody: *Thelotornis* (Bird snakes, page 100)
- Pupil round; head short to moderately long; habit short or moderately slender: go to 19
19 - Scales keeled and in 19-21 rows at midbody; head very short and eye large: *Dispholidus* (Boomslang, page 99)
- Scales smooth and in 11-21 rows at midbody; head of moderate length and eye of moderate size: go to 20
20 - Rostral large and projecting, snout pointed and beak-like: go to 21
- Rostral of normal size; snout rounded and not beak-like: go to 22
21 - Snout strongly hooked in profile; loreal not longer than deep; preocular usually well separated from frontal; tail long, 53-125 subcaudals:
*Rhamphiophis* (Beaked snakes, page 86)
- Snout not hooked in profile; loreal longer than deep; preocular in contact with frontal; tail short, 28-45 subcaudals:
*Dipsina* (Dwarf beaked snake, page 87)
22 - Nostril pierced between at least 2 shields: go to 23
- Nostril pierced in single, sometimes semi-divided, nasal shield: go to 25
23 - Maxillary teeth interrupted below anterior part of eye by 2 much enlarged, fang-like teeth; nostril pierced between 2 or 3 nasal shields:
*Psammophis* (Sand and Grass snakes, page 89)
- Maxillary teeth almost equal in size and continued without interruption to the gap separating them from the posterior pair of enlarged poison fangs: go to 24

TYPICAL SNAKES

24- Nostril pierced between 2 nasal shields only; tail long, with 80 + subcaudals:                                    *Dromophis* (Olympic snakes page 87)
- Nostril pierced between 2 nasal shields and an internasal shield; tail
short, subcaudals not exceeding 80:
                                    *Psammophylax* (Skaapstekers, page 87)
25- Mandibular teeth small and subequal in size; anal entire:      go to 26
- Mandibular teeth much enlarged in front; anal scale divided:
                                    *Hemirhagerrhis* (Bark snakes, page 85)
26- Snout hollowed on either side, just anterior to the eye; scales in 17
rows at midbody:            *Amplorhinus* (Many-spotted snake, page 82)
- Snout not hollowed on either side, just anterior to the eye; scales in
21 rows at midbody:
                        *Montaspis* (Cream-spotted Mountain snake, page 83)

## Old World Snakes
### SUBFAMILY LAMPROPHIINAE

This subfamily includes some of Africa's most typical snakes. They are
characterized by vertebral and hemipenial features. They lack enlarged
fangs, and none is venomous. Most are terrestrial, some are of burrowing
habits, and others are either aquatic or semi-aquatic.

There are 14 genera with about 45 species; six genera (none of which is
endemic) with 25 species (15 of which are endemic) occur in the southern
African subregion.

## Water Snakes    *Lycodonomorphus*

These medium-sized, aquatic snakes have a cylindrical body with a small
head that is barely distinct from the neck. The eyes are moderately large,
with round (sometimes elliptical) pupils. The scales are smooth, in 19-25
rows. The tail is moderately long, with paired subcaudals, and is longer
in males, with an obvious hemipenial bulge. Females grow larger.

They are mainly nocturnal, although some species forage during the
day. They are very common in suitable habitat. Prey consists mainly of
frogs and tadpoles and sometimes fish. These snakes capture their food
underwater beneath stones, in crannies, etc. Large prey is constricted.
They are oviparous. Harmless to man, they lack fangs and venom glands.
Most have a gentle disposition and very rarely bite.

Found throughout central and E. Africa, there are seven species. Four of
these, two of which are endemic, enter the subcontinent.

### Dusky-bellied Water Snake
*Lycodonomorphus laevissimus* **(Pl. 33)**
*(Endemic) max. SVL 751 mm male, 1 085 mm female.*

This solid, smooth-scaled snake has a small, flattened head and small eyes
with round pupils that sit well on top of the head. The first upper labial
has a backward projection. There are 154-179 ventrals and 53-89 subcaudals. The back is dark olive-grey to brown-black, sometimes with a pale
streak on the lower flank. The upper lip is spotted. The belly is cream to
yellow, with a broad, central, dark band. **Biology and breeding:** Locally
common, this snake is aquatic, foraging mostly in water. Small frogs, fish
and tadpoles are swallowed while the snake is submerged. It lays 8-17 eggs
in summer. It is a bad-tempered species, biting readily and giving off a
foul cloacal smell. **Habitat:** Pools in slow-moving, well-wooded streams,

but entering grassland streams in Swaziland. **Range:** E. Cape, through former Transkei and KwaZulu-Natal to SE Mpumalanga and Swaziland. **Subspecies:** No races are now recognized.

**Mulanje Water Snake**  *Lycodonomorphus leleupi* **(Pl. 32)**
*Max. SVL 580 mm male, 750 mm female.*
This snake is similar to the dusky-bellied water snake, *L. laevissimus* (above), but is slightly smaller, has a shorter tail (51-76 subcaudals), and lacks a dark belly band. The first upper labial has a backward projection. The back and upper lip are olive-black. The belly is dull orange with dark infusions. The tail has a dark stripe below. **Biology and breeding:** Similar in habits and behaviour to the common brown water snake, *L. rufulus* (page 73), but is diurnal. It lays up to nine eggs (25 x 13 mm) in summer. **Habitat:** Small streams, pans, and vleis. **Range:** E. Zimbabwe and adjacent Mozambique, north through Malawi to Democratic Republic of Congo (former Zaïre). **Subspecies:** Two races recognized but only *L.l. mlanjensis* occurs on the subcontinent. The typical race, *L.l. leleupi*, occurs in E. Democratic Republic of Congo and has a darker belly.

*L.l. mlanjensis*

**Common Brown Water Snake**  *Lycodonomorphus rufulus* **(Pl. 32)**
*(Endemic) max. SVL 552 mm male, 702 mm female.*
This snake is similar to the Mulanje water snake, *L.l. mlanjensis* (page 73), but is slightly smaller, has vertical pupils, and lacks the backward projection to the first upper labial. Subcaudals number 53-86. The back is uniform olive-brown, the upper lip and belly pale yellow-pink, and the tail darker below. **Biology and breeding:** These nocturnal water snakes are common under cover around water margins, and feed mainly on frogs. They are powerful constrictors. They tame easily and make gentle pets. The female lays 6-23 eggs (12-21 x 20-42 mm) in midsummer. They hatch after an incubation period of about 60-65 days and the young measure about 197-216 mm. **Habitat:** Small streams, pans and vleis. **Range:** Eastern half of the subcontinent, extending along the coast to W. Cape.

**Floodplain Water Snake**  *Lycodonomorphus obscuriventris* **(Pl. 33)**
*Max. SVL 440 mm male, 575 mm female.*
This snake is similar in habits and appearance to the Mulanje water snake, *L.l. mlanjensis* (page 73), but is much smaller and has a short tail (37-52 subcaudals). Females grow larger. The back is uniform dark olive to blackish. The upper lip has a pale stripe. The belly is orange-yellow, and sometimes faintly spotted, and the tail is darker. **Biology:** None. Found during the day and evening, foraging for frogs in marginal vegetation around still water. **Habitat:** Lowland floodplain pans and vleis. **Range:** Mozambique floodplain and adjacent regions, including S. Malawi. **Subspecies:** Previously a southern race of Whyte's water snake, *L. whytii*, which is now restricted to Tanzania and N. Malawi.

# House Snakes  *Lamprophis*
These characteristic African snakes are small to medium-sized; only a few exceed a metre in length. The eyes are small, with vertical pupils (as is usual in nocturnal snakes). The scales are smooth, with the anal undivided and the subcaudals paired.

Most house snakes are terrestrial, although some live underground (in termite nests, etc.) and others forage in rock cracks. These harmless constrictors are attracted to houses by food (usually rodents, but some also take reptiles). Oviparous, they lay white, oval eggs. Males have a prominent hemipenial bulge.

Thirteen species are found throughout the continent, with isolated populations in Arabia (*L. arabicus*) and even on the Seychelles (*L. geometricus*). There are seven species on the subcontinent, six of which are endemic.

### Brown House Snake     *Lamprophis fuliginosus* (Pls. 3 and 28)
*Max. SVL 656 mm male, 783 mm female.*
A large house snake with an obvious head and small body scales (27-29 rows). It is uniform red-brown in colour (snakes from arid areas are light orange). Large, old snakes are darker, almost black. There are two pale yellow streaks on the side of the head, which sometimes extend onto the front half of the body. The belly is off-white. The young sometimes have indistinct, pale lateral spots that may persist in adults. Xanthic specimens are known. **Biology and breeding:** Terrestrial, these snakes forage for rodents and other small vertebrates (including bats) at night. In arid regions they frequently eat lizards. They bite readily at first, but settle down easily in captivity. Up to 16 eggs (25-50 x 12-24 mm) are laid in summer, and these take 60-90 days to develop. Hatchlings measure 190-260 mm TL. In captivity, the female may lay clutches every 1-2 months during the breeding season. **Habitat:** Common in highveld grassland and arid karroid regions, but found everywhere and tolerant of urban sprawl. **Range:** Throughout southern Africa and most of the continent. **Subspecies:** A thin, pale, large-eyed form from the Namib and ProNamib may be a separate species (*L. mentalis*).

### Olive House Snake     *Lamprophis inornatus* (Pl. 32)
*(Endemic) Max. SVL 637 mm male, 975 mm female.*
This large house snake has 21-25 scale rows and small eyes. It is uniform olive-green in colour and occasionally almost dark brown: the belly is light grey-green. **Biology and breeding:** This snake is similar to the brown house snake, *L. fuliginosus* (above), but prefers moister habitats. It usually eats small mammals (for example the striped fieldmouse, *Rhabdomys pumilie*), but also eats lizards and other snakes. The female lays 5-15 eggs (32-43 x 24-25 mm) in October-December; these hatch in 70-90 days. The young measure 192-240 mm TL. **Habitat:** Moist coastal bushveld and fynbos, extending into grassveld. **Range:** Coastal belt from SW Cape to East London, extending through KwaZulu-Natal lowlands and Mpumalanga escarpment to N. Province.

### Spotted House Snake     *Lamprophis guttatus* (Pl. 17)
*(Endemic) max. SVL 427 mm male, 615 mm female.*
A small, slender house snake with 21-25 scale rows and relatively large eyes. Its coloration is blotched, and regionally variable. There is a series of blotches on the back, arranged in alternating or adjacent pairs that may merge to form a zigzag. In the north, the body is pinkish-grey or brown, distinctly marked with dark brown, often dark-edged spots. The colour is duller in E. Cape, becoming light brown or tan in W. Cape, with only diffuse spots on the front of the body. The belly is yellowish-white. **Biology and breeding:** Common in rocky habitats, sheltering in cracks and under flakes during the day, and feeding at night on geckos and sleeping skinks and lacertids. It is a shy snake, easily stressed in captivity.

The female lays 3-6 elongate eggs (38 x 20 mm) in midsummer.
**Habitat:** Karroid areas to mesic savannah. **Range:** Inland mountains of
Cape and Cape fold mountains, to S. Namibia and through KwaZulu-Natal
to Mpumalanga and N. Province; one record from adjacent Mozambique.

### Aurora House Snake
*Lamprophis aurora* **(Pls. 25 and 32)**
*(Endemic) max. SVL 459 mm male, 643 mm female.*

This beautiful short, stocky house snake has 21-23 scale rows and a short
tail (35-58 subcaudals). The body is green (rich olive to citrine) above,
with a prominent orange-yellow stripe along the backbone, and the belly
is white, with adjacent scale rows usually yellow. Adults are drabber than
the sparkling juveniles, which are speckled with a pale bar on each scale
and have a black-spotted head. **Biology and breeding:** Unfortunately,
this snake is not common; it is a secretive, terrestrial species, shy and
rarely attempting to bite. Its staple diet is nestling rodents. The female
lays 8-12 eggs (35-41 x 19-20 mm) in summer; hatchlings measure
200 mm TL and emerge after 72-78 days incubation. **Habitat:** Grassland,
entering coastal bush and fynbos. **Range:** Highveld of Gauteng and Free
State, extending into KwaZulu-Natal and E. Cape. Isolated records from
S. Cape and W. Cape escarpment.

### Fisk's House Snake
*Lamprophis fiskii* **(Pl. 19)**
*(Endemic) max. SVL 310 mm male, 327 mm female.*

A small house snake with a blunt head and a short tail. The scales are
smooth and in 21-23 rows, the loreal as long as it is deep, and the subcaudals number 28-34. The head is lemon-yellow in colour with symmetrical dark blotches. The body is lemon to dirty yellow, attractively
marked with a double row of alternating dark brown blotches (sometimes
fused on the forebody to form a zigzag pattern) and the belly is creamy
white. **Biology and breeding:** Little is known of this rare snake's habits
and behaviour; a few specimens have been collected on roads at night
(SA RDB, Rare). It lives underground and constricts and eats small lizards.
When threatened, it hisses and tightly coils and uncoils the front and rear
of its body. A female laid eight eggs in summer. **Habitat:** Karroid sandy
veld. **Range:** Widely scattered localities around Great Karoo.

### Yellow-bellied House Snake
*Lamprophis fuscus* **(Pl. 32)**
*(Endemic) max. SVL 460 mm male, 635 mm female.*

This medium-sized, slender house snake has a small head and 19 body
scale rows. It is uniform olive-brown to light olive-green above; the upper
lip and scale rows bordering the belly are yellow-green and the belly is
light yellow. **Biology:** These snakes are generally rare, and are usually
found in old termite nests. They rarely bite, and do not settle easily in
captivity. The diet is mainly lizards, and possibly nestling rodents.
**Habitat:** Grassveld and fynbos. **Range:** Cape Town to Mpumalanga
and Swaziland.

### Swazi Rock Snake
*Lamprophis swazicus* **(Pl. 28)**
*(Endemic) max. SVL 423 mm male, 560 mm female.*
This very slender snake has an obvious head, bulging eyes and 17 scale
rows. It is dark red-brown to light beige; the belly is creamy white. The
scales may be dark-edged. **Biology:** The Swazi rock snake is similar in
habits and behaviour to the spotted house snake, *L. guttatus* (page 74),

being nocturnal, sheltering during the day in rock cracks and feeding on small lizards. **Habitat:** Rock outcrops in savannah. **Range:** Mpumalanga escarpment and NW Swaziland.

## Wolf Snakes   *Lycophidion*

These small snakes are peculiar to Africa. The body is cylindrical with the flattened head barely distinct from the neck. The eyes are small, with vertical pupils. The front teeth in the upper and lower jaw are long and recurved (hence 'wolf' snake), but these snakes lack venom glands and are harmless to man. The scales are smooth, in 17-19 rows. The anal is undivided. The tail is short, with the subcaudals paired. The tail is longer in males.

Nocturnal, they shelter during the day under cover, emerging to hunt at dusk. Prey consists mostly of diurnal lizards (skinks, lacertids, etc.) which are caught sleeping in their retreats. They are gripped by the large teeth of the wolf snake, extracted from their retreat and then constricted. Snakes are sometimes taken. Slow-moving and relatively docile, these snakes will bite only if provoked. They are oviparous.

At least 17 species are found throughout sub-Saharan Africa, with eight occurring on the subcontinent, four of which are endemic.

### Cape Wolf Snake   *Lycophidion capense* (Pl. 36)
*Max. SVL 440 mm male, 558 mm female.*

*L.c. capense*

A small snake that grows larger in the southern part of its range. It has a flattened head. The postnasal touches the first upper labial. The ventrals number 159-205. Coloration is usually uniform dark brown (particularly in the E. Cape) to black, sometimes with each scale white-tipped and a white- or black-speckled belly. **Biology and breeding:** This common terrestrial species prefers well-vegetated situations. Cape skinks are commonly eaten, whilst the Cape thick-toed gecko forms an important part of the diet in the Free State. The female lays 3-9 eggs (22 x 10 mm) in early summer; they may hatch in only 51 days. Hatchlings measure 120 mm TL. **Habitat:** Varied; grassland and savannah, entering coastal bush and fynbos in the Cape. **Range:** Throughout most of the subcontinent, except Namib Desert and most of Cape. Isolated records from S. Cape and S. Namib Desert. Elsewhere, through E. Africa to Egypt. **Subspecies:** Three races are recognized, only the typical race occurring on the subcontinent and north to S. Tanzania. Replaced by *L.c. loveridgei* from NE Tanzania to Somalia (including the off-shore islands), and by *L.c. jacksoni* from S. Sudan and Ethiopia to Uganda and E. Democratic Republic of Congo (former Zaïre).

### Variegated Wolf Snake   *Lycophidion variegatum* (Pl. 29)
*Max. SVL 323 mm male, 389 mm female.*

A small, slender wolf snake. The postnasal is separate from the first upper labial. There are 185-204 ventrals. Its speckled coloration is similar to that of some Cape wolf snakes but the white markings are more extensive; the belly is dark, sometimes with pale marks. **Biology and breeding:** It prefers rocky areas, hunting for sleeping skinks and geckos in rock cracks. Three eggs have been recorded in the largest female. **Habitat:** Usually found in rock outcrops in moist savannah. **Range:** From the Lebombo Range in N. Zululand, through to the Mpumalanga escarpment and to Zimbabwe and S. Zambia.

**Spotted Wolf Snake**                  *Lycophidion multimaculatum*
*Max. SVL 286 mm male, 475 mm female.*
A small snake that grows smaller in the southern part of its range. It has
a flattened head. The postnasal touches the first upper labial. The ventrals
number 159-182 in males, 153-188 in females. Coloration is varied; in the
south the head is covered in uniform pale stippling and the body is red-
brown to grey with white stippling, except for a paired series of irregular
dark blotches down the back, which may fuse to form crossbands. The
belly is white, but the chin may be dark. **Biology:** A nocturnal, terrestrial
species that hunts skinks and lacertids asleep in their burrows. **Habitat:**
Found in moist savannah. **Range:** Just entering Caprivi Strip. Elsewhere
through Angola, Zamibia and Democratic Republic of Congo (former
Zaïre), to W. Tanzania and Gabon.

**Namibian Wolf Snake**              *Lycophidion namibianum* (Pl. 25)
*(Endemic) max. SVL 315 mm male, 530 mm female.*
A small species that lacks a postnasal and has a flattened head. There are
193-207 ventrals in males, 202-213 in females. The body is usually reddish
to dark brown with heavy pale speckling and variable pale markings. The
belly and the lower flanks are white, with the ventral scales usually with a
dark brown centre. **Biology:** Similar to variegated wolf snake. **Habitat:**
Rocky desert and arid savannah. **Range:** Restricted to N. Namibia.

**Hellmich's Wolf Snake**              *Lycophidion hellmichi* (Pl. 25)
*Max. SVL 345 mm male, 427 mm female.*
This small, slender snake is similar to the Cape wolf snake, *L. capense*
(page 76), but has higher ventral (199-211) and subcaudal (33-45) counts.
The head is dark brown with vague symmetrical white stippling on the
crown and white lips. The body is dark brown with the scales white-
tipped, and sometimes with a thin (three scales wide) white dorsal stripe.
The lower flanks are white, the belly dark brown with white edges to the
ventrals. **Habitat:** Rocky arid savannah. **Range:** Mainly in western
Angola, with a single record from the Kaokoveld in N. Namibia.

**Eastern Wolf Snake**          *Lycophidion semiannule* (Pls. 36 and 98)
*(Endemic) max. SVL 220 mm male, 310 mm female.*
This is a very small species that lacks a postnasal and has few ventrals
(144-150). The head is black, with some white stippling, and a silvery or
yellowish band around the snout. The body is black, heavily stippled in
white to give a blue-grey appearance, except for 30-34 solid black cross
bars on the body and about seven on the tail. The belly is black, with the
ends of the ventrals stippled with white. **Biology:** This terrestrial species
is rare and secretive, sheltering beneath dune vegetation. **Habitat:**
Coastal thicket. **Range:** Restricted to Bazaruto Archipelago and the
Inhambane region of Mozambique.

**Pygmy Wolf Snake**          *Lycophidion pygmaeum* (Pls. 36 and 98)
*(Endemic) max. SVL 197 mm male, 262 mm female.*
This very small species lacks a postnasal and has few ventrals (140-155).
The body and head is black, with a broad white band around the snout.
On the back the scales are stippled in white, except towards the rear. The
belly is uniform black, except for light white stippling on the throat and
on the ventral edges. **Biology and breeding:** A secretive, terrestrial

species that shelters in grass tussocks and beneath logs. Feeds on dwarf burrowing skinks (*Scelotes* sp.). A large female contained three eggs. Hatchlings measure 100-110 mm TL. **Habitat:** Coastal grassland and thicket, entering pine plantations. **Range:** Endemic to N. Zululand.

### Dwarf Wolf Snake
*Lycophidion nanum* (Pl. 36)
*(Endemic) max. SVL 210 mm male, 248 mm female.*
The smallest wolf snake, it has a blunt, flattened head, small eyes and vertical pupils. Its scalation is similar to that of the eastern wolf snake, *Lycophidion semiannule* (above), but it has only 6-7 upper labials, six lower labials, and scales in 17 rows to the tail. The back and belly are uniform blue-black, with a stippled white band around the snout. **Biology and breeding:** This secretive species is a specialist feeder on amphisbaenians (*Chirindia*). The female lays two elongate eggs (26 x 6 mm). **Habitat:** Floodplain with miombo woodland. **Range:** Central Mozambique Plain.

## File Snakes *Mehelya*

These peculiar African snakes may be closely related to the wolf snakes, *Lycophidion* (page 76). The body is almost triangular in cross-section, with the broad, flat head very distinct from the neck. They have large nostrils, and smallish eyes with vertical pupils. The body scales are strongly keeled and almost conical, in 15-19 rows, often non-overlapping; the scales along the backbone are enlarged and have two keels. The anal is undivided. The tail is longish, with paired subcaudals. The common name derives from the similarity of the body in shape and texture to a three-cornered file.

Nocturnal and terrestrial, file snakes are very secretive, and are rarely seen in spite of being widely distributed. They are constrictors, feeding on small vertebrates; some are specialist feeders on snakes. The oviparous females are larger than the males. Harmless to man, they lack fangs and venom glands. They are very docile, never attempting to bite, but are restless in the hand.

Ten species are distributed throughout most of sub-Saharan Africa, with three on the subcontinent, none of which is endemic.

*M.c. capensis*

### Cape File Snake
*Mehelya capensis* (Pl. 25)
*Max. SVL 1 220 mm male, 1 612 mm female.*
This large snake has a very flat head and a thickset, triangular body. Two labials enter each eye. The scales are strongly keeled, in 15 rows, with those on the spine fused to the backbone. There is extensive bare skin between the scales. There are 193-244 ventrals and 44-58 subcaudals. The back is grey to grey-brown, and sometimes dark olive to purple-brown, with a white to yellow vertebral stripe. The skin between the scales is pink-purple. The belly is ivory-white to cream, extending onto the flanks. **Biology and breeding:** The Cape file snake is a formidable predator on other snakes (even venomous species, to whose venom it appears immune), and also eats other small vertebrates, particularly plated lizards. It never bites when captured, but may empty its bowels. A few (5-13) large eggs (47-55 x 20-31 mm) are laid in leaf litter. Young measure 390-420 mm TL. In captivity, eggs hatch in 90-100 days. Females may lay two clutches in a summer. **Habitat:** Mainly savannah, but entering coastal forest and arid regions. **Range:** In the east from KwaZulu-Natal, through Mpumalanga, N. and NW provinces, Zimbabwe and Caprivi Strip to N. Namibia. Elsewhere, to Cameroon and Somalia. **Subspecies:** Three

races are recognized, with only the typical race occurring in the subcontinent. *M.c. fiechteri* occurs in Somalia, whilst *M.c. savorgnani* extends along the northern border of the central rainforest, from Kenya to Cameroon.

### Angola File Snake

*Mehelya vernayi* **(Pl. 36)**

*Max. SVL 1 090 mm male, 1 155 mm female.*

This species is similar in appearance to the Cape file snake, *M. capensis* (above) but has three labials entering each eye. The scales are in 19 rows and the ventrals number 256-268. It lacks the white vertebral stripe of the Cape file snake, and the back is dark red-brown on the forebody, with the scales increasingly pale-centred towards the tail, giving it a speckled appearance. The belly is cream-yellow. **Biology and breeding:** Similar in behaviour and habits to the Cape file snake; toads and lizards have been found in the gut contents. A few eggs (37 x 15 mm) are laid. **Habitat:** Rocky mountainous country. **Range:** N. Namibia to W. Angola.

### Black File Snake

*Mehelya nyassae* **(Pl. 36)**

*Max. SVL 437 mm male, 520 mm female.*

This small species has two labials entering each eye, the scales in 15 rows, ventrals numbering 165-184, and 51-77 subcaudals. The back is uniform dark brown to purple-brown above. The skin between the scales is pink. The belly is dark olive to black, or white to cream-olive. **Biology and breeding:** This snake is similar in behaviour and habits to the Cape file snake, *M. capensis* (above), but eats mainly lizards, particularly skinks. The female lays up to six eggs. The young measure 200-220 mm TL. **Habitat:** Savannah, entering coastal forest. **Range:** Eastern regions from KwaZulu-Natal to Kenya, possibly extending through Botswana to central Namibia.

## Slug Eaters   *Duberria*

These stout-bodied little snakes have a small head that is hardly distinct from the neck. The small eyes have round pupils, and each nostril pierces a single nasal. The scales are smooth, in 15 rows. The anal is undivided. The tail is short, with paired subcaudals.

These gentle, slow-moving, shy snakes forage among grass roots and rotting timber in damp situations. The diet consists exclusively of slugs and land snails. The slug eater follows a slime trail and simply swallows the prey at its end. The females are larger than the males and give birth to small numbers of live babies. There are two species, both of which enter the subcontinent and one of which is endemic.

### Common Slug Eater

*Duberria lutrix* **(Pl. 28)**

*Max. SVL 355 mm male, 360 mm female.*

A short small-headed snake, with 116-142 ventrals. The back is brick-red to pale brown above, sometimes with a broken black line along the backbone. The flanks are paler, being grey to light brown. The belly is cream, edged with a dark, dotted line. **Biology and breeding:** This is a common species in suitable habitat, and a boon to gardeners and farmers. Inoffensive, it rolls into a tight spiral when alarmed (hence the Afrikaans name 'tabakrolletjie'). Six to 22 babies (larger numbers in larger females) are born in late summer (January-February); they measure 80-109 mm TL. Gravid females can become obese, and the babies may weigh more than the spent mother. **Habitat:** Savannah, entering coastal bush and fynbos. **Range:** Cape fold mountains, through E. Cape to KwaZulu-Natal,

◼ *D.l. lutrix*

◻ *D.l. rhodesiana*

Gauteng, Mpumalanga and N. Province to Zimbabwe. Elsewhere, through E. Africa to Ethiopia. **Subspecies:** There are six races, two of which occur on the subcontinent. *D.l. lutrix* has two postoculars, and broken black dorsolateral lines; it occurs in South Africa. *D.l. rhodesiana* has one postocular, and lacks dorsolateral lines; it is found in Zimbabwe.

**Variegated or Spotted Slug Eater**     *Duberria variegata* **(Pl. 16)**
*(Endemic) max. SVL 225 mm male, 343 mm female.*
This small, stout snake is similar to the common slug eater *D. lutrix* (above), but has a more prominent snout and 91-110 ventrals. The back is brown to olive or dark brown, with three rows of blackish blotches that may form crossbars and are sometimes obscured by pale speckling. The belly is dirty yellow with dark reticulation, particularly at the rear.
**Biology and breeding:** Similar in habits to the common slug eater, this species has not been observed to form a coiled defensive posture. Seven to 20 young (larger litters in larger snakes) are born in late November-January; they measure about 90-100 mm TL. **Habitat:** Coastal forest and savannah. **Range:** N. Zululand and adjacent Mozambique.

## Mole Snake     *Pseudaspis*
This genus contains a single, widely distributed species.

**Mole Snake**                          *Pseudaspis cana* **(Pls. 18, 28 and 35)**
*Max. SVL 1 265 mm male, 1 280 mm female; to 2 m TL in SW Cape.*
A large thick, solid snake with a slightly hooked nose. The body scales are smooth (but sometimes keeled in black snakes from W. Cape), in 25-31 rows. Each nostril is pierced between two nasals. The anal is divided. The eyes have round pupils. Coloration is variable. The young are blotched, the body being light red-brown with four rows of dark, pale-edged spots (the centre pair may fuse to form a zigzag pattern); the adults are plain (the juvenile pattern is sometimes retained), usually light to red-brown, but occasionally olive, grey, dark brown or black (common in W. Cape). Males have thicker, longer tails. **Biology and breeding:** Mole snakes are extremely useful, harmless constrictors that live underground in abandoned animal burrows and feed on moles, rodents and other small mammals. Juveniles also eat lizards. Some eat eggs, which they swallow whole. They are aggressive when first caught, and often bite and twist, leaving deep gashes that may require stitches. They calm down in captivity and make good pets, although they are prone to long fasts. Males fight in mating season and bite each other severely. They mate in late spring (October), and 25-40 (up to 95) young are born during March-April, each measuring 200 mm TL. **Habitat:** Sandy scrubland in SW Cape, highveld grassland and mountainous and desert regions. **Range:** Throughout southern Africa (and on Robben Island). Elsewhere, north to Angola and Kenya.

# Old World Water Snakes
SUBFAMILY NATRICINAE

These snakes are mainly restricted to the Northern Hemisphere, with only a few species entering Africa. They are gentle, inoffensive nocturnal denizens of swamps and wet forests. They feed mainly on small frogs and fish. Only two genera, with three species (none endemic) enter the northern parts of the subcontinent.

# Marsh Snakes   *Natriciteres*

These small, inconspicuous snakes have a cylindrical body with a small head that is barely discernible from the neck. The eyes are largish, with round pupils. The internasals are paired. The scales are smooth, in 15-19 rows. The anal is sometimes divided. The tail is moderately long, with paired subcaudals.

Diurnal and terrestrial, they are found sheltering under cover in damp situations. They feed on fish and frogs. Females are oviparous, and larger than males. They are docile and rarely bite. If grabbed by the tail, they spin wildly, breaking it off. This caudal autotomy, common in lizards but rare in snakes, may be an adaptation to predation by fish and wading birds. Unlike lizards, the tail is not regenerated. Harmless to man, they lack fangs and venom glands. Three species are distributed throughout tropical Africa, with two entering the subcontinent, neither of which is endemic.

### Forest Marsh Snake                 *Natriciteres variegata* (Pl. 33)
*Max. SVL 276 mm male, 330 mm female.*

A small, thickset snake with smooth scales in 17 rows at the front and 15 rows at the rear. There are usually eight lower labials, the first four touching the anterior chin shields. Ventrals number 125-143, and subcaudals 60-84. The back is dark olive to chestnut-black above (sometimes with a faint yellow collar), with a broad, darker band down the backbone, usually bordered by a row of minute white dots. The top lip is barred in yellow and black. The belly is yellow to orange with dark grey edges. **Biology and breeding:** Shelters under cover at forest fringes, feeding in pools on frogs and fish-eating spiders. Lays 5-6 eggs. **Habitat:** Montane and lowland evergreen forest. **Range:** Isolated populations in N. Zululand and Mozambique and eastern escarpment of Zimbabwe. Elsewhere, through E. and central Africa to Sierra Leone. **Subspecies:** Four races, with only *N.v. sylvatica* occurring on the subcontinent. Distinguished from: the typical race (which occurs from Sierra Leone to the Democratic Republic of Congo) which has 15 scale rows at midbody; from *N.v. bipostocularis* (which occurs in Democratic Republic of Congo, Angola and Zambia) by having three postoculars; and from *N.v. pembana* (occurring on Pemba Island, off Tanzania) by its higher ventral and subcaudal counts.

*N.v. sylvatica*

### Olive Marsh Snake          *Natriciteres olivacea* (Pls. 33 and 37)
*Max. SVL 290 mm male, 407 mm female.*

A small snake similar to the forest marsh snake, *N. variegata* (above), but with 19 scale rows at the front and 17 at the rear; there are nine lower labials, the first five touching the anterior chin shields. In colour similar to the forest marsh snake, but lacks the yellow collar and is more often olive in colour. **Biology and breeding:** Similar to that of forest marsh snake, and inhabits vleis and pans; has been observed to eat winged termites. It tames well and is very docile in captivity. The female lays 6-8 eggs (22 x 9 mm) in early summer. **Habitat:** Savannah. **Range:** S. Mozambique, Zimbabwe and N. Botswana, north to Sudan and W. Africa.

# Swamp Snakes   *Limnophis*

There are two species in the genus, only one of which enters the extreme northern regions of the subcontinent. They are small, inconspicuous snakes with a cylindrical body, and are distinguishable from the marsh snakes, *Natriciteres* (above), by having a single, triangular internasal.

**Eastern Striped Swamp Snake** *Limnophis bangweolicus* (Pl. 25)
*Max. SVL 495 mm male, 500 mm female.*
This snake has a small head that is barely distinct from the neck. The eyes are largish, with round pupils. The sixth upper labial is very large, often touching the parietal. The scales are smooth, in 19 rows. The anal is divided. The tail is short, with paired subcaudals. The back is dark olive-brown, flanked by a paler stripe; the sides pale, with 3-4 black-edged scale rows simulating thin stripes. The belly is yellow to brick-red. **Biology and breeding:** Poorly known, feeds on fish and amphibians. Lays eggs. **Habitat:** Marshy areas. **Range:** Okavango and Zambezi drainage basins. **Subspecies:** Previously a race of *L. bicolor*, which is restricted to Angola.

# SNAKES WHOSE RELATIONSHIPS REMAIN UNRESOLVED

The following species are unusual African snakes whose relationships to other snakes have not been resolved. Various theories concerning their affinities have been proposed, but these are not uniformly accepted. Many are endemic to the subcontinent.

## Western Keeled Snake  *Pythonodipsas*

This unusual snake is easily recognized by its small, irregular head shields, a condition usually found only in pythons and adders. There is a single species in the genus.

**Western Keeled Snake** *Pythonodipsas carinata* (Pl. 16)
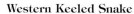
*Max. SVL 515 mm male, 770 mm female.*
The body is cylindrical, with smooth (or faintly keeled) scales, in 21 rows. The head is very flat and distinct from the neck. The eyes are largish, with vertical pupils. The nostrils are situated on top of the snout. The anal is entire, and the tail longish with undivided subcaudals. The back is yellow-olive, pale buff, sandy or grey above, with a double series of dark-edged, brown to grey-brown blotches that may form a zigzag or crossbars. The flanks have smaller, less distinct bars. The head is variegated in the body colours. The belly is white, sometimes spotted on the sides. **Biology and breeding:** Nocturnal and terrestrial. Feeds on small lizards, particularly geckos and skinks, which it constricts. Prey are captured in their retreats or ambushed when active. Females grow much larger than males and feed more often on rodents. Probably oviparous (not confirmed). Viper-like in appearance, and may mimic the horned adder, *Bitis caudalis*. Has large back fangs, bites readily. Not venomous. Settles well in captivity, but should be fed sparingly. **Habitat:** Rocky desert. **Range:** W. Namibia to SW Angola.

## Many-spotted Snake  *Amplorhinus*

An unusual snake of nondescript appearance. It has prominent grooved back fangs and its venom is considered relatively harmless, although clinical symptoms were recorded once. The single species in this genus is endemic to the subcontinent. It may be related to natricine snakes.

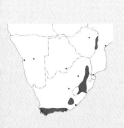

**Many-spotted Snake** *Amplorhinus multimaculatus* (Pl. 18)
*(Endemic) max. SVL 428 mm male, 471 mm female.*
The body of this snake is cylindrical, with a small head that is just distinct from the neck. The eyes are of moderate size, with round pupils. The

scales are smooth (except over the posterior back and tail base), in 17 rows. The anal is undivided. The tail is of moderate length, with divided subcaudals. The back is green or olive-green to brown above, usually with a series of dark brown to black blotches, and sometimes with a pale dorso-lateral stripe; scattered scales are often pale-edged, giving a flecked effect. The belly is dull green to blue-grey. **Biology and breeding:** Secretive, but locally common. Forages for frogs and lizards in reed beds and waterside vegetation. Bites readily and may coil into a tight spring, similar to the common slug eater, *Duberria lutrix* (page 79). Its venom has caused local pain, inflammation and swelling that resolved in a short time; the bite also bled freely but severe haemorrhage did not develop. Antivenom is unnecessary and probably ineffective. Four to eight (max. 12) young, measuring 125-200 mm TL, are born in late summer. **Habitat:** Mountain streams and vleis. **Range:** Cape fold mountains, KwaZulu-Natal and Mpumalanga Drakensberg; an isolated population on Zimbabwe's eastern escarpment.

## Cream-spotted Mountain Snake *Montaspis*

Poorly known, only recently described (1991). It resembles, and may be related to, the many-spotted snake *Amplorhinus multimaculatus* (above).

**Cream-spotted Mountain Snake** *Montaspis gilvomaculata* **(Pl. 98)** *(Endemic) max. SVL 372 mm male, 416 mm female.*
The body of this small snake is cylindrical, with a small head that is just distinct from the neck. The eyes are of moderate size, with round pupils. The scales are smooth and in 21 rows. The anal is undivided. The tail is of moderate length, with divided subcaudals. It has prominent grooved back fangs. The back is olive to chocolate brown above. The dorsal head shields, and particularly the lips are speckled with cream. The throat is cream with brown-edged scales. The belly scales are brown, pale-edged, dotted and speckled with small cream spots. Beneath the tail is brown, becoming straw-coloured at the tip. **Biology and breeding:** Secretive and rare, this snake feeds on frogs that it hunts in reed beds and waterside vegetation. It chews large frogs, restraining them in body coils. When held it never bites, but struggles, flattens the body and may discharge foul-smelling cloacal contents. A female contained six ova in March. Active even at low temperatures. **Habitat:** Mountain streams and vleis. **Range:** Restricted to high altitudes in KwaZulu-Natal Drakensberg.

## Shovel-snout Snakes *Prosymna*

These small, strange African snakes are not obviously related to any other group. The body is cylindrical, with the head not distinct from the neck. The snout is characteristically depressed, forming an angular horizontal 'shovel' that is sometimes upturned. The scales are usually smooth, in 15-21 rows. The anal is undivided. The tail is short, ending in a spine.

They burrow in loose soil (one species inhabiting rock cracks), feeding almost exclusively on reptile eggs. The shell is punctured by the maxillary teeth and the egg, which may contain a well-developed embryo, is swallowed whole. They lay a few (3-6) elongate eggs. Some species have an unusual defensive display, forming a tight 'watchspring', usually with the head hidden beneath the coils. When touched they wildly coil and uncoil. Harmless to man, they lack fangs or venom glands. There are 13 species distributed throughout sub-Saharan Africa, with seven occurring on the subcontinent, three of which are endemic.

## Mozambique Shovel-snout       *Prosymna janii* (Pl. 16)

*(Endemic) max. SVL 210 mm male, 275 mm female.*
A small snake with a rounded, angular snout, and eyes with round pupils. It has few ventrals (107-129), and keeled scales in 15-17 rows. The body is yellow to pale red-brown above, with a series of paired, large, dark brown to black blotches that are larger on the forebody. The belly is uniform cream-white. **Biology and breeding:** Rarely found, except in spring when males come to the surface to search for females. In defensive display, the front of the body is inflated and raised, and moved slowly to and fro with the mouth open. Hard-shelled gecko eggs commonly eaten. Up to five eggs laid in December. **Habitat:** Coastal dune forest. **Range:** S. Mozambique, including Inhaca Island, Bazaruto Archipelago, and N. Zululand.

## Sundevall's Shovel-snout    *Prosymna sundevallii* (Pls. 16 and 29)

*(Endemic) max. SVL 270 mm male, 330 mm female.*
This small snake has smooth scales in 15 rows. The snout is upturned. The pupils are round. The paired internasals touch each other (or are just apart). There are 131-170 ventrals. The body is pale to dark brown above, with numerous light and dark mottlings, and sometimes with a series of dark vertebral blotches. The belly is white. **Breeding:** Lays 3-5 elongate eggs (28 x 9 mm). Hatchlings measure 100-110 mm TL. **Habitat:** Dry areas, including savannah woodlands, highveld and karroid areas, entering fynbos and mesic thicket in the Cape. **Range:** Eastern half of the subcontinent. **Subspecies:** Two races: *P.s. sundevallii* has its internasals separated, paired spots, and a longer tail; occurs from Gauteng to Cape, with a few records from N. Cape/S. Botswana border; *P.s. lineata* has its internasals touching, single spots, and a shorter tail; occurs in Mpumalanga, N. Province, Zimbabwe, with an isolated record from N. Zululand.

■ *P.s. sundevalli*

□ *P.s. lineata*

## Two-striped Shovel-snout       *Prosymna bivittata* (Pl. 19)

*(Endemic) max. SVL 274 mm male, 315 mm female.*
This slender snake has smooth scales in 15 rows. The snout is upturned. The pupils are round. The paired internasals are well separated. Ventrals number 154-180. The back is purple-brown to red-brown, with a broken orange stripe on the backbone. The belly is white. **Breeding:** The female lays up to 4 eggs (27 x 7 mm). **Habitat:** *Acacia* savannah, entering sandveld. **Range:** N. and NW provinces, through S. Zimbabwe and Botswana, to Namibia and Namaqualand.

## Angola Shovel-snout       *Prosymna angolensis*

*Max. SVL 225 mm male, 300 mm female.*
A small snake with an angular snout, and smooth scales in 15 rows. There is a single, bandlike internasal. Ventrals number 121-163. The tail is very short (16-26 subcaudals). The back is light yellow-brown, with a paired series of black spots (which may be absent); the scales are sometimes dark-edged with a pale centre. The belly and flanks are yellow-white. **Habitat:** Savannah. **Range:** N. Namibia and Caprivi Strip, north to Angola and Zambia, east to Geoverega, Botswana, and Hwange, S. Zimbabwe.

## South-western Shovel-snout       *Prosymna frontalis* (Pl. 26)

*Max. SVL 290 mm male, 380 mm female.*
This small, slender snake has an angular snout. The scales are smooth, in 15 rows. There is a single, bandlike internasal. The eyes have vertical

pupils. Ventrals number 153-199. The tail is long (32-54 subcaudals). The body is light brown to chestnut above; the scales are dark-edged, giving a striped or mosaic effect. It has a broad, dark brown to black collar (which is followed by fainter crossbars in juveniles). The belly is white. **Habitat:** Rocky areas in arid regions. **Range:** N. Cape, to Namibia and S. Angola.

### East African Shovel-snout — *Prosymna stuhlmannii* (Pl. 29)
*Max. SVL 225 mm male, 255 mm female.*
A small snake with an angular snout. Its smooth scales are in 15 rows. It has a single, bandlike internasal. There are 124-164 ventrals. The tail is long (17-39 subcaudals). The back is usually metallic blue-black, sometimes with the scales pale-centred; a paired series of small white spots flanking the backbone may be present. The tip of the snout is greenish-yellow and the belly is white, and sometimes brown-black. **Biology and breeding:** The defensive 'watchspring' display has not been recorded in this species. The female lays 3-4 eggs (19-30 x 6-8 mm). **Habitat:** Savannah, extending into wooded hills. **Range:** N. Zululand, to Mpumalanga, Zimbabwe and Mozambique. Elsewhere through E. Africa to S. Somalia. **Subspecies:** Previously treated as a southern race of *P. ambigua*, which is more robust and restricted to Central Africa and Angola.

### Visser's Shovel-snout — *Prosymna visseri* (Pl. 98)
*Max. SVL 263 mm male, 310 mm female.*
This small snake has a rounded snout, a single internasal, and a very large prefrontal touching the first upper labial. The scales are smooth, in 15 rows. The eyes have round pupils. Ventrals number 189-208, and subcaudals 37-57. The back is dark brown, with a pale yellowish vertebral stripe (which may be broken). The belly is white. **Biology:** It differs from other shovel-snout snakes in that it lives in deep granite cracks in rocky areas, where it feeds on gecko eggs. **Habitat:** Rock outcrops in Mopane tree savannah. **Range:** S. Angola; one specimen recorded recently from Kamanjab in N. Namibia.

## Sand Snakes and Relatives
### SUBFAMILY PSAMMOPHINAE

These snakes share certain vertebral and dental features and are unusual in having a vestigial, tube-like hemipenis. Varying from very small to large in size, most are diurnal, fast, active terrestrial snakes while some are partly arboreal (living under tree bark) and others burrow in loose sand. They are rare in forest or thick bush, and are usually found in savannah or semi-desert, with some entering montane grassland. Egg-laying is usual, but there is one viviparous species. All possess large back fangs, and some have toxic saliva, although only a very few species are clinically dangerous. Serious envenomation has been reported for the Mediterranean *Malpolon*, and mild envenomation for some local *Psammophis*.

The subfamily is distributed throughout Africa, with some entering Europe and the near East; one species is present on Madagascar. There are eight genera, with six on the subcontinent, one of which is endemic.

## Bark Snakes — *Hemirhagerrhis*
These small arboreal snakes have a short maxillary with 9-10 teeth, followed after a gap by two curved fangs.

There are three species in the genus, two of which occur in the region. The other species, *H. kelleri*, occurs in the dry savannahs of Ethiopia and Somalia.

### Eastern Bark or Mopane Snake
*Hemirhagerrhis nototaenia* (Pl. 16)

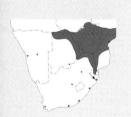

*Max. SVL 300 mm male, 335 mm female.*
A small, slender snake with a flattened head, an obvious neck, small eyes with vertical pupils and a semi-divided nasal. The body is cylindrical with smooth scales in 17 rows. The tail is longish, with 68-98 paired subcaudals. The back is grey or grey-brown, with a dark vertebral stripe that is flanked by, and often fused with a series of black spots, forming crossbars or a zigzag. The top of the head is black. The belly is dirty white, mottled with grey. The tail is paler, with the last third often yellow or orange to salmon pink. **Biology and breeding:** They shelter under loose bark, feeding on day geckos, small skinks, and occasionally small frogs. These are eaten while the snake hangs head-down from vegetation. They may also eat gecko eggs. They never bite. The female lays 2-8 elongate eggs (24 x 6 mm). **Habitat:** Savannah. **Range:** Extreme N. KwaZulu-Natal and Mpumalanga lowveld, into Zimbabwe and Mozambique, and through N. Botswana to N. Namibia and S. Angola. Elsewhere, to tropical E. Africa, reaching S. Sudan. **Subspecies:** None: The western race is now treated as a full species (below).

### Viperine Bark Snake
*Hemirhagerrhis viperinus* (Pl. 16)

*Max. SVL 270 mm male, 295 mm female.*
A small, slender snake, similar in scalation to the eastern bark snake (above), but with fewer ventrals (154-177) and subcaudals (52-75). The back is more boldly patterned with larger, somewhat triangular dark spots. It usually lacks a vertebral stripe. The last half of the tail is creamy to chestnut-yellow. **Biology:** Found sheltering in deep rock cracks, where it eats small, diurnal geckos (Namib day geckos and dwarf day geckos). **Habitat:** Granite outcrops in arid savannah. **Range:** Scattered records in central and N. Namibia and S. Angola.

## Beaked Snakes   *Rhamphiophis*
These are large, stout snakes with a shortened skull and a hooked snout. They are terrestrial, searching underground in rodent burrows for their food. There are five species, one of which occurs in the region.

### Rufous Beaked Snake
*Rhamphiophis rostratus* (Pl. 34)

*Max. SVL 1 105 mm male, 1 070 mm female.*
A large, stout-bodied snake. The head is distinct from the body, and has a prominent, hooked snout. The eyes are largish, with round pupils. The body is cylindrical and stout with smooth scales in 17-19 rows. The anal is divided. The tail is long, with paired subcaudals. The back is uniform yellowish-brown to red-brown, with the scales sometimes pale-centred. The head has a dark stripe on the sides. The belly is cream to yellow-white. **Biology and breeding:** Slow-moving and diurnal; shelters in mammal burrows and termitaria. Eats a variety of small vertebrates, including other snakes; juveniles also take insects. They rarely bite and although they hiss and strike when first captured, they tame well. The female lays 8-17 large cylindrical eggs (34-40 x 20-22 mm) often staggered

over a few days. **Habitat:** Sandy thornveld or bushveld. **Range:** In north entering Caprivi and N. Botswana; in east from Mpumalanga, through N. Province, Zimbabwe (where it is absent from the central plateau), Mozambique floodplain, and north to Sudan. **Subspecies:** Previously treated as a southern race of *R. oxyrhynchus*, which occurs in W. Africa (reaching Uganda) and lacks the head stripe, and has a single preocular.

## Dwarf Beaked Snake    *Dipsina*
The genus is endemic to the subcontinent, and contains a single species.

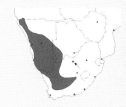

### Dwarf Beaked Snake    *Dipsina multimaculata* (Pls. 15 and 17)
*(Endemic) max. SVL 321 mm male, 323 mm female.*
This small, slender snake has a distinct head with a prominent, hooked snout. The eyes are largish with round pupils. The body is cylindrical and slender with smooth scales in 17 rows. The anal is divided. The tail is short with paired subcaudals. The back may be various shades of buff, grey and pink-brown with 3-5 rows of darker blotches that may be pale-centred and/or fuse to form crossbars. The back of the neck has a dark V-shape. The head has an eye-stripe. The belly is white to pink-cream with dark lateral spots. **Biology and breeding:** Hides beneath stones or in loose sand at the base of bushes, ambushing small lizards particularly barking geckos and small lacertids. Docile, but when threatened may adopt a coiled posture that mimics the horned adder, *Bitis caudalis* (page 116). The female lays 2-4 eggs (22-27 x 8-9 mm, 1,3-1,4 g). They hatch after 53 days (at 28°C); young measure 115-126 mm TL. **Habitat:** Rocky sandy areas. **Range:** Cape karroid areas, through SW Botswana to Namibia.

## Olympic Snakes    *Dromophis*
These slender, medium-sized snakes have the maxillary teeth longest in the middle, and the anterior mandibular teeth the largest.
   There are three species in the genus, one of which occurs in the region. *D. praeornatus* is restricted to W. Africa, from Senegal to the Central African Republic. A new species has recently been discovered in N. Mozambique.

### Lined Olympic Snake    *Dromophis lineatus*
*Max. SVL 880 mm male, 768 mm female.*
Slender with a cylindrical body and a distinct head. The eyes are medium-sized, with round pupils. The scales are smooth, in 15-17 rows. The anal is divided. The tail is long with paired subcaudals. The back is olive in colour, with three thin greenish yellow stripes. The scales are black-edged. The belly is greenish-yellow to pale green, usually with distinctive black bars on the sides of the ventrals. **Biology and breeding:** Diurnal, forage around rivers and swamps for frogs and small mammals. Gentle and rarely bite. Lay 6-9 eggs (23-27 x 12-18 mm). **Habitat:** Low, waterside vegetation. **Range:** Extreme W. Zimbabwe, Caprivi Strip. Through tropical Africa to Sudan.

## Skaapstekers    *Psammophylax*
These solid-bodied snakes have a distinct head, and moderately sized eyes with round pupils. The maxillary teeth are the same size to slightly larger in the rear; the mandibular teeth are largest at the front. Skaapstekers' bodies are cylindrical, with smooth scales in 17 rows. The anal is divided. The tail is of moderate length, with paired subcaudals.

These are terrestrial grassland snakes that forage during the day and evening. They feed on a wide variety of small vertebrates which they bite, then grip until the prey has been subdued by the venom. They may bite if they are restrained. The venom is clinically unimportant, and no serious symptoms have been reported; experimentally, it is very toxic, but yields are minute. The common name is ludicrous; it translates literally as 'sheep stabber'; it is doubtful if they produce enough venom to kill a rat, let alone a sheep. Reproduction is varied, the species showing interesting maternal care in cold climates.

There are three species in the genus, all occurring in the region. None is endemic.

### Spotted or Rhombic Skaapsteker
*Psammophylax rhombeatus* **(Pls. 17 and 22)**
*Max. SVL 1 200 mm male, 932 mm female.*
A medium-sized snake that has a smallish head with a rounded snout. The rostral is usually deeper than it is broad, and sometimes separates the internasals. There are usually two anterior temporals. Ventrals number 143-177, and subcaudals 60-84. The back is yellowish-brown to pale olive, with three (rarely four) rows of dark-edged blotches down the back that may fuse to form a zigzag or irregular stripes. The upper lip is dark-spotted. The belly is yellowish with dark blotches. **Biology and breeding:** Common in moist grasslands, this species actively pursues its prey. The diet includes lizards, frogs, rodents, birds, and even other snakes. It may bite, but only if provoked. It tames well. Up to 30 eggs (20-35 x 12-18 mm) are laid in a hole; the female guards the eggs by coiling around them. They take only 35-45 days to hatch and the young measure 180-220 mm TL. **Habitat:** Highveld grasslands, mesic thicket and fynbos, entering karroid areas. **Range:** Widespread in the highveld, entering coastal KwaZulu-Natal and S. Cape, with scattered records in Little Namaqualand and Namibia. Elsewhere in S. Angola. **Subspecies:** Two races are recognized, with only the typical race occurring on the subcontinent; it is replaced in S. Angola by *P.r. ocellatus*, which has a different colour pattern and more than 172 ventrals.

*P.r. rhombeatus*

### Striped Skaapsteker
*Psammophylax tritaeniatus* **(Pl. 22)**
*Max. SVL 734 mm male, 680 mm female.*
This is a medium-sized snake. It has a small head, with a pointed snout. The rostral is usually broader than it is deep. The eyes are small. The tail is shortish (49-69 subcaudals). The back is grey to pale grey-olive with three distinct, black-edged, dark brown stripes, one of these forming a vertebral line that may be divided by a fine yellowish line. The lateral stripes pass through the eyes. The upper lip and belly are uniform white to cream. **Biology and breeding:** These gentle, beautiful and inoffensive snakes forage in grass and hunt for small mammals (the young take lizards and small frogs). When disturbed, they make a dash for cover and then freeze; they are very well camouflaged and easily overlooked. They wriggle wildly in the hand, but never bite. The female lays 5-18 eggs (23-28 x 11-15 mm, 2-3 g) in a hole, but she is not known to guard the eggs. Hatchlings measure 130-220 mm TL. **Habitat:** Open grassland and savannah. **Range:** Central part of the region, from S. Free State through Gauteng and N. Province, Zimbabwe, N. Botswana and Namibia, north to Angola and Tanzania.

**Grey-bellied Grass Snake** *Psammophylax variabilis* (Pl. 22)
*Max. SVL 835 mm male, 620 mm female.*
A medium-sized snake. The head is small, with a rounded snout. The
rostral is always broader than it is deep. The eyes are small. There is one
anterior temporal. The tail is shortish (49-61 subcaudals). The back is grey
or olive-brown, sometimes with three thin (one scale wide), dark stripes
which may be white-flecked. The upper lip is grey-white. The belly is
uniform grey. **Biology and breeding:** These snakes eat a wide variety
of small mammals, as well as fish. They are viviparous; about four fully
formed babies, measuring 151-155 mm TL, are born in December.
**Habitat:** Floodplain grasslands (elsewhere in montane grassland).
**Range:** Restricted locally to Chobe floodplain. Elsewhere, through central
and E. Africa to Ethiopia. **Subspecies:** Three races are recognized, with
only the typical race occurring in the region.

*P.v. variabilis*

# Sand and Grass Snakes *Psammophis*

These small to large snakes have the head distinct from the neck, and
moderate to large eyes with round pupils. There are 10-15 maxillary
teeth, the largest at the front of the eye, and two large, grooved fangs at
the back of the eye. The anterior mandibular teeth are distinctly enlarged.
Usually the first four lower labials touch the anterior chin shields. The
body is cylindrical, with smooth scales in 11-19 rows. The anal is
sometimes divided. The tail is long, with paired subcaudals.

These fast, active diurnal snakes inhabit savannah or arid scrubland, but
are sometimes restricted to montane grassland. Some species (*P. sibilans*
and *P. schokari*) polish themselves with a nasal gland secretion which
reduces skin water-loss. Prey (small vertebrates) is pursued, grabbed and
chewed until the venom takes effect, then swallowed head first. These
snakes usually struggle wildly when first caught and the larger species bite
readily. When they are caught by the tail, they spin wildly causing it to
break off. The tail tip cone may be regenerated resulting in false low
subcaudal counts. Truncated tails are more common in some species
(63% in *P. biseriatus*) than in others (8% in *P. crucifer*). They tame well, but
require frequent food. The venom is usually harmless, but a bite from the
Kenyan *P. biseriatus* caused mild haemorrhage; pain, swelling and nausea
has been noted in some *P. brevirostris* and olive grass snake bites. They
are oviparous.

This is a large genus containing 23 species which are found throughout
Africa, with five species entering the near East. Nine occur in the region,
only one of which is endemic.

**Western Sand Snake** *Psammophis trigrammus* (Pl. 34)
*Max. SVL 750 mm male, 540 mm female.*
A very slender snake, with 17 scale rows. There are nine upper labials
(numbers five and six enter the eye). The first five lower labials touch the
anterior chin shields. Ventrals number 183-197. The anal is divided. The
tail is long (132-155 subcaudals). The body is pale olive to grey-brown
anteriorly, and reddish to yellowish behind; sometimes black-edged scales
along the back form a stripe that may be flanked by a yellowish-white
stripe. The belly is off-white, with a light grey to olive median band.
**Biology:** This very fast snake chases skinks and lacertids during the
heat of the day. **Habitat:** Arid scrubland. **Range:** Richtersveld, through
Namibia to S. Angola.

## Karoo Sand Snake or Whip Snake
*Psammophis notostictus* (Pl. 23)
*Max. SVL 680 mm male, 733 mm female.*
This slender snake has 17 scale rows and eight upper labials (numbers four and five enter the eye). There are two preoculars. Ventrals number 155-183. The anal is undivided. The tail is long (80-107 subcaudals). Coloration may be uniform or striped. The back is light grey to dark brown, with paler flanks; sometimes there is a pale stripe or spots along the backbone and a pale stripe on the side. The edge of the belly has white and grey stripes, the rest being off-white with grey blushes. **Biology and breeding:** This snake is a very fast predator on skinks and lacertids, which it chases during the heat of the day. It is the most common snake in karroid areas; many specimens are killed while crossing roads. A gravid female contained three eggs (28 x 6 mm) in October. **Habitat:** Arid scrubland and karroid regions. **Range:** Cape provinces and S. Free State, through Namibia to S. Angola.

## Cape, Namib and Fork-marked Sand Snakes
*Psammophis leightoni* (Pl. 23)
*Max. SVL 960 mm male, 798 mm female.*
Slender snakes with 17 scale rows and eight upper labials (numbers four and five enter the eye). There is one preocular. The posterior nasal is divided, as is the anal. Coloration may be striped or blotched (see Subspecies). **Biology and breeding:** These snakes chase and eat small vertebrates, mainly rodents and lizards, but also take other snakes. A gravid female contained eight eggs (25 x 9 mm) in October. The hatchlings measure 220-240 mm TL. **Habitat:** Coastal fynbos, desert and semi-desert, entering savannah. **Range:** Western regions, from Cape Town to N. Province and S. Angola. **Subspecies:** There are three races, all of which occur in the region. The Cape sand snake, *P.l. leightoni*, has the top of the head spotted or barred, 155-161 ventrals, and 92-97 subcaudals; it is found in SW Cape and is threatened by habitat destruction (SA RDB, Vulnerable). The fork-marked sand snake, *P.l. trinasalis*, has the top of the head striped, 150-172 ventrals and 84-102 subcaudals; it is found in E. Namibia, Botswana, N. Cape, NW Province, Free State to N. Province. The Namib sand snake, *P.l. namibensis*, has the top of the head spotted or barred, 167-187 ventrals, and 94-112 subcaudals; it is found in Namaqualand, extending through Namib Desert to S. Angola.

*P.l. leightoni*

*P.l. namibensis*

*P.l. trinasalis*

## Jalla's Sand Snake
*Psammophis jallae* (Pl. 23)
*Max. SVL 730 mm male, 640 mm female.*
This snake has 15 scale rows, and seven upper labials (numbers three and four enter the eye). There is one preocular. The posterior nasal is divided, as is the anal. Ventrals number 154-175. The tail is long (84-112 subcaudals). The back is light grey to olive-brown, usually with a broad, black-edged dark band (sometimes with yellow vertebral spots), bordered by a narrow white-yellow streak. The flanks are buff, often with a red-brown stripe. The belly has a broad olive-yellow central stripe which is sometimes dark-edged, with the outer ventral edges white to cream. The throat has a characteristic blue-black colour. **Biology:** A rare snake. The diet consists mainly of skinks and lacertids. **Habitat:** Grassland and savannah. **Range:** N. and NW provinces, into Zimbabwe and W. Zambia, and through Botswana to N. Namibia and SE Angola.

## Stripe-bellied Sand Snake
**Psammophis subtaeniatus (Pls. 22 and 98)**
*Max. SVL 900 mm male, 885 mm female.*
This is a slender snake with 17 scale rows. There is one preocular. The posterior nasal is divided, as is the anal. The back is grey-olive to brown (and paler at the rear) with a broad, black-edged dorsal stripe, flanked by a cream to yellowish stripe, then a dark lateral stripe and a black stripe. The head has pale, dark-edged blotches. The belly has a bright yellow, black-edged stripe, bordered at the edge by a white stripe. **Biology and breeding:** Readily climbs into low bush, and will eat small birds in addition to lizards and rodents. Very fast and difficult to catch, although many are killed by birds of prey. The female lays 4-10 eggs (32 x 12 mm). **Habitat:** Open dry savannah, thornveld and bushveld. **Range:** Northern regions from coast to coast. Elsewhere, to E. Africa. **Subspecies:** Two races are recognized, and both occur in the region. *P.s. subtaeniatus* has nine upper labials and 106-132 subcaudals; it is found over most of the region, except in Mozambique, reaching its southern limit in N. Zululand. *P.s. orientalis* has eight upper labials, 94-116 subcaudals, and its head markings and pale dorsolateral stripes are faint; it is found in Mozambique.

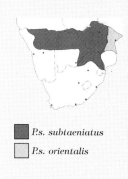

P.s. *subtaeniatus*

P.s. *orientalis*

## Dwarf Sand Snake
**Psammophis angolensis (Pl. 22)**
*Max. SVL 320 mm male, 352 mm female.*
This is a very small, slender snake with only 11 scale rows. It has eight upper labials (numbers four and five enter the eye). There is one preocular. The posterior nasal is usually undivided, while the anal is divided. Ventrals number 135-156. The tail is short (57-82 subcaudals). The back is grey to yellow-bronze, with a broad brown-black dorsal stripe, and a faint, broken black stripe on the lower flank. The head is dark brown, with three narrow, pale crossbars and 1-2 dark neck collars. The lips, throat and belly are yellow-white. **Biology and breeding:** This small, secretive snake forages in grass tussocks, under fallen logs, etc., feeding on small lizards and frogs. It never bites, but is difficult to tame. The female lays 3-5 elongate, small eggs (15-18 x 5-6 mm). **Habitat:** Moist and dry wooded savannah. **Range:** N. Province and Mpumalanga, through Zimbabwe, N. Botswana and Namibia, north to the Democratic Republic of Congo and Tanzania.

## Leopard and Short-snouted Grass Snakes
**Psammophis brevirostris (Pl. 34)**
*Max. SVL 950 mm male, 760 mm female.*
These are slender snakes with 17 scale rows, and eight upper labials (numbers four and five enter the eye). There is one preocular, and the snout is short and only slightly longer than the eye width. The posterior nasal is usually undivided, while the anal is divided. Ventrals number 146-174. The tail is long (72-109 subcaudals). Coloration is usually striped (see Subspecies). **Biology and breeding:** Alert and active, they are frequently seen crossing roads. They eat small vertebrates. They bite readily when first caught. Females lay 4-15 eggs (28 x 15 mm) in early summer; they hatch in about 60 days (27°C), and females may lay two clutches per season. The young are 190-250 mm TL. **Habitat:** Varied; eastern race in highveld and montane grassland, western race in rocky arid savannah. **Range:** A patchy distribution on the subcontinent (see Subspecies). **Subspecies:** Two races are recognized, both occurring in the region. *P.b. leopardinus* has variable coloration, the back being light

P.b. *leopardinus*

P.b. *brevirostris*

red-brown to light olive, usually with a pale buff chain pattern on the forebody and pale yellow stripes on the rear. There are pale bars on the back of the head. The chin and throat have grey blotches. The belly is off-white, sometimes with grey bands. It is found in Namibia and S. Angola. In typical *P.b. brevirostris*, the back is olive-brown, with a broad dorsal stripe of black-edged scales, flanked by pale dorsolateral stripes. There is sometimes a narrow, broken white stripe down the backbone. The belly is white. This race occurs in the highveld and adjacent regions, extending to S. KwaZulu-Natal coast and north into E. Africa, and with a relict population in E. Zimbabwe. *P. sibilans*, to which this snake was previously referred, is now restricted to N. Africa.

### Olive Grass Snake
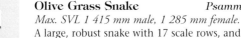

*Psammophis mossambicus* **(Pl. 23)**
*Max. SVL 1 415 mm male, 1 285 mm female.*

A large, robust snake with 17 scale rows, and eight upper labials (numbers four and five enter the eye). There is one preocular and the snout obviously longer than the eye width. The posterior nasal is usually undivided, while the anal is divided. The snout is not flattened. Ventrals number 151-183. The tail is long (82-110 subcaudals). The back is olive-brown (paler towards the tail), sometimes with the scales black-edged, forming thin black lines or with scattered black flecks on the forebody. The belly is white-yellow, sometimes with black streaks. **Biology and breeding:** The olive grass snake is similar to the short-snouted grass snake, *P. brevirostris* (above) but forages more readily in marshy areas. It occasionally eats other snakes, even young black mambas, with which it may be confused. It should be treated with respect; it bites readily, and its venom may cause nausea and pain; antivenom is ineffective in the treatment of this snakebite. The female lays 10-30 eggs (28-40 x 10-20 mm) in dead leaves, etc., in midsummer. They hatch in about 65 days (27°C) and the young measure 275-300 mm TL. **Habitat:** Moist savannah and low-lying grasslands. **Range:** Northern part of the region, extending south along KwaZulu-Natal coast. Elsewhere, to Kenya. Previously referred to *P. phillipsii*, which is now restricted to W. African forests.

### Cross-marked or Montane Grass Snake

*Psammophis crucifer* **(Pls. 23 and 34)**
*(Endemic) max. SVL 490 mm male, 621 mm female.*

This small, robust snake has 15 scale rows, and eight upper labials (numbers four and five enter the eye). There is one preocular. The posterior nasal is usually undivided, while the anal is divided. The snout is not flattened. Ventrals number 136-165. The tail is short (61-81 subcaudals). The back is silver-grey to olive-brown, with a broad, dorsal, black-edged, brown stripe; there is a similar stripe with a white lower border on the flank. The head has dark-edged, cream-yellow crossbars. The belly is yellow-orange, often with grey lateral streaks. Occasional specimens are uniform olive-grey with an off-white belly. **Biology and breeding:** This grass snake occurs in the temperate zones, and is active on mountain plateaus and in moist grasslands. It eats mainly lizards, but also takes frogs. It wriggles wildly when caught, but rarely bites, and it tames well. The female lays 5-13 eggs (18-21 x 10 mm, exceptionally up to 32 mm long) in midsummer. The eggs may hatch in 45 days, and the young measure 195 mm TL. **Habitat:** Found in highveld and montane grass-land, entering fynbos. **Range:** Cape fold mountains and KwaZulu-Natal midlands, on to the highveld of the Free State and extending along the old escarpment of the northern provinces, with relict populations in Namaqualand and E. Zimbabwe.

## Colubrine Snakes
### SUBFAMILY COLUBRINAE

This subfamily contains the common snakes of the Northern Hemisphere including the racers, rat snakes, king snakes and their allies. Although poorly represented in Africa, it does include a number of clinically important species. They are distinguished by an asymmetrical hemipenis, with a simple sulcus. Back fangs have developed independently in a number of lineages, while in one group (the egg eaters) the teeth are greatly reduced. Included here are a number of groups sometimes placed in separate tribes or even elevated to distinct subfamilies (for example boigines, philothamnines, etc.). They are distributed worldwide, but occur mostly in the northern hemisphere. There are 70-80 genera with over 400 species; eight genera with 16 species occur on the subcontinent. Three species are endemic.

## African Smooth Snakes   *Meizodon*
This is an endemic African genus (extending just into Arabia) of small, secretive snakes, related to European smooth snakes and rat snakes. They are oviparous. There are five species, with one entering the subcontinent.

### Semiornate Snake   *Meizodon semiornatus* (Pl. 26)
*Max. SVL 455 mm male, 600 mm female.*
A small, slender snake with a flat head, and eyes with round pupils. Scales are smooth, in 21 rows at midbody; tail moderately long. Back is grey to olive-brown, with irregular black crossbars on front of body. Head is black, with eye partially ringed with white. Throat is white, belly grey. **Biology and breeding:** Shy and diurnal; forages in thick vegetation along river courses for skinks, day geckos and frogs. Shelters beneath bark or in hollow logs, where 2-3 individuals may be found. Rarely bites; harmless. (SA RDB, Peripheral.) Lays 2-3 large, elongate eggs (35 x 10 mm). **Habitat:** Arid and mesic savannah. **Range:** N. Zululand, Swaziland, and Kruger National Park, through Mozambique Plain and Zimbabwe to E. Africa and Yemen. **Subspecies:** The typical race extends through most of the range, and is replaced in Sudan and Chad by *M.s. tchadensis*.

*M.s. semiornatus*

## Green and Bush Snakes   *Philothamnus*
These agile, diurnal African snakes have slender, usually green bodies, an obvious head, and large eyes with round pupils. The body scales are smooth and usually in 15 rows at midbody. Harmless to man, they lack fangs and venom glands, but are often mistaken for green mambas or boomslang. Most species are terrestrial, but they readily climb low vegetation. Inhabiting damp areas, they feed on small vertebrates, particularly amphibians, which they grab but do not constrict. There are 19 species throughout sub-Saharan Africa, with five on the subcontinent, one of which is endemic.

### Spotted Bush Snake   *Philothamnus semivariegatus* (Pls. 30 and 99)
*Max. SVL 825 mm male, 850 mm female.*
A very slender snake with a flat, distinct head and a long tail. There are two pairs of temporals on each side of the head, and three upper labials

enter each eye. The ventrals and subcaudals are strongly keeled and laterally notched. The body is bright green to olive, usually with dark spots and bars on the forebody (these are sometimes absent in specimens from Mpumalanga), becoming grey-bronze towards the rear. The head is green or blue-green and the eyes have golden irises. The belly is greenish-white to yellowish (bright lemon yellow in Namaqualand). **Biology and breeding:** This beautiful, graceful snake hunts among shrubs and bushes on rocky ridges or along river courses for geckos, chameleons and tree frogs. An expert and speedy climber, it is difficult to detect in foliage. Its vision is excellent, and prey and danger are quickly spotted. It is often seen with the head and neck undulating sideways while the body remains motionless. In threat display, the neck is inflated, revealing the bright blue skin, and it may strike. It takes time to settle in captivity. The female lays 3-12 elongate eggs (28-41 x 8-12 mm) in midsummer. Hatchlings measure 230-260 mm TL. **Habitat:** Open forest or savannah, extending into arid regions. **Range:** Northern regions, extending into Kalahari and N. Cape, reaching Namaqualand in the west and Port Elizabeth in the east. Elsewhere, through central Africa to Sudan and Guinea.

### Ornate Green Snake *Philothamnus ornatus* (Pl. 25)

*Max. SVL 420 mm male, 595 mm female.*
A slender snake with a rounded head, two temporals on each side of the head, and three labials entering each eye. It has a longish tail (86-100 smooth subcaudals). The back is emerald to olive-green, with a yellow-edged, red-brown dorsal stripe, and a white to bronze-cream belly. **Biology:** This snake lives in reed beds alongside streams, and eats small amphibians. It is shy and rarely bites. **Habitat:** Mesic savannah. **Range:** It has a patchy distribution; E. Zimbabwe and Okavango Swamp, and elsewhere to Angola and Lake Malawi.

### Western Green Snake *Philothamnus angolensis* (Pl. 30)

*Max. SVL 790 mm male, 808 mm female.*
A slender snake with two temporals on each side of the head, and three labials entering each eye. The tail is long (87-120 smooth subcaudals). The body is uniform bright emerald to olive-green, often with scattered blue-white spots. The skin between the scales is black, and the belly is pale green to yellowish-green. **Biology and breeding:** This active snake climbs into reed beds along river courses and vleis and feeds on small reed birds and lizards, as well as frogs. In threat display, it inflates the throat, showing the black skin (similar to the boomslang), and bites readily (SA RDB, Peripheral). The female lays 5-8 (max. 16) eggs in summer (December-February); these vary in size (25-43 x 9-18 mm). Communal nesting sites in rotting vegetation may contain up to 85 eggs. These hatch in about two months. The young measure 220-260 mm TL. **Habitat:** Mesic savannah. **Range:** It has a patchy distribution; N. Zululand and adjacent Mozambique, E. and central Zimbabwe, Okavango Swamp and Caprivi Strip, and central Namibia. Elsewhere, north to Cameroon.

### Green Water Snake *Philothamnus hoplogaster* (Pl. 30)

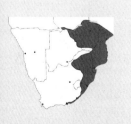

*Max. SVL 662 mm male, 685 mm female.*
This small, slender species has two temporals on each side of the head, and two labials entering each eye. There are 73-106 smooth subcaudals. The body is uniform bright emerald to blue-green, sometimes with black

bars on the forebody. The skin between the scales is black. The belly is bluish-white to yellow. **Biology and breeding:** This alert, active snake hunts in reed beds alongside vleis and streams. It is an expert swimmer. The diet consists mainly of small frogs and fish, but lizards may also be taken. The young also eat grasshoppers. The neck is not inflated in threat display. The female lays 3-8 elongate eggs (25-34 x 8-12 mm) in early summer. The young measure 150-200 mm TL, and are darker than the adults. **Habitat:** Varied; coastal bush, fynbos, and arid and mesic savannah. **Range:** E. Cape coast, through KwaZulu-Natal, Mpumalanga, N. Province and S. Mozambique to Zimbabwe. Elsewhere, to Kenya.

### Eastern Green Snake

*Philothamnus natalensis* **(Pl. 30)**
*(Endemic) max. SVL 788 mm male, 766 mm female.*
This slender snake may easily be confused with the green water snake, *P. hoplogaster* (above). It differs in being larger, having keeled ventrals and subcaudals (see Subspecies) and two pairs of temporals on each side of the head. The body is uniform bright green above (juveniles sometimes have dark bars on the forebody), and pale green below. **Biology and breeding:** This snake is similar in habits and behaviour to the green water snake. **Habitat:** Varied; wet montane and dry forest, and miombo woodland. **Range:** W. Cape (to Riversdale), through E. Cape, KwaZulu-Natal and Mpumalanga to Zimbabwe and S. Mozambique. **Subspecies:** Two races: *P.n. natalensis* has keeled subcaudals and nine upper labials; occurs in N. Zululand to S. Mozambique. *P.n. occidentalis* has smooth subcaudals and eight upper labials; occurs over the southern part of the range.

■ *P.n. natalensis*
□ *P.n. occidentalis*

# Egg Eaters   *Dasypeltis*

These unusual African snakes have numerous adaptations for feeding exclusively on birds' eggs. The mouth is almost toothless, with minute teeth embedded in the thick gums, and the skin of the neck and lower jaw is very elastic. The head is small, the moderately sized eyes have vertical pupils, and there is no loreal scale. The body scales are strongly keeled, particularly the lateral rows.

Egg eaters are capable of swallowing eggs with a diameter three times that of their head. The egg is taken into the throat and moved back and forth. Special 'gular' teeth (which are actually projections into the gullet from the backbone) saw through the shell. The liquid content is then swallowed, and the collapsed shell regurgitated. Only fresh eggs are eaten. As a defence against predators (jackals, mongooses, etc.), they mimic venomous adders; they have similar colour patterns, and can 'hiss' by forming a nested horseshoe shape of their coils and rubbing their serrated lateral scales together. They strike readily, with the mouth agape; while this is effective defence, these snakes are quite harmless. They are oviparous. Nocturnal and mainly terrestrial, they will readily climb trees and rock faces in search of birds' nests.

There are six species, with three occurring on the subcontinent, one of which is endemic.

### Common or Rhombic Egg Eater

*Dasypeltis scabra* **(Pl. 15)**
*Max. SVL 595 mm male, 964 mm female.*
A slender, solid snake with a small, rounded head. The lateral body scales are small and have serrated keels. The tail is short (38-78 subcaudals); males have longer tails. The back is slate-grey, light brown or olive-brown,

with a median series of dark, squarish blotches flanked by narrow dark bars. The top of the head has two narrow, V-shaped marks followed by a similar prominent mark on the nape. Lining of the mouth is black. Belly is white, and sometimes flecked. The occasional red-brown, patternless specimen may be confused with the southern brown egg eater (below). **Biology and breeding:** This snake is very common, but is rarely seen. It feeds gluttonously in spring and summer, laying down fat for the winter fast. Colour patterns vary to match the local soil colour and mimic venomous species; the brown-red specimens in the west mimic the horned adder (page 116), and the grey-black specimens along the east coast mimic the night adder (page 113). It lays 6-25 eggs (36 x 18 mm) in summer; these take 80-90 days to hatch. The young measure 210-240 mm TL. In captivity, two clutches may be laid per season. One specimen lived 31 years. **Habitat:** Absent only from true desert and closed-canopy forest. **Range:** Throughout the subcontinent. Elsewhere, to Sudan in the north and Gambia in the west.

### Southern Brown Egg Eater      *Dasypeltis inornata* (Pl. 28)
*(Endemic) max. SVL 784 mm male, 895 mm female.*
This species is similar to the common egg eater, *D. scabra* (above), but has a longer tail (69-92 subcaudals) and slightly smaller, unserrated lateral scales. Its uniform coloration is reddish-brown, and sometimes yellow-olive to dark brown, with dark skin between the scales. The belly is white to dirty yellow. **Biology and breeding:** This snake is similar in behaviour and habits to the common egg eater. The female lays 8-17 eggs (21-35 x 14-20 mm) in summer. The egg surface is pimpled. The young measure 230-280 mm TL. **Habitat:** Prefers open coastal woodland. **Range:** Found in Alexandria in the E. Cape through KwaZulu-Natal, to Mpumalanga and Swaziland.

### East African Egg Eater      *Dasypeltis medici* (Pl. 15)
*Max. SVL 600 mm male, 760 mm female.*
This species is similar to the common egg eater, *D. scabra* (above), but has a longer, more slender tail (71-109 subcaudals), and reduced and serrated lateral scales. The back is pinkish to red-brown, sometimes with a darker brown vertebral stripe interrupted by white patches. The flanks have narrow vertical bars. The head and neck have about five faint V-shaped marks. The lining of the mouth is pink. The belly is cream with brown stippling. **Biology and breeding:** This snake's habits and behaviour are poorly known (SA RDB, Peripheral). The female lays 6-28 eggs (24 x 8 mm). **Habitat:** Found in lowland evergreen forest. **Range:** Found in N. Zululand (Sodwana), through the Mozambique Plain and the eastern escarpment of Zimbabwe, to Kenya. **Subspecies:** Two races are recognized, with only the typical race occurring on the subcontinent. *D.m. lamuensis* has an unpatterned body and fewer ventrals, and occurs from Somalia to Tanzania.

D.m. medici

# Herald Snakes    *Crotaphopeltis*
These nocturnal, terrestrial African snakes have a short, flattened head and big eyes with vertical pupils. The scales are mainly smooth and in 17-21 rows. They lack large venom glands. Herald snakes inhabit marshy areas, feeding on amphibians. They are oviparous. There are six species, with two occurring on the subcontinent.

## Herald or Red-lipped Snake    *Crotaphopeltis hotamboeia* (Pl. 33)

*Max. SVL 701 mm male, 710 mm female.*

A small snake with a broad, obvious head and a short tail. The scales are in 19 rows at midbody and are dull, but the head is iridescent when the skin is freshly shed. The back is olive to green-black above, sometimes with white dots. The head is iridescent blue-black, and the upper lip is orange-red (but white or blackish in the north). The belly is uniform white. **Biology and breeding:** The presence of this snake in South Africa was first noted in the Eastern Province Herald newspaper, hence its unusual common name. Living in marshy areas, it feeds at night on amphibians; the prey is grabbed and held until it has been immobilized by the venom. The Herald snake has large, blade-like back fangs. It is belligerent, and when threatened, it flattens its head and flares its lips, which results in a viper-like appearance. It bites readily, and the wound bleeds freely, but no toxic symptoms have been recorded in a bite by this species. It tames well. The female lays 6-19 eggs (26-32 x 10-13 mm) in leaf litter in early summer; these hatch in 61-64 days. Young measure 130-180 mm TL. **Habitat:** Savannah and open woodland. **Range:** Eastern half of the region, from SW Cape to Zimbabwe. Elsewhere, to tropical Africa.

## Barotse Water Snake    *Crotaphopeltis barotseensis* (Pl. 33)

*Max. SVL 545 mm male, 470 mm female.*

This snake looks similar to the Herald snake, *C. hotamboeia* (above), but has a more elongate body and smooth, glossy body scales in 17 rows. The back is uniform light grey-brown, with dark-edged scales. The head is not dark. The belly is pale brown. **Biology and breeding:** This aquatic species feeds on frogs. It has a gentle disposition and rarely bites. The female lays 6-8 eggs in February. **Habitat:** Papyrus swamp. **Range:** Okavango Swamp, along Chobe River to upper Zambezi River.

## Tiger Snakes    *Telescopus*

These nocturnal, very slender snakes are found throughout Africa, extending into Europe and the near East. Elsewhere, they are called cat snakes because of their large eyes and vertical pupils. They are usually found in dry, rocky regions or open savannah. The diet consists mainly of birds, lizards and occasionally bats. There are seven species in the genus, with two in southern Africa, one of which is endemic. An undescribed species from Namibia is known.

## Eastern Tiger Snake    *Telescopus semiannulatus* (Pl. 19)

*Max. SVL 624 mm male, 880 mm female.*

A thin-bodied snake with a distinct head and large eyes with vertical pupils. The scales are smooth, in 19 rows at midbody. The anal is divided. The head is uniform orange, with a dark nape band and brown-orange eyes. The body is orange-pink to dull salmon, with 22-50 dark blotches that are larger on the forebody. The belly is uniform yellowish to orange-pink. **Biology and breeding:** Mainly terrestrial, these snakes regularly climb dead trees, old thatched huts, etc. They are slow-moving and unpredictable. When first encountered, they will strike readily and often. In captivity, they become calmer, but may still bite. Small roosting birds, bats, lizards and rodents are eaten. The venom is mild and innocuous to man. Females lay 6-20 elongate eggs (30 x 16 mm) in moist leaf litter in summer; these hatch in 71-85 days. Hatchlings measure 170-230 mm TL.

*T.s. semiannulatus*

*T.s. polystictus*

In captivity, females may retain sperm and lay eggs every two months during summer. **Habitat:** Savannah and sandveld. **Range:** N. bushveld (reaching Pretoria), eastern lowveld (reaching mid-KwaZulu-Natal) and extending through Kalahari bushveld into Namibia and N. Cape. Elsewhere, to Kenya and Democratic Republic of Congo. **Subspecies:** Two races: *T.s. semiannulatus* has 20-50 dark blotches on the back; it is found in Kalahari and eastern regions. *T.s. polystictus* has 52-75 dark blotches on the back; occurs in highveld regions of Namibia, extending into Richtersveld.

### Beetz's Tiger Snake — *Telescopus beetzii* (Pl. 19)
*(Endemic) max. SVL 435 mm male, 590 mm female.*
A slender snake with 21 scale rows at midbody and an undivided anal. It is sandy-buff on the body, with a series of dark round blotches on the back (30-39 on body, and 12-20 on tail), and a small dark spot on the crown. The belly is pinkish-tan. **Biology and breeding:** Rare; lives on rock outcrops, sheltering in cracks during the day and emerging at night to feed on lizards. Usually only found dead on roads. Lays 3-5 elongate eggs (10-14 x 33-55 mm) in December; these hatch after 80-90 days. Young measure 170-190 mm TL. **Habitat:** Rocky, arid regions. **Range:** S. Namibia, extending through Karoo to Laingsburg and SW Free State. Absent from Namib Desert.

## Cat-eyed Tree Snakes  *Dipsadoboa*
Endemic, nocturnal, African tree snakes, the cat-eyed tree snakes have a long, slender body, a flattened, distinct head, and eyes with vertical pupils. They are closely related to the Herald snakes, *Crotaphopeltis* (page 96), but differ in having well-developed venom glands and posterior gular shields. Arboreal, they shelter during the day under bark or in hollow stumps, emerging at night to feed. They are oviparous.
There are ten species in the genus, with two entering the subcontinent.

### Marbled Tree Snake — *Dipsadoboa aulica* (Pl. 31)
*Max. SVL 660 mm male, 630 mm female.*
This small, slender snake has smooth scales in 17 rows at midbody, an obvious head with the loreal entering the eye, the anal undivided, and a longish tail (subcaudals 75-97 in males, 74-86 in females). The back is brown to light brown, with 38-50 faint white crossbars. The head is finely marbled with white, and the tongue is white. The belly is off-white, laterally flecked with red-brown. Older specimens are less brightly barred. **Biology and breeding:** This snake shelters during the day in hollow logs, under bark, in thatched roofs, etc., emerging at dusk to feed on geckos and tree frogs, although it will also eat toads, skinks and even small rodents. They often hunt in reed beds, homing in on calling reed frogs. When disturbed it adopts an open coiled posture with the head well raised. It bites readily but is not dangerous. The female lays 7-8 small eggs (23-28 x 10-13 mm) in midsummer. Hatchlings measure about 180 mm TL. **Habitat:** Lowveld riverine forest. **Range:** N. Zululand, through Swaziland, E. Mpumalanga and Mozambique Plain, entering E. Zimbabwe, and to S. Malawi. **Subspecies:** No races are now recognized.

### Cross-barred Tree Snake — *Dipsadoboa flavida*
*Max. SVL 493 mm male, 480 mm female.*
This small, slender snake has smooth scales in 17 rows at midbody, an obvious head with the loreal entering the eye, the anal undivided, and a

long tail (subcaudals 90-106 in males, 79-100 in females). The top of the head is marbled, with the pale yellow reticulation restricted mainly to the scale edges (and more extensive in the typical race). Body coloration is varied (see Subspecies). **Biology:** A nocturnal and terrestrial or semi-arboreal species, that usually shelters in crevices and under loose bark of bamboos or miwale palms. The diet comprises mainly geckos and tree frogs. **Habitat:** Coastal thicket and dune forest. **Range:** Coastal regions of E. Africa, from Somalia to S. Mozambique. **Subspecies:** Two races are recognized; typical *D.f. flavida* is restricted to the Mulanje Plateau in S. Malawi, and has a pale upper surface with 65-95 red-brown spots on the body. Broadley's cross-barred tree snake, *D.f. broadleyi*, is found from S. Somalia, coastal Kenya and Tanzania, to S. Mozambique (reaching Maputo), and has a red-brown upper surface with 58-82 pale cross-bars.

# Racers   *Coluber*
These thin, diurnal snakes are active hunters in open woodland and semi-desert. They lack back-fangs, have large eyes with round pupils, and the body scales are smooth and large. They are mainly distributed in the northern hemisphere, with a secondary radiation into Saharan Africa, adjacent Arabia and the Horn of Africa. Only a single species (*C. smithi*) crosses the equator into S. Kenya, and the recent discovery of a new species in N. Namibia was therefore completely unexpected. Currently approximately 35 species are recognized, with a single species occurring in the New World. Only a single, endemic species occurs in southern Africa.

### Cunene Racer                    *Coluber* sp. (Pl. 99)
*Max. SVL 290 mm.*
A medium-sized to large snake with paired subcaudals (about 90) and a divided anal scute. The body scales are smooth, have two apical pits, and are in 23 rows at midbody. The relatively long tail is about a third of the SVL. The body is pale grey above, becoming white on the sides and belly and beneath the tail. Numerous irregular broad dark crossbands occur on the back, with a series of irregular black vertical bars or two rows of spots on the sides. These markings fade at the base of the tail. The snout and lips are yellowish and the top of the head uniform grey-brown. **Biology:** A shy, terrestrial species. The banded pattern suggests that it may mimic the venomous black-necked spitting cobra (page 109). **Habitat:** Stony ground (dolomite) with thick *Colophospermum* scrub. **Range:** Known only from two specimens from the Cunene Valley.

# Boomslang   *Dispholidus*
This snake is distinguished by its distinct head and very large eyes, keeled body scales in oblique rows, and large back fangs. Males develop bright colours, while the juveniles and females are brown-olive. Its venom prevents blood clotting, that can cause death. There is one species in the genus.

### Boomslang                    *Dispholidus typus* (Pl. 31)
*Max. SVL 1 290 mm male, 1 260 mm female.*
A large snake with a distinct head, and very large eyes with round pupils. The body scales are keeled, in 19 oblique rows at midbody. Coloration is very variable. Juveniles are twig-coloured, often with blue skin between the scales on the forebody; the head is dark brown above and white below.

*D.t. typus*

They have jewel-like, emerald-green eyes and a yellow throat. Adult females are light olive or brown, with white to brown bellies. Males are more brightly coloured, and occur in various colour phases: They may be leaf-green (and sometimes powder-blue), with a light green belly and occasionally black skin between the scales; or bright green or yellow with black-edged scales, giving a cross-barred appearance, with the head vermiculated in black; or black with dark grey, black-edged belly scales; or brick-red to rust-red, with an orange-pink belly. **Biology and breeding:** These snakes are dangerous but shy. They hunt during the day. Their excellent vision aids them in catching prey, which consists of small vertebrates, particularly chameleons and birds. Prey is actively pursued, seized and chewed to introduce the toxic venom, which quickly kills the victim. When cornered, a boomslang will inflate its neck to expose the brightly coloured skin, and may strike. The amount of venom injected is minute (1 mg), but it is a potent haemotoxin that prevents blood clotting, causing death from haemorrhage. Symptoms of poisoning may not develop for 24-48 hours. A specific antivenom is required for the treatment of this snakebite, and is available only at major city hospitals. Blood or plasma transfusions may be given to replace lost clotting factors if antivenom is unavailable. Envenomation is rare, and it is usually snake handlers who are bitten. Mating occurs in spring, and 10-14 (occasionally up to 25) eggs (40 x 20 mm) are laid in tree hollows or leaf litter in summer. Incubation takes 2-3 months. The young measure 290-330 mm TL. **Habitat:** Open bush and savannah; also found in sparsely wooded grassland in the Winterberg, E. Cape. **Range:** Found throughout sub-Saharan Africa, occurring in the northern parts of the region and extending along the east and south coast to Cape Town. **Subspecies:** Two races are recognized. *D.t. typus* occurs in southern Africa and throughout sub-Saharan Africa, excluding deserts. It is replaced by *D.t. punctatus* in forested regions of S. Democratic Republic of Congo, Angola and Zambia.

# Twig Snakes   *Thelotornis*

These arboreal snakes are distinguished by their lance-shaped head, large eyes with keyhole-shaped pupils, extremely long tail and large back fangs. Diurnal, they rely on their cryptic coloration and slow movement to ambush their prey. The genus contains two species; *T. kirtlandii* is restricted to the rain forests of central and W. Africa, while the other species enters the northern savannahs of the subcontinent.

### Twig or Vine Snake   *Thelotornis capensis* (Pls. 18 and 31)
*Max. SVL 1 062 mm male, 975 mm female.*
This extremely thin snake has a lance-shaped head and large eyes with keyhole-shaped pupils. The body scales are feebly keeled, in 19 oblique rows at midbody. The tail is very long. The body is twig-coloured, being grey-brown with black and pink flecks, with a series of diagonal pale blotches. The top of the head is green or blue-green, with varied markings (see Subspecies). The belly is pink-grey, with many dark grey blotches. Males have longer tails and fewer ventrals than females. **Biology and breeding:** These beautifully camouflaged snakes can move swiftly if disturbed. The pupil shape and loreal groove allow stereoscopic vision. The diet is very varied, and includes lizards, frogs, small birds and even other snakes. They hunt by ambush, and eat many terrestrial species, striking them from above. Prey is killed by envenomation, and is

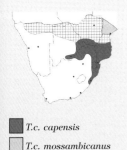

T.c. capensis

T.c. mossambicanus

T.c. oatesii

100

swallowed while the snake hangs downwards. It inflates its neck when threatened. The venom is potently haemotoxic, causing similar symptoms to that of the boomslang's, and, as with envenomation by the boomslang, a victim can experience a 24- to 48-hour 'latent' period before symptoms become evident, although blood tests will reveal clotting abnormalities earlier. This venom is not neutralized by the boomslang-specific anti-venom; treatment must rely on blood or plasma transfusions to replace clotting factors. Fatalities are known, but are rare. Males engage in combat in the mating season. The female lays 4-18 small, elongate eggs (36 x 16 mm) in summer (December-January); these hatch in March, after 60-90 days. The young measure 230-331 mm TL and weigh 3-4 g. A female may lay two clutches per season. **Habitat:** Savannah, coastal thicket and forest fringe. **Range:** E. and S. Africa, replaced in the rain forests of central and W. Africa by *T. kirtlandii*. **Subspecies:** Three races are recognized; all occur on the subcontinent. *T.c. capensis* is a small race (800-1 360 mm TL), with fewer than 162 ventrals, and a blue-green head that is heavily speckled with black; it occurs in KwaZulu-Natal, Swaziland, Mpumalanga, N. Province and adjacent areas. *T.c. oatesii* is the largest race (900-1 680 mm TL), with more than 162 ventrals, and a blue-green head with a black Y-shaped mark on the crown; it is found in northern areas of Namibia and Botswana, and most of Zimbabwe. *T.c. mossambicanus* is 800-1 400 mm long, and its head is uniform green; it occurs in Mozam-bique, intergrading with other races along the southern border.

# Cobras, Mambas and Relatives
## FAMILY ELAPIDAE

These snakes are usually medium to large in size, with well-developed, fixed fangs at the front of the mouth, and venom glands. The head is covered with large shields, but lacks a loreal. The eyes usually have round pupils. The body is covered with shiny, pitless scales, which are keeled in the rinkhals. They are often brightly banded, particularly the juveniles.

Elapids are mostly terrestrial, and there are many burrowing forms; some are arboreal and others aquatic. They usually lay eggs although a few species are viviparous. The family includes many of the most poisonous snakes, although these are rarely common enough to cause a large incidence of snakebite. However, the bigger species are 'confident' of their abilities and will stand their ground. Many have familiar defensive displays.

Elapids are distributed throughout the tropical regions, sub-Saharan Africa and Australia. Two subfamilies are recognized, including the completely aquatic sea snakes (which are sometimes treated as a separate family). There are about 250 species in 61 genera; seven genera containing 17 species (six of which are endemic) occur on the subcontinent.

KEY TO THE SOUTHERN AFRICAN GENERA IN THE ELAPIDAE

1 - Tail flattened and oar-like; body scales bead-like, non-overlapping; ventrals much narrower than body; marine:
>> *Pelamis* (Yellow-bellied sea snake, page 111)
  - Tail cylindrical; body scales overlapping; ventrals as broad as body; terrestrial:  go to 2
2 - 3 preoculars, widely separated from nasal; prefrontals in contact with labials; more than 90 subcaudals:
>> *Dendroaspis* (Mambas, page 110)

- 1-2 preoculars, in contact with nasals and separating prefrontals from labials; fewer than 75 subcaudals:                                    go to 3
3 - Internasals not bordering nostril: dorsal scales in 13 rows at midbody:
*Elapsoidea* (Garter snakes, page 104)
  - Internasals bordering nostril; dorsal scales in 15 or more rows at midbody:                                    go to 4
4 - Only a single postocular; scales in 15 rows at midbody:
*Homoroselaps* (Harlequin snakes, page 102)
  - Two or more postoculars; scales in 17 or more scale rows at midbody:
go to 5
5 - Rostral very large and shield-like:
*Aspidelaps* (Coral and Shield-nose snakes, page 103)
  - Rostral not enlarged:                                    go to 6
6 - Dorsal scales strongly keeled; body and tail short (116-150 ventrals, 33-47 subcaudals); viviparous:
*Hemachatus* (Rinkhals, page 109)
  - Dorsal scales smooth; body and tail long (175-288 ventrals; 50-78 subcaudals); oviparous:
*Naja* (Cobras, page 106)

# African Elapids
SUBFAMILY ELAPINAE

## Harlequin Snakes    *Homoroselaps*

The taxonomic relationships of these snakes remain confused. Initially called dwarf garter snakes (*Elaps*) and placed with cobras and mambas in the family Elapidae (because they have fixed front fangs), they were later believed to be related to African burrowing snakes, Atractaspididae (page 60). Recently, however, they have been returned to the family Elapidae. They are now believed to be the most primitive living elapids, and may form a basal stock linking the elapids and atractaspidids.

They are small and brightly coloured snakes, their heads are barely distinct from their necks, and their small eyes have round pupils. Each nostril pierces a single nasal, and the maxillary is extended, bearing a large, hollow front fang. The body is cylindrical, with smooth scales in 15 rows. The anal is divided, and the tail is short, with paired subcaudals.

Harlequin snakes are docile and rarely bite. They burrow in loose soil and forage underground in tunnels and cracks, and are often exposed in old termitaria or under stones. They feed on other burrowing reptiles, which are seized, and killed by venom. They are oviparous. There are two species and both are endemic to South Africa.

### Spotted Harlequin Snake    *Homoroselaps lacteus* (Pl. 19)
*(Endemic) max. SVL 596 mm male, 628 mm female.*

This small, slender snake has six upper and six lower labials, 160-209 ventrals, and 24-43 subcaudals. Different colour phases occur in different regions: the back is yellowish-white with numerous broken black bands, and usually with an red-orange-yellow vertebral stripe (southern and western regions); the body is black, each scale with a yellow dot, and with a bright orange-yellow vertebral streak (northern regions); intermediate colour patterns, in which the black back has irregular yellow-white cross-bars and a vertebral series of red to orange spots, occur from East London to Port Elizabeth. **Biology and breeding:** This snake is common in

certain regions, living in old termite nests, under stones, etc. It is known to eat legless skinks, blind snakes and other snakes, but rarely feeds in captivity. Its venom has not been studied. Bites are very rare because of its small gape and reluctance to bite. Three known cases suffered mild to severe swelling of the limb with mild haemorrhage, swollen lymph vessels and painful glands that resolved in 3-4 days; the only neurological symptoms were persistent headaches that lasted for 24 hours. Polyvalent antivenom is ineffective in the treatment of this snakebite. Usually 6-9 eggs (up to sixteen in very large females) are laid in November-December. They vary in size (extremes 22-28 x 8-10 mm in one female, and 14-18 x 11-12 mm in another) and take about 50 days to hatch. The hatchlings measure 132-148 mm TL. **Habitat:** Varied; semi-desert to savannah and coastal bush. **Range:** Found in the southern parts of the region, from Namaqualand to N. Province.

### Striped Harlequin Snake

*Homoroselaps dorsalis* **(Pl. 24)**
*(Endemic) max. SVL 258 mm male, 248 mm female.*
This small, very slender snake has six upper and five lower labials, 210-239 ventrals, and 22-33 subcaudals. The body is black above, with a conspicuous yellow stripe along the backbone. The lips, belly and lower flanks are yellow-white. **Biology and breeding:** It is very secretive and known only from a few specimens. It feeds exclusively on thread snakes (*Leptotyphlops*) which it catches underground in their burrows. Females lay 2-4, small elongate eggs. Its venom has not been studied as yields are minute. There have been no recorded bites by this species. **Habitat:** Prefers grassland. **Range:** Found in the highveld, extending to KwaZulu-Natal midlands.

# Coral and Shield-nose Snakes   *Aspidelaps*

These small elapids are distinguished by the enlarged rostral shield. They live underground in burrows or beneath stones, emerging at night to feed on small vertebrates. When threatened, they rear up and spread a narrow hood. They huff and puff a lot, and may strike with the mouth closed, but not always. This is a comic performance, but one to heed: the venom is neurotoxic, and a few deaths have been recorded. There are two species in the genus, one of which is endemic to the region.

### Coral Snake

*Aspidelaps lubricus* **(Pls. 20 and 26)**
*Max. SVL 687 mm male, 600 mm female.*
A short, solid snake with a large rostral shield on the nose, smooth scales in 19 rows at midbody, and usually a characteristic banded pattern. The head is reddish, with a black crossbar between the eyes, an arrow shape on the top, and a broad nuchal collar. The body is orange to coral-red, with 20-47 black crossbands that decrease in width towards the tail. The belly is yellowish, with the crossbars completely encircling the body in the young, but fading in adults, leaving only the first 2-3 intact. In the northern races, the colour pattern fades (see Subspecies for details). **Biology and breeding:** The coral snake is a bad-tempered clown. Although it does well in captivity, it rarely forgives its captor. It is fond of rocky outcrops. The diet consists mainly of small vertebrates, particularly other reptiles. Its venom is poorly known, but is apparently neurotoxic. Venom yield for *A.l. infuscatus* has been recorded at 50 mg, with an LD50 300 µg/kg. The effectiveness of antivenom is unknown.

■ *A.l. lubricus*

☐ *A.l. cowlesi*

▦ *A.l. infuscatus*

Bites from the southern race have not resulted in serious symptoms, but a bite from *A.l. infuscatus* was reported to have killed two children. Lays 3-11 eggs (50-54 x 15 mm) in December; these hatch in 59-71 days. The young measure 170-180 mm TL. In captivity, lay clutches every two months during summer. **Habitat:** Karroid and sandveld regions, entering dry valley plains in S. and E. Cape. **Range:** Western regions of subcontinent; throughout karroid regions, but reaches Port Elizabeth and Cape Town, and extends through Namibia to S. Angola. **Subspecies:** Three races: *A.l. lubricus* rarely grows longer than 600 mm, is conspicuously banded, and has 20-28 subcaudals; found through Karoo to S. Namibia. *A.l. infuscatus* grows larger, has a black head, and a grey-brown body with vague dark crossbands; occurs in central Namibia. *A.l. cowlesi* has a pale head and uniform grey-brown body; occurs in Kaokoveld, SW Angola. The latter two are poorly defined, and not easily distinguished from each other.

### Shield-nose Snake         *Aspidelaps scutatus* (Pls. 18 and 26)
*(Endemic) max. SVL 630 mm male, 640 mm female.*
A short, thickset snake with a short, broad head and a very large rostral, 21-25 scale rows at midbody, and keeled posterior body scales. The back is pale grey-brown, yellowish, or buff to orange, with a series of dark blotches that are well-developed in the eastern race, and fade towards the tail. The head and neck are mostly black with a white eye-stripe and throat band. The belly is white. **Biology and breeding:** Burrows in sandy soil using its nose as a 'bulldozer'. Feeds at night, and has a varied diet, taking small mammals, amphibians, lizards, and even other snakes. In defence, it may sham death. The few case histories recorded exhibited pain and mild neurological symptoms (ptosis, slurred speech and partial paralysis) that persisted for 2-3 days. There has been one recorded death from a bite by this species. The effectiveness of antivenom in the treatment of the bite is unknown. Lays 4-10 eggs, and may coil around them to protect them. **Habitat:** Savannah and sandveld. **Range:** In a wide band through the northern regions of the subcontinent. **Subspecies:** Three races are recognized and all occur on the subcontinent. *A.s. scutatus* has poorly defined markings, a short tail (25-30 subcaudals in males, 20-24 in females), and averages 450 mm in length, rarely growing to longer than 600 mm; it occurs through N. Namibia, Botswana, W. Zimbabwe and NW Province. *A.s. intermedius* is the same colour and size as the typical race, but has a medium-length tail (32-35 subcaudals in males, 27-31 in females); it is found in the eastern regions of N. Province and Mpumalanga. *A.s. fulafula* has well-defined markings, a long tail (33-39 subcaudals in males, 30-33 in females), and is a large snake, often growing to longer than 600 mm; it is found in SE Zimbabwe and S. Mozambique.

*A.s. scutatus*
*A.s. fulafula*
*A.s. intermedius*

## Garter Snakes    *Elapsoidea*
These small to medium-sized burrowing elapids have a small head, a short tail, and 13 scale rows at midbody. They are often brightly banded, particularly when young. The different species are easily confused due to the uniform scale counts and the different juvenile and adult colour patterns.

Garter snakes burrow in sandy or humic soils, coming to the surface at night. Most eat other reptiles, although small mammals and amphibians are also taken. They are oviparous.

There are eight species, widely distributed through sub-Saharan Africa, with four occurring in southern Africa, one of which is endemic.

## Günther's Garter Snake        *Elapsoidea guentheri* (Pl. 21)

*Max. SVL 560 mm male, 385 mm female.*

This solid, medium-sized snake has a rounded snout, 131-156 ventrals in both sexes, and four lower labials touching the anterior chin shields. It is banded, with pale and dark crossbands of the same width. In juveniles, the body is black, with 16-20 crossbands, and 2-4 on the tail; in adults, the bands fade, and the back becomes a uniform grey-black with the belly steel-grey. **Biology and breeding:** These snakes are known to eat other snakes, skinks, occasionally amphibians and even termite alates. No details are known about their venom, and no case histories have been recorded. Up to 10 eggs are laid in late summer. **Habitat:** Miombo woodland. **Range:** Central plateau of Zimbabwe, extending into adjacent Democratic Republic of Congo, Angola and Zambia.

## Angolan Garter Snake        *Elapsoidea semiannulata* (Pl. 21)

*Max. SVL 532 mm male, 467 mm female.*

E.s. semiannulata

Medium-sized snakes with a moderately rounded snout, 137-161 ventrals in males and 136-152 in females (rarely more than 150 in the typical race), and three lower labials touching the anterior chin shields. The pale bands or paired white rings are at least half the width of the dark bands. In juveniles, the head is white and the back black, with 12-17 narrow white or yellow bands; in adults (longer than 20 cm), the pale bands darken in the centre to leave paired, narrow rings which persist in large adults. The belly is uniform white. **Biology and breeding:** Not common, this slow-moving snake is inoffensive. Its diet consists mainly of skinks, geckos, amphibians, and sometimes small snakes. The female lays up to 10 small eggs (20 x 8-10 mm). **Habitat:** Varied; including arid and mesic savannah, but absent from very arid areas. **Range:** Locally restricted to N. Namibia and Caprivi Strip; extralimitally through central Africa to Senegal. **Subspecies:** Only two races are now recognized; only the typical race occurs on the subcontinent. It is replaced from W. Zambia to Senegal by *E.s. moebiusi*, which usually has more than 150 ventrals.

## Boulenger's Garter Snake   *Elapsoidea boulengeri* (Pls. 21 and 37)

*Max. SVL 710 mm male, 603 mm female.*

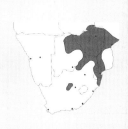

Very similar to, and previously confused with the Angolan garter snake (*E. semiannulata*, above). It is a medium-sized snake with a moderately rounded snout, 140-161 ventrals in males and 138-155 in females, and three lower labials touching the anterior chin shields. The pale crossbands or paired white rings are much narrower than the dark ones. In juveniles, the head is white and the back black, with 12-17 narrow white or yellow bands, in adults (longer than 20 cm), the pale bands darken in the centre to leave paired, narrow rings which disappear completely in large adults (longer than 35 cm). The belly is dark grey or brown, rarely white. **Biology and breeding:** A slow-moving snake with a preference for eating skinks and small snakes, although geckos and occasionally frogs may be eaten. It is prone to cannibalism. Its venom has not been studied; a bite caused pain and swelling, and transient nasal congestion. The female lays 4-8 eggs (20 x 8-10 mm) in the early summer. **Habitat:** Prefers mesic savannah. **Range:** This species is restricted to the moister eastern regions of the subcontinent, reaching as far south as Zululand and the N. Cape, and extending northwards to E. Zambia and the coastal regions of Tanzania.

■ *E.s. fitzsimonsi*

☐ *E.s. decosteri*

▦ *E.s. longicauda*

|||| *E.s. media*

▧ *E.s. sunderwallii*

## Sundevall's Garter Snake
*Elapsoidea sunderwallii* (Pls. 21, 32 and 37)
*(Endemic) max. SVL 930 mm male, 650 mm female.*
This snake is medium to large in size, depending on the race. It has a slightly pointed snout. Males have 152-180 ventrals, while females have 138-161. The juveniles are strongly marked with almost equal-sized bands of cream or pink and dark chocolate, and the head and belly are pale, with a dark extension onto the crown of the head. In adults the pale bands darken from the centre to form paired rings that usually disappear (but persist in the typical race) and the body becomes slate grey to black, and the belly and adjacent body scales pink-buff, and sometimes mottled.
**Biology and breeding:** These are slow-moving snakes, and are reluctant to bite. They settle well in captivity. The diet is varied, and includes snakes, lizards and their eggs, rain frogs, rodents and moles. Rarely seen, they are usually collected in old termitaria, under stones or on roads at night. The venom has not been studied. There have been few recorded bites; symptoms for a bite from *E.s. longicauda* included nausea, vomiting, loss of consciousness and blurred vision; these symptoms resolved in two or three days without the use of antivenom. A bite from *E.s fitzsimonsi* caused only pain and swelling. The female lays up to 10 small eggs.
**Habitat:** Varied; coastal forest, highveld grassland, and arid and mesic savannah. **Range:** Southern Africa, from central Namibia to S. Mozambique and KwaZulu-Natal. **Subspecies:** There are five races: *E.s. sunderwallii* is the largest, with juveniles and adults both having 19-34 pale bands; it occurs in KwaZulu-Natal to SE Mpumalanga. The other races are distinguished by scalation. *E.s. media* has 13-23 subcaudals, and 157-168 ventrals in males and 140-154 ventrals in females; it is found in Gauteng, NW Province, Free State and N. Cape. *E.s. fitzsimonsi* also has 13-23 sub-caudals, and 167-180 ventrals in males and 156-161 ventrals in females; it is found in Botswana and Namibia. *E.s. longicauda* is the largest race and has 22-33 subcaudals, and 152-159 ventrals in males and 138-144 ventrals in females; it is found in N. Province, SE Zimbabwe and S. Mozambique. *E.s. decosteri* also has 22-33 subcaudals, and 164-179 ventrals in males and 148-156 ventrals in females; it occurs in Zululand and S. Mozambique.

## Cobras  *Naja*
The cobras are large, stockily built, terrestrial snakes with smooth scales. They are alert, active foragers, pursuing and capturing small vertebrates. When threatened, they lift the forebody and spread a characteristic hood. Four African species have modified fangs and can 'spit' venom up to three metres. Bites from spitters and non-spitters present with different symptoms, but all are potentially dangerous. All cobras are oviparous.

They are distributed through Asia and Africa. Upper Miocene fossils are known from France. There are eight African species, and all but three of these occur in southern Africa; one is endemic.

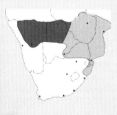

■ *N.a. anchietae*

☐ *N.a. annulifera*

### Snouted Cobra
*Naja annulifera* (Pls. 20 and 27)
*Max. SVL 2 125 mm male, 1 946 mm female.*
This thick-set snake has a large head and 17-19 smooth scale rows at midbody. Suboculars are present. Coloration is variable, but is usually yellow-grey to brown or blue-black; old specimens are darker. The belly is yellowish, with dark blotches. It has a dark throat band which is more conspicuous (black) in juveniles. The banded phase of this species, which

is found throughout the range, has 7-9 yellowish bands on the body and two on the tail. This banding develops in snakes that are longer than 600 mm, and is more frequent in males. Males grow slightly larger than females. **Biology and breeding:** Nocturnal, the snouted cobra emerges at dusk to forage for small vertebrates. It is often seen basking at its retreat (old termite nests, hollow logs, etc.) in the morning sun. The diet is varied, often including toads and other snakes, and occasionally birds' eggs; it may become a pest in poultry runs. Very large adults frequently eat puff adders. Adults are aggressive towards one another, and readily bite. Spreads a broad hood in threat display. The eastern race is less aggressive, whereas the western *N.a. anchietae* is more willing to continue an argument. When cornered, it may sham death. This cobra is a non-spitter. Bites are common in some districts, and are usually inflicted on the lower leg, at night. Initial symptoms include a burning pain and slight swelling, followed rapidly by neurological symptoms, and often death from respiratory failure. The venom yield is 175-300 mg; 25-35 mg is fatal in humans. A victim of its bite requires large doses of antivenom. The female lays 8-33 large, oval eggs (47-55 x 25-30 mm) in loose soil or disused termitaria in early summer. Hatchlings measure 240-340 mm TL. **Habitat:** Savannah, particularly common in bushveld and lowveld. **Range:** Widely distributed in the southern half of Africa. **Subspecies:** There are two races, both of which occur on the subcontinent. *N.a. annulifera* has 19 scale rows; it occurs in the eastern regions, from N. KwaZulu-Natal, through lowveld of Mpumalanga and N. Province to W. Botswana, and north to N. Zambia. *N.a. anchietae* has 17 scale rows and does not grow longer than 2 100 mm; it is found in N. and central Namibia through N. Botswana to NW Zimbabwe. The Eygptian cobra, *N. haje haje*, is now treated as a separate species, occurring from E. Africa, north and south of Sahara Desert, to Atlantic Ocean; a separate race, *N.h. arabica*, occurs in the semi-desert of W. and S. Arabia.

### Forest Cobra                              *Naja melanoleuca* (Pl. 27)
*Max. SVL 2 050 mm male, 1 564 mm female.*

This is the largest of the African cobras (up to 2 690 mm TL in the north) but is a slender snake, with highly polished scales in 19 rows at midbody. It has one preocular and a broad rostral. The head and foreparts are yellow-brown, heavily mottled in black, becoming shiny blue-black towards the tail. The lower labials are often white with black edges. The belly is pale white-cream, often with dark blotches. **Biology and breeding:** This cobra is fond of water. It may climb into low bush. It is crepuscular, and more active on overcast days than the snouted cobra. The diet is varied and includes most small vertebrates, even fish. This alert snake is rarely cornered, but it will spread a narrow hood and bite readily if necessary. It is long-lived; 29 years is known in captivity (SA RDB, Peripheral). It is a non-spitter. Its venom is neurotoxic, but it bites very rarely and no deaths have been recorded locally. Males have been observed in combat in breeding season. The female lays 15-26 large eggs (60 x 30 mm) in leaf litter, hollow logs, etc. These hatch after an incubation period of 75-91 days. The hatchlings measure approximately 380 mm TL. **Habitat:** Prefers tropical and subtropical rain forest and coastal thicket. **Range:** Found in the forests of Africa, from Senegal to Ethiopia, south to Angola and Mozambique Plain, just entering E. Zimbabwe and Zululand (to Durban).

## Cape Cobra                           *Naja nivea* (Pls. 20 and 27)

*(Endemic) max. SVL 1 510 mm male, 1 442 mm female.*

This relatively small, slender cobra has a broad head, and smooth but dull scales in 19-21 rows. There is one preocular and a narrow rostral. Coloration is varied, with some phases common in certain regions. The yellow cobra is butter-coloured to dirty yellow (particularly in Botswana), sometimes speckled with brown; the brown or speckled cobra is bright reddish-brown to mahogany, with darker and paler flecks (common in SW Cape); and the black cobra is purplish-black (found in Great and Little Namaqualand). Juveniles are dirty yellow, often finely speckled in dark brown, and have a prominent black throat band. **Biology and breeding:** Active during the day and early evening, this snake feeds on a wide spectrum of prey, including other snakes. It will climb low trees and raid sociable weaver colonies. It is common around Karoo farms, to which it is attracted by rodents. It is long-lived; 26 years is known in captivity. It is a memorable sight when foraging in the veld. Unfortunately, it is both nervous and deadly. It spreads a broad hood and confidently disputes its right of way. It is a non-spitter. The venom is syrupy and as toxic as the black mamba's. The average venom yield is 120 mg (max. 250 mg); 15-20 mg is fatal in humans. The venom is neurotoxic, and death usually occurs from the rapid onset of paralysis. Large volumes of antivenom are urgently required in the treatment of the bite, and long periods of assisted breathing (up to 25 days) may be necessary before the paralysis disappears. Bites are not uncommon; this species is responsible for the majority of fatal snakebites in the Cape provinces. The female lays 8-20 large eggs (60 x 30 mm, 25-30 g) in a burrow; hatchlings measure 340-350 mm TL. **Habitat:** Arid karroid regions, particularly along river courses, entering well-drained open areas along the southern coast. **Range:** Through the Cape provinces, in the east to East London, and north to S. Namibia and adjacent Botswana and Free State.

## Mozambique Spitting Cobra or M'fezi

*Naja mossambica* (Pl. 27)

*Max. SVL 1 285 mm male, 1 270 mm female.*

A small cobra with a blunt head and 23-25 scale rows. It has two preoculars and 11-14 scales bordering the parietals. The back is pale grey to dark olive above, with each scale edged in black. The belly is salmon-pink to yellowish. There are irregular black crossbands or blotches on the throat. **Biology and breeding:** A nocturnal species, although juveniles may forage during the day. The varied diet includes rodents, lizards, toads, and grasshoppers. It is very common in lowveld regions and often forages around houses at night. It spreads a broad hood and 'spits' readily. Although it feeds well in captivity, it rarely tames. It produces copious amounts (200-300 mg) of dilute venom, which it sprays at the intruder's eyes, causing agonizing and instant pain; 40-50 mg of this venom is fatal in humans. Bites are frequent in Zululand and the Mpumalanga lowveld. The venom causes a 'skipping' skin necrosis that often requires skin grafts; neurotoxic symptoms are minor, and fatalities are exceptionally rare. It lays 10-22 small eggs (35 x 20 mm) in summer. Hatchlings measure 230-250 mm TL. **Habitat:** Savannah regions, and cleared areas in former forest. **Range:** Eastern regions, from S. KwaZulu-Natal through Mpumalanga, Gauteng, N. and NW provinces, N. Botswana to NE Namibia. Elsewhere to S. Tanzania.

# Black-necked Spitting Cobra    *Naja nigricollis* (Pls. 20 and 35)
*Max. SVL 1 470 mm male, 2 000 mm female.*

N.n. *nigricollis*

N.n. *nigricincta*

N.n. *woodi*

This cobra has a broad head with a rounded snout, 17-21 scale rows,
two preoculars and 7-10 scales bordering the parietals. Coloration is varied
(see Subspecies). **Biology and breeding:** The typical race is common in
moist savannah, and is more aquatic than the other subspecies. It is mainly
nocturnal, although the juveniles and *N.n. woodi* are active during the
day. The diet is varied, and is similar to that of the Mozambique spitting
cobra, *N. mossambica* (page 108), except that the western and southern
races take more lizards and rodents, and *N.n. woodi* commonly hunt large
puff adders. It is a nervous species that readily spreads a hood and 'spits'.
The venom is relatively toxic, causing minor neurological symptoms and
extensive necrosis, bleeding and haematological abnormalities. Venom
yields are large (200-350 mg); 40-50 mg is fatal in humans. Bites are
common in N. Namibia, but have been poorly studied. The typical race
causes many severe snakebites in W. Africa. The female lays 10-22 eggs
(35 x 20 mm). **Habitat:** The typical race favours moist savannah; the
two southern races rocky arid regions. **Range:** Sub-Saharan Africa, from
Senegal to Kenya, through W. Zambia to Caprivi Strip, and south through
Namibia to W. Cape. **Subspecies:** Three races; two of which are endemic
to the subcontinent and may together be a different species. The typical
race, *N.n. nigricollis* (the black-necked spitting cobra) just enters the region
in the Caprivi Strip; it is large, with 176-219 ventrals, a uniform olive-
brown to black back, a yellow to red belly, and a broad, dark throat band.
The western barred spitting cobra or zebra snake, *N.n. nigricincta*, is
smaller (max. 1 500 mm TL), with 192-226 ventrals, a light grey to pink-
brown back and belly, ringed with 51-86 black bands on the body and
13-32 black bands on the tail, and a wide, dark throat band that is prominent in juveniles; it occurs in central and N. Namibia. The black spitting
cobra, *N.n. woodi*, is of medium size (max. 1 800 mm TL), with 223-228
ventrals, a uniform black back, and a dark grey belly streaked with black,
while juveniles are grey with a black head and neck; it occurs in S. Namibia,
through Namaqualand to Citrusdal in south and Prieska in the east.

# Rinkhals    *Hemachatus*
The rinkhals is a close relative of the true cobras, but has keeled scales, no
solid teeth on the maxilla, and is viviparous.
    The single species in the genus is endemic to southern Africa.

### Rinkhals    *Hemachatus haemachatus* (Pls. 20 and 35)
*(Endemic) max. SVL 1 075 mm male, 1 152 mm female.*

This stocky snake has a broad head and keeled scales in 17-19 rows.
Coloration is varied, with specimens in E. Cape to KwaZulu-Natal midlands and the Inyanga Highlands of Zimbabwe being conspicuously banded
in dark-brown to black, alternating with pale grey, yellowish or orange;
inland, particularly on the highveld, the back is uniform dark brown to
black, sometimes speckled with lighter greys and browns. The belly is
dark, with 1-2 pale crossbands on the throat (hence its common Afrikaans
name); these may fade in old specimens. Juveniles are conspicuously
banded. **Biology and breeding:** Nocturnal, but sometimes active on
overcast days. It has catholic tastes, eating small vertebrates, particularly
rodents and toads. In defence, it rears and spreads a broad hood. Sprays
venom up to 2-3 m, usually aims it at the intruder's face. If this fails, it

will sham death, rolling on to its back with the mouth agape. Settles well and has lived for more than 11 years in captivity, often being a gluttonous feeder. Its venom is neurotoxic, with deaths resulting from respiratory paralysis. Less dangerous than the true cobras, as its venom is more dilute for spitting. If the venom enters the eyes, it causes great pain and some-times blindness; the eyes must be washed immediately with a bland liquid. The local antivenom is effective. Fatalities are rare. Twenty to 30 (max. 63) live babies are born in late summer (December-March). New-born young measure 162-225 mm TL; weigh 4,3-6,6 g. **Habitat:** Grassland, from the coast up to 2 500 m. **Range:** Common on highveld and in KwaZulu-Natal grasslands; relict populations in montane grasslands of old escarpment in the W. and E. Cape and Zimbabwe (Inyanga), and along S. Cape coast.

## Mambas   *Dendroaspis*

These large agile, diurnal elapids have a long, flat-sided head and elongate bodies with long tails. All except the black mamba are strictly arboreal. They actively pursue their prey, striking rapidly and often until it succumbs to the toxic venom. These are probably the most feared of all the African snakes, but only the black mamba commonly bites. They are oviparous.

There are four species, which are found throughout most of tropical Africa, with two entering the subcontinent.

### Black Mamba                    *Dendroaspis polylepis* **(Pl. 35)**

*Max. SVL 2 330 mm male, 2 530 mm female; exceptionally up to 4 300 mm TL.*

A large, streamlined snake with a narrow, coffin-shaped head and smooth scales in 23-25 oblique rows. The back is uniform gunmetal to olive-brown, but never really black; the belly is pale grey-green, sometimes with dark blotches, and the mouth lining is black. **Biology and breeding:** Active and terrestrial. Eats fledgling birds and small mammals (rats and dassies). Prey is pursued and stabbed with the fangs until it collapses from the toxic venom. Digestion is rapid. It is long-lived (up to 20 years in captivity), and territorial, having a favoured home in a termite nest, a hollow log or a rock crevice. If disturbed, it will retreat unless cornered. It is confident in defence; rears the front third of the body, spreads a narrow hood and gapes the mouth, revealing the black lining. Bites readily and often. Its hollow 'hiss' is best heeded – if you step back, the snake will also retreat. The venom is neurotoxic and cardiotoxic, yielding 100-400 mg; 10-15 mg is fatal in humans. Its bite is extremely serious, and requires large volumes of antivenom (up to 10 ampoules) to counteract the venom. The victim may be fully conscious, but all the muscles are paralyzed; death from respiratory failure usually occurs in 7-15 hours. In spring, males fight by raising and intertwining their bodies; this is often mistaken for mating. Twelve to 17 eggs are laid (70-91 x 30-35 mm; 47-54 g) in termite nests, etc. These hatch in 80-90 days. Young measure 529-604 mm TL; growth is rapid, a black mamba may reach 2 000 mm in length in its first year. **Habitat:** Savannah and open coastal bush, usually below 1 500 m. **Range:** Northern parts of subcontinent (absent from desert), extending south along KwaZulu-Natal coast to Port St Johns. Elsewhere, to Senegal and Somalia.

### Green Mamba                    *Dendroaspis angusticeps* **(Pl. 30)**

*Max. SVL 1 453 mm male, 1 480 mm female.*

This large, slender snake has a narrow, coffin-shaped head and smooth scales in 19 oblique rows. The back is uniform bright green (bluish-green in hatchlings). The belly is yellowish-green, and the mouth lining is white. **Biology and breeding:** Active and arboreal; feeds almost exclusively on birds and small mammals, although juveniles may eat chameleons. Shy and rarely seen. When cornered, it is less belligerent than the black mamba, threatening and biting only as a last resort. It has lived for more than 14 years in captivity. The venom is neurotoxic; it is less potent than the black mamba's, and the venom yield is smaller (60-100 mg). Bites are uncommon, and cause mild paralysis and, rarely, death. Males engage in combat in breeding season. Up to 10 eggs (58 x 26 mm) are laid in a hollow log or leaf litter in summer. They hatch after 70-80 days. The young measure 350-400 mm TL. **Habitat:** Coastal bush and dune and escarpment forest. **Range:** Restricted to KwaZulu-Natal coastal regions and forests along E. Zimbabwe escarpment. Elsewhere, to E. Africa.

# Sea Snakes
## SUBFAMILY HYDROPHIINAE

As their name implies, sea snakes are completely aquatic. They have numerous adaptations to marine life, including a nasal salt gland to purge excess salt, a flattened, oar-like body, valved nostrils, and a large lung. The belly scales are greatly reduced in size.

They feed on marine life, particularly eels and fish eggs. All are venomous and many have very toxic venoms. Fortunately, they are docile but are very common in some waters (for example Vietnam and Malaysia), and bites and fatalities are regionally common. A specific antivenom is required in the treatment of their bite. Viviparous, they give birth in the surface waves. They never normally come ashore.

Sea snakes are closely related to Australian terrestrial elapids. There are 45-50 species in 13-14 genera, restricted mainly to the coastal waters of Australasia. A single, vagrant species occasionally washes ashore on our eastern and southern coast.

## Yellow-bellied Sea Snake     *Pelamis*

An unusual snake, adapted to feeding on small fish in surface waters. There is a single species in the genus. Occurs throughout the Indo-Pacific.

**Yellow-bellied Sea Snake**                *Pelamis platurus* **(Pl. 25)**
*Max. SVL 650 mm male, 660 mm female.*
The body of this snake is laterally flattened, with an oar-like tail. The head is narrow, with an elongate, flat-topped snout which has valved nostrils. There are no enlarged belly scales. Its striped coloration is characteristic, although uniform yellow specimens do occur. The dark brown or black back contrasts with the cream, yellow or light-brown belly. The tail is yellow, with black spots. **Biology and breeding:** Sea snakes accumulate in slicks where surface currents meet, sheltering in floating seaweed and debris, and ambushing small fish. They shed their skin with a 'knotting' behaviour, rubbing one part of the body against another. They are excellent swimmers, being able to move either backwards or forwards with ease, but are helpless when washed ashore. Can dive easily to depths of 50 m, and spend 87% of their time underwater, for periods up to 213 minutes. They have few predators as their venom is very toxic to fish; it is possible that their bright coloration is aposematic. The venom of sea snakes occurring in local waters has not been studied. Elsewhere (in

Panama), it is mildly neurotoxic (LD50 130 µg/kg), watery, and yields are small (1-2 mg, max. 4,4 mg). Myotoxic symptoms are not present in this species. No bites or deaths have been recorded in southern Africa. It is unlikely that local antivenom is effective in the treatment of a bite from this species. They give birth to 3-8 live young (250 mm TL) in March-October. **Habitat:** Ocean surface waters. **Range:** Throughout warm Indo-Pacific, from Kenya to Baja California. Vagrants are washed south in Agulhas Current and strand on KwaZulu-Natal and Cape beaches. Usually excluded from the Atlantic Ocean by the cold Benguela Current along the W. Cape coast. A report, in 1996, of two specimens from Swakopmund, Namibia, is exceptional and is the first that shows a meaningful extension of the species' range into the S. Atlantic Ocean.

# Vipers
FAMILY VIPERIDAE

These snakes have large, erectile fangs at the front of the mouth. The head is distinct and usually covered with small, irregular, overlapping scales (night adders have large head shields like those of the colubrids). The eyes usually have vertical pupils. The body scales are strongly keeled (but smooth in night adders). The body is stocky, with a short tail and usually with a blotched colour pattern.

These short to large snakes are mainly terrestrial, although some species are arboreal, one is a burrowing species, and several are semi-aquatic. They are usually nocturnal or crepuscular, and feed on small vertebrates. Prey is ambushed and killed by the venom. Most are viviparous, but some primitive groups lay eggs.

Adders and vipers are found throughout the world except on most oceanic islands, Australia and Madagascar. They are frequently found in temperate climates (the European adder, *Vipera berus*, extends almost to the Arctic Circle). There are four subfamilies: the Azemiophinae (consisting of a single rare viper, *Azemiops feae* from SE Asia); the Causinae (the night adders, from Africa); the Viperinae (the true vipers, from Eurasia and Africa); and the Crotalinae (the pit-vipers from Asia and the Americas).

There are about 200 species in 28 genera; 15 species (eight of which are endemic) in three genera occur on the subcontinent.

fragmented and keeled
scales (typical vipers)

smooth, 'colubrid'-type
scales (night adders)

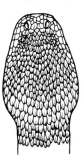 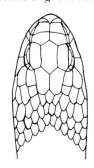

**The head scales of southern African vipers**

1 - Head large, much broader than neck, and covered with small, keeled
    scales; pupils vertical; viviparous:                          go to 2
   - Head small, only slightly larger than neck, and covered with large,
    symmetrical shields; pupils round; oviparous:
                                  *Causus* (Night adders, page 112)
2 - Nasal separated from rostral by small scales; no enlarged supraorbital
    shield:                        *Bitis* (African adders, page 114)
   - Nasal in contact with rostral or separated by nasorostral shield; large
    supraorbital shield present:    *Proatheris* (Swamp viper, page 119)

# Night Adders
## SUBFAMILY CAUSINAE

## Night Adders   *Causus*

These small, primitive vipers are distributed throughout sub-Saharan
Africa. They are nocturnal, but they have round pupils. They rarely grow
to longer than a metre, and have a short, blunt head and large head
shields. The scales are smooth or feebly keeled; the tail is short.

Night adders live in forests or moist savannah, feeding mainly on frogs
and toads. Their venom glands are large, extending 50-70 mm into the
neck in some species. Venom yields are large, but the venom is weak and
causes mainly localized pain and swelling. Fatalities are exceptionally rare.
The venom can be neutralized with the use of polyvalent antivenom, but
symptoms rarely merit its use. All night adders are oviparous. There are six
species, two of which occur in our region. Neither is endemic.

### Common or Rhombic Night Adder   *Causus rhombeatus* (Pl. 15)
*Max. SVL 830 mm male, 680 mm female.*
A medium-sized adder with a rounded snout, and soft, feebly-keeled scales
in 17-21 rows at midbody. Ventrals number 134-155. The back is various
shades of grey to olive or light brown to pinkish-brown, with 20-30 dark,
pale-edged rhombic blotches over the body and tail (these are sometimes
absent, particularly in northern populations). The back of the head has a
characteristic, dark V-shape. The belly is cream to pinkish-grey. **Biology
and breeding:** It rests during the day in undergrowth, under stones or
logs, in termitaria, etc., and forages at night. Its eyesight is poor, and prey
is detected mainly by smell. Sometimes aggressive, it huffs and strikes
readily, but tames quickly. The venom glands are large, extending into
the neck; they yield 20-30 mg of mild, dilute venom that causes pain
and swelling. There are no recorded fatalities for a bite by this snake.
Antivenom is effective, but rarely necessary. It lays 15-26 eggs (26 x 16 mm)
in summer; these take 70-85 days to hatch. Young measure 130-160 mm
TL. In captivity clutches may be laid 2-3 times a year. **Habitat:** Mesic
savannah. **Range:** This night adder is found in the eastern regions,
from Riversdale in the W. Cape, through KwaZulu-Natal and northern
provinces to Zimbabwe, N. Botswana and Caprivi Strip. Elsewhere to
Nigeria and Sudan.

### Snouted Night Adder          *Causus defilippii* (Pl. 15)
*Max. SVL 392 mm male, 387 mm female.*
This small adder has an upturned snout, a stout build and a more distinct
head than that of the common night adder, *C. rhombeatus* (above).

It has 17 scale rows at midbody, and 108-126 ventrals. The body is pale brown to pinkish-brown on the flanks, with a darker brown back, and a series of 20-30 black, triangular blotches on the back and tail. The back of the head bears the characteristic V-shape. The belly is pearl-white, and grey in juveniles. **Biology and breeding:** Feeds almost exclusively on small amphibians. Does not burrow, despite its snout shape. The symptoms and toxicity of its venom are similar to those of the common night adder, but the yields are smaller. The venom glands are short, not extending into the neck. There are no known fatalities for a bite by this species. Antivenom is effective, but rarely necessary. Males engage in combat in the breeding season. It lays 6-8 eggs (23 x 15 mm) in summer; these take 90-100 days to hatch. The young measure about 100 mm TL. **Habitat:** Common in lowveld, tolerating dry savanna. **Range:** Low-lying KwaZulu-Natal, lowveld of Mpumalanga and N. Province, Mozambique and Zimbabwe, to Tanzania.

## African Adders    *Bitis*

This is the largest group of African vipers, containing both the largest and the smallest viperines. All are terrestrial, stocky species, and some attain gross proportions. The head shields are fragmented. The tail is very short, especially in the females. There is a well-developed supranasal sac above the nostril that may be comparable to the heat-sensitive organ of pit-vipers.

Prey is captured by ambush; if it is small, it is held in the mouth but it is usually released until it succumbs to the venom, and then eaten at leisure. All African adders are viviparous.

African adders are present throughout sub-Saharan Africa, with one species (*Bitis arietans*) also occurring in Arabia. There are 17 species, one extinct, with twelve on the subcontinent, eight of which are endemic.

### Puff Adder                      *Bitis arietans* **(Pls. 3 and 12)**

*Max. SVL 1 090 mm male, 1 100 mm female (to 1 700 mm in East Africa).*
This thick, heavily built snake has a large, flattened, triangular head and large nostrils which point vertically upwards. The scales are heavily keeled in 29-41 rows at midbody. The body is yellow-brown to light brown, with black, pale-edged chevrons on the back and bars on the tail; sometimes the chevrons are lost in the general speckled colouring. There are dark blotches on the crown of the head and between the eyes, and two oblique bars from the eye to the lip. The belly is white or yellow, with a few scattered blotches. Snakes from E. Cape and KwaZulu-Natal are more brightly coloured. Rare striped patterns are known to occur. Males are slightly smaller and more brightly coloured than females. **Biology and breeding:** This common adder is a sluggish snake. It emerges at dusk, lying in cover and ambushing prey, which includes mainly rodents, some-times birds and even other snakes; a tortoise was recorded once. It has effective camouflage. If disturbed, it adopts a strike posture and usually warns by giving a deep, hollow hiss; once heard, it is not easily forgotten. It strikes readily. The puff adder normally moves in 'caterpillar' fashion, leaving a straight, deep track in sand. It may climb into low scrub to bask, particularly when gravid. It often swims, and lies on warm roads at night (the latter usually with dire consequences). It lives for up to 14 years in captivity if it is provided with plenty of warmth and sunshine. The venom is cytotoxic, often causing extensive swelling, pain and necrosis.

*B.a. arietans*

Yields are large (100-350 mg; 100 mg is fatal in humans). The long fangs (12-18 mm) inject the venom deeply, and bites are usually inflicted on the lower leg. Bites are common, but only a small proportion proves fatal; nonetheless, this snake causes over 60% of serious bites in the region, and is responsible for most of the fatalities. Death usually results from kidney failure and other complications caused by the extensive swelling. It is essential to treat a victim of its bite for fluid loss into swollen tissue, and antivenom should be used in serious cases. In the E. Cape, males engage in combat and trail and mate with females in spring (rarely autumn); further north mating occurs more often in late autumn. Large litters, usually consisting of 20-40 young (150-200 mm TL) are born in late summer. Very large females from E. Africa may have up to 156 young, a world record for any snake. **Habitat:** Absent only from desert, dense forest and mountain tops. **Range:** Throughout the subcontinent, north through the whole of Africa to S. Arabia. **Subspecies:** Two races are recognized. The typical race occurs throughout Africa, and is replaced in Somalia by *B.a. somalica*, which has keeled subcaudals.

### Gaboon Adder — *Bitis gabonica* (Pls. 3 and 12)

*Max. SVL 1 230 mm male, 1 350 mm female.*

This large, fat adder is redeemed by its beautiful colours. It has a big, flat triangular head, with a pair of enlarged, horn-like scales on the snout, and 33-46 scale rows at midbody. The back has an attractive geometric pattern of rich purple and brown, interspersed with pastel colours. The head is buff, with a dark mid-dorsal line and a spot above the jaw angle, and dark and light stripes that radiate from the eye to the lip. The belly is buff, with dark grey blotches. **Biology and breeding:** This snake is a memorable sight. Its complex coloration is ideal camouflage among leaf litter.

B.g. gabonica

Surprisingly tolerant, it huffs and puffs a lot but rarely bites. Adapts well to captivity, enjoying the good life and growing fat. In nature, it prefers to hunt among forest edge and secondary growth where it ambushes large rodents, ground birds and even toads. Favoured prey includes vlei rats and the woodland mouse. Its strike is very fast, and its fangs are massive (up to 40 mm). This adder is rare in the region and is deservedly protected (SA RDB, Vulnerable). The venom is cytotoxic and is produced in large amounts (450-600 mg); 90-100 mg is fatal in humans. Bites are very rare. Symptoms include massive swelling and pain, and extensive necrosis. The use of antivenom is essential, and the victim should be treated for fluid loss. Males engage in combat, and only dominant males mate with females. Gestation may take 12 months; 16-43 young (up to 60 in W. African race) are born in late summer; these measure 240-370 mm TL and weigh 25-45 g. It breeds every 2-3 years. Known to hybridize with the puff adder and rhinoceros viper. **Habitat:** Locally in coastal dune thicket and remnant montane forest, where it prefers forest edge. **Range:** Locally restricted to coastal forests of N. Zululand, eastern escarpment forests of E. Zimbabwe. Elsewhere, through central and E. Africa to Nigeria. **Subspecies:** Two races: typical race occurs in the region, and is replaced in W. Africa by *B.g. rhinoceros*, which has larger nasal horns and only one dark eye-stripe.

### Berg Adder — *Bitis atropos* (Pl. 12)

*(Endemic) max. SVL 470 mm male, 490 mm female.*

A small adder with an elongate head that lacks raised ridges or horns above the eyes. The scales of the head and body are keeled and in 29-33 rows at midbody. The subcaudals are smooth. Coloration varies according to the region. The back is dark brown to greyish-olive, with a paired series of triangular, black, pale-edged blotches on the sides, separated by a narrow, yellow-white streak. There is a dark arrowhead on the crown, and two pale streaks on either side of the head. The belly is off-white with grey smears, and occasionally grey-black overall. Snakes from SE Mpumalanga are reddish and may be poorly marked. **Biology and breeding:** Common in suitable habitat. Irascible when first caught, it rarely tames. Fond of basking in grass tussocks on rocky ledges. Juveniles eat amphibians, while adults also take lizards and rodents. Yields 22-28 mg of venom. Unusual minor neurological symptoms occur in victims, including drooping of eyelids and loss of smell and taste; symptoms resolve in 1-2 days, bite rarely results in swelling or necrosis. No fatalities known. Antivenom is ineffective in treatment. Mating may occur in autumn, prior to hibernation; 4-9 (max. 15) young born in late summer. Young measure 107-145 mm TL. **Habitat:** Montane grassland (up to 3 000 m), and coastal and montane fynbos. **Range:** S. Cape fold mountains from Cedarberg to Port Elizabeth, in isolated populations on KwaZulu-Natal and Mpumalanga Drakensberg, and Chimanimani and Inyanga mountains in Zimbabwe.

### Horned Adder

*Bitis caudalis* (Pl. 13)

*Max. SVL 372 mm male, 548 mm female.*

This small, squat adder has a single horn on the ridge above each eye (although this may rarely be absent). The head is triangular. The scales are strongly keeled, in 23-31 rows at midbody. Coloration is blotched, and regional variations occur. The back varies in colour from light grey (Etosha Pan) through buff to reddish (N. Cape and Kalahari) or greyish-olive to light brown (Karoo), with a series of dark (sometimes pale-edged and/or pale-centred) dorsal and lateral blotches. The top of the head has a broad, dark V-shape or hourglass-shape, and dark bars may radiate from the eye to the jaw angle. The tail tip is often black. The belly is uniform cream-white. Females have short tails, keeled subcaudals and duller colours. **Biology and breeding:** Common. Prefers to lie in the shade of small scrub and shuffles down into the sand, which aids concealment and offers protection from heat. Active at dusk, it may sidewind in loose sand. The diet consists mainly of small lizards (rodents and amphibians are also eaten) that are captured by ambush, and may be attracted to enter the snake's range by the waving black tail tip of the latter. The snake usually holds on to the prey. The horned adder hisses and strikes at first, but tames well (except those from N. Province). The venom is mild, causing swelling, pain and some necrosis. No fatalities known, antivenom rarely necessary. Males engage in combat in breeding season. Mating occurs in October-November, gestation takes 90-110 days. Four to 15 (max. 27) young (100-150 mm TL) born in December-February, coinciding with the hatching of lizard eggs. **Habitat:** Sandy mesic and xeric savannah (entering rocky ridges in Gauteng), but absent from mobile dunes. **Range:** Widespread in arid western region, throughout Karoo and Kalahari to S. Angola, reaching S. Zimbabwe, Gauteng, NW and N. provinces.

### Many-horned Adder

*Bitis cornuta* (Pl. 13)

*(Endemic) max. SVL 402 mm male, 498 mm female.*

A medium-sized stocky adder with a large tuft of 2-4 horns above each eye. The scales are in 25-31 rows at midbody with the subcaudals keeled at the tail tip in males, and keeled throughout in females. There are 132-152 ventrals in females, 127-146 in males. The back is grey (sometimes reddish-brown inland from Kleinsee) with four rows (the central two may fuse) of dark, angular pale-edged blotches. The top of the head has symmetrical dark markings that may form an arrowhead. The belly is dirty white, and sometimes speckled. **Biology and breeding:** Shelters in rock cracks or rodent burrows in rocky areas. Never sidewinds or shuffles into loose sand. Active at dusk and in the early morning. Diet consists of lizards (mainly lacertids and skinks), supplemented by rodents and amphibians. Irascible, it rarely tames in captivity but may feed well. Experimentally, its venom is as toxic as that of the puff adder, *B. arietans* (page 114), but yields are small. Symptoms from the few known bites are similar to those of the horned adder, *B. caudalis* (page 116); no fatalities are known. Mates in October-November; 7-12 young, measuring 130-150 mm TL, are born in late summer. **Habitat:** Mountains or gravel plains. **Range:** S. Namibia, through Namaqualand to SW Cape. **Subspecies:** None.

### Desert Mountain Adder                    *Bitis xeropaga* (Pl. 13)
*(Endemic) max. SVL 406 mm male, 558 mm female.*

This small, relatively slender adder has raised ridges over the eyes, but no horns. The number of scale rows around the neck may be the same as or greater than that at midbody (25-27). The subcaudals are usually smooth. The back is dirty buff or ash to dark grey, with 16-34 bars, each consisting of a median dark brown rectangle flanked on each side by a white spot and a light brown region. There is no dark mark on the top of the head. Three to four white bars radiate from the eye to the mouth. The belly is light dusky-grey with dark speckles. **Biology and breeding:** Similar to many-horned adder, *B. cornuta* (page 116), but they are not found together. Does not sidewind or bury in sand. Accepts skinks and mice in captivity. Nothing is known about its venom; no recorded bites. (SA RDB, Restricted.) Little known about its breeding; 4-5 young born in late summer. **Habitat:** Sparsely vegetated rocky hillsides and mountain slopes. **Range:** Lower Orange River from Augrabies Falls to Richtersveld and Aus in Namibia.

### Red Adder                               *Bitis rubida* (Pl. 14)
*(Endemic) max. SVL 335 mm male, 386 mm female.*

A small, squat adder in which the tuft of horns above the eyes are small or absent. The scales are in 25-29 rows at midbody. There are 133-143 ventrals in females, 126-138 in males. The back is dull brown to red-brown, with faint darker blotches (up to 30) on the body. The belly is light brown, with the blotches restricted to the sides. Males are smaller than females. **Biology and breeding:** Shelters beneath rock slabs on mountain slopes or plateaus. Active during early morning or evening, feeding on lizards (geckos, skinks and lacertids). Larger snakes also take rodents. Settles well in captivity. Nothing known about its venom; no recorded bites. Recently described (1997). Up to ten young (120-138 mm TL) born in late summer (February). **Habitat:** Succulent Nama Karoo, rocky mountain fynbos. **Range:** Cedarberg, through Tanqwa and Robertson Karoo, to the valleys of Little Karoo and foothills of Roggeveldberg and Komsberg.

### Plain Mountain Adder                    *Bitis inornata* (Pl. 14)
*(Endemic) max. SVL 256 mm male, 302 mm female.*
A small, squat adder that lacks horns above the eyes. The scales are in

27-30 rows at midbody. There are 130-138 ventrals in females, 126-137 in males. The posterior subcaudals are faintly keeled. The back is dull brown to red-brown, with faint darker blotches. The belly is light brown, with the blotches restricted to the sides. Males are smaller than females. **Biology and breeding:** Shelters in grass tussocks and beneath rock slabs on mountain plateaus. Active during early morning, feeding on lizards, (skinks and lacertids) and rodents. Settles well in captivity, but is sensitive to high temperatures. Hibernates during winter snows. Nothing is known about its venom; no recorded bites. (SA RDB, Restricted.) Six to eight young (125-152 mm TL) born in late summer. **Habitat:** Rocky mountain grassland. **Range:** Restricted to Sneeuberg near Graaff-Reinet and Cradock.

### Albany Adder                                    *Bitis albanica* (Pl. 99)
*(Endemic) max. SVL 281 mm male, 384 mm female.*

A small, squat adder in which the tuft of horns above the eyes is small. The scales are in 27-29 rows at midbody. There are 129-138 ventrals in females, 120-131 in males. The back is greyish with a bold series of black and white dorsolateral blotches (15-22) that may fuse on the hind body. The belly is dark grey with pale-edged ventrals. Males are smaller than females. **Biology:** Nothing is known about this very rare adder, which may be endangered by habitat destruction. There have been no recorded bites. Only recently recognized as a distinct species (1997). **Habitat:** Mesic succulent thicket and Bontveld. **Range:** Restricted to the Algoa Bay region of the E. Cape.

### Southern Adder                                  *Bitis armata* (Pl. 99)
*(Endemic) max. SVL 330 mm male, 374 mm female.*

A small, squat adder in which the tuft of horns above the eyes are small or absent. The scales are in 25-29 rows at midbody. There are 124-128 ventrals in females, 115-125 in males. The back is grey, heavily stippled in black with a series of black and white paired dorsolateral blotches (22-28). The belly is pale, with dusky infusions on the sides or edge of the ventrals. Males are smaller than females. **Biology and breeding:** The southern adder often shelters beneath limestone rock slabs among thick shrubs on coastal plains. It is active mostly during the early morning or evening, feeding mainly on lizards (skinks and lacertids). Larger snakes also take rodents. It settles well in captivity. Nothing is known about its venom, and there have been no recorded bites. It has only recently been recognized as a separate species (1997). Up to six young (125-152 mm) are born in late summer. **Habitat:** Coastal fynbos. **Range:** Agulhas Plain in the S. Cape, from Hermanus to Potberg, with an isolated population around Langebaan.

### Namaqua Dwarf Adder                             *Bitis schneideri* (Pl. 14)
*(Endemic) max. SVL 250 mm male, 254 mm female.*

This is the smallest adder. Its eyes are situated on either side of its rounded head. There is a small ridge over each eye, bearing a small hornlike scale. Scales are in 23-27 rows at midbody. Ventrals number 104-129 and sub-caudals are keeled (but smooth near the tail base in males). Coloration is varied and matches local soil colour. On coastal white sands the back is grey to brownish-grey, with three series of rounded, dark, pale-centred blotches, and is speckled with black. On the red sands of the Obib dune sea, S. Namibia, the body becomes red-orange with fainter blotches.

The head has a pale arrowhead. The tail tip is sometimes black. The belly is dirty yellow, speckled with black. **Biology and breeding:** Often shuffles into loose sand at the base of grass tussocks, leaving only its head exposed. Mainly nocturnal, it eats small geckos and frogs. It sidewinds readily. Its habitat is threatened by alluvial diamond mining (SA RDB, Vulnerable). Its venom is very mildly cytotoxic; symptoms include local swelling and pain. Antivenom is unnecessary in the treatment of its bite, and there have been no recorded fatalities. Three to four young, measuring 110-130 mm TL, are born in late summer. **Habitat:** Prefers semi-stable, vegetated coastal sand dunes. **Range:** Found in the southern regions of the Namib Desert, from Lüderitz Bay in Namibia to coastal Little Namaqualand.

### Péringuey's Adder

*Bitis peringueyi* **(Pl. 14)**
*Max. SVL 223 mm male, 237 mm female.*
This very small adder has its eyes situated on top of its rounded, flat head. There is no supraorbital ridge. Scales are in 23-31 rows at midbody. Ventrals number 117-144, and the subcaudals are smooth except towards the tail tip. The back is pale buff to orange-brown, or pale greyish-yellow, with three series of faint, dark spots (those on the flanks are pale-centred), and irregularly stippled with pale and dark spots. The back of the head sometimes has faint dark marks. The belly is whitish, occasionally with dark reddish-brown spots on the sides; 25% of snakes have a black tail tip. **Biology and breeding:** This snake is famous for its ability to sidewind; this unusual locomotion involves undulating the body in smooth, lateral curves, lifting most of the body from the sand. Sidewinding enables the snake to move swiftly over hot, loose dunes. It shuffles completely into loose sand, leaving only its eyes exposed, and sometimes its black tail tip, which it waves to attract desert and sand lizards. It drinks fog droplets that condense on its flattened body. It is endangered by over-collecting for the pet trade, and rarely lives long in captivity. Its venom is very mild, causing pain and local swelling; antivenom is unnecessary in the treatment of its bite. There have been no recorded fatalities. Three to 10 minute young (measuring 80-110 mm TL) are born in March-April. **Habitat:** This species usually prefers the fine, wind-blown sand of true Namib Desert. **Range:** Occurs in two population along the West coast, from Rotkop in S. Namibia to S. Angola.

## Lowland Swamp Viper *Proatheris*

This is a small viper with fragmented head shields, except for an enlarged supraocular, strongly keeled scales and a nonprehensile tail.

There is a single species, that just enters the subcontinent. It was previously placed in the genus *Atheris*.

### Lowland Swamp Viper

*Proatheris superciliaris* **(Pl. 14)**
*Max. SVL 513 mm male, 600 mm female.*
A robust snake with an elongate head and a large supraorbital scale. The pupils are vertical. The scales are strongly keeled, in 27-29 rows at midbody. The tail is longish (32-45 paired subcaudals). The back is grey-brown, with three rows of blackish spots, separated by a series of yellow-ish bars that form an interrupted lateral line. The top of the head has three black chevrons. The belly is off-white, with black markings. The undersurface of the tail is straw-yellow to orange, particularly in juveniles.

**Biology and breeding:** This terrestrial snake shelters in rodent burrows, emerging at dusk to feed on small frogs (particularly reed frogs). Larger adults also feed on small rodents. Aggressive when first captured, but tames readily. Its venom has not been studied; there have been no recorded bites. Males engage in combat in the breeding season (June-July). After 177-184 days gestation, 3-16 young (135-208 mm TL) born in November-December. They prefer to feed on small frogs, occasionally taking lizards as well. Sexual maturity may be reached in 18-20 months in males, but only 2-3 years in females. The young may wave their bright yellow tails to lure prey within striking distance. **Habitat:** Prefers low-lying marshes and floodplains. **Range:** Mozambique Plain from Beira north to Quissanga, up the Zambezi River to Lake Malawi and extreme SW Tanzania.

# WORM LIZARDS
## SUBORDER AMPHISBAENIA

These very unusual reptiles were for a long time classed as lizards but have now been placed in a separate suborder within the Squamata. Fossils date back to the N. American Palaeocene epoch (65 million years ago). Among many other features, worm lizards are distinguished by an enlarged medial tooth on the premaxillary bone, a reduced right lung (in snakes and legless lizards the left lung is reduced), and a unique middle ear. They are the most specialized burrowing reptiles, capable of driving tunnels through hard soils, and are rarely seen above ground.

All are limbless (except the Mexican *Bipes*, which has front legs) and most retain only vestiges of the limb girdles. They lack external ears and have backward-facing nostrils, adaptations which prevent the entry of sand. Their eyelids are fused and the very reduced eyes lie deep below the translucent skin. The body is often cylindrical, and is covered with smooth, squarish scales which are arranged in distinctive rings (annuli), causing these lizards to look like worms, hence the common name. These annuli are divided into dorsal and ventral sets by a faint longitudinal groove. The skin is separated from the underlying body, being attached only by three muscle sets per vertebra. This specialization allows the head and body to move within the skin so that a ramming motion can be generated for burrowing. To withstand these pressures, the skull is short and robust, with the braincase ringed by frontal bones for extra strength. Primitive species, and those inhabiting loose soils, are round-snouted, and the head is covered with close-fitting, enlarged head shields. Some species have evolved a hardened cutting edge to the snout that may form a horizontal spade or a vertical keel. This is used to scrape soil from the front of the burrow and compact it into the walls.

These squamates are small to medium-sized, the largest, at 750 mm, being from S. America. Most feed on invertebrates, especially ants and termites. Large prey is located by scent and vibration, gripped between the few, large teeth, and torn to bits by being dragged into the burrow. Some S. American species are large enough to eat small vertebrates. Males have hemipenes and fertilization is internal. The majority lay eggs, although some retain these within the body and give birth to live young. Most are flesh-coloured, and some have darker dorsal pigmentation. The tail in larger species is usually short and rounded, sometimes pigmented and often heavily scarred. This is because in defence it may be waved in the air, mimicking the head and deflecting attacks away from the vital organs;

in fact, the name 'amphisbaena' means 'two-headed'. In many smaller species the tail is longer and can be shed, but not regenerated. There are about 155 species in 21 genera and four families. These are distributed throughout most of sub-Saharan Africa and tropical S. America, with scattered populations in Arabia, Spain and N. America. Two families occur in Africa, with only the Amphisbaenidae reaching southern Africa.

## Tropical Worm Lizards
### FAMILY AMPHISBAENIDAE

This is by far the largest family of worm lizards, with 15 genera containing about 145 species, most of which are distributed through Africa and S. America. The family contains both round-headed and spade-snouted forms. There are nine African genera, containing 65 species, with 17 species (seven of which are endemic) in four genera occurring on the subcontinent.

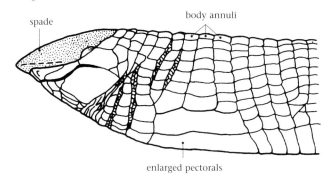

The head of a spade-snouted amphisbaenid

KEY TO THE SOUTHERN AFRICAN GENERA IN THE AMPHISBAENIDAE
1 - Segments of the pectoral region not elongate; snout rounded, without a sharp cutting edge:                                    go to 2
  - Segments of pectoral region elongate; snout with sharp horizontal cutting edge:                                    go to 3
2 - Body slender; head shields fused into 1 or 2 shields:
            Chirindia (Pink round-headed worm lizards, page 121)
  - Body not slender; head shields all distinct:
            Zygaspis (Purple round-headed worm lizards, page 122)
3 - Nasals well separated by rostral; tail short, bluntly rounded:
            Monopeltis (Spade-snouted worm lizards, page 124)
  - Nasals usually touching above rostral; tail long, terminating abruptly in a callous pad:        Dalophia (Blunt-tailed worm lizards, page 126)

## Pink Round-headed Worm Lizards     Chirindia

These small, elongate worm lizards have a rounded head and extensive fusion of the head shields. The nasal, first upper labial and prefrontal, and sometimes other shields, are all fused behind the rostral into a large shield. Restricted to E. and southern Africa, there are four Tanzanian species and two in southern Africa; one of these is endemic.

C.l. langi

C.l. occidentalis

## Lang's Round-headed Worm Lizard    *Chirindia langi* (Pl. 42)
*(Endemic) SVL 120-140 mm; max. SVL 158 mm.*
A small, elongate worm lizard with a rounded head. There are three upper labials, and the ocular is fused with the second upper labial. There are 242-309 body annuli, with 27-35 segments per annulus (see Subspecies). Males have 4-6 preanal pores (see Subspecies). The tapering tail has a rounded tip and 24-28 caudal annuli. The body is uniform unpigmented flesh-pink throughout. **Biology:** This worm lizard burrows in loose soil, and is usually discovered beneath stones or rotting logs. It eats mainly termites. When caught, it wiggles wildly to escape and will shed its tail if grasped (17-19% of specimens have truncated tails). Predators include snakes (particularly purple-glossed and quill-snouted snakes), jackals and ratels. **Habitat:** Sandy Kalahari soils, entering mopane woodland on clay soils. **Range:** N. Province and adjacent Mozambique. **Subspecies:** Two races are recognized. *C.l. langi* is longer (av. 133 mm TL), with more body annuli (275-309), but fewer segments (usually 30) per annulus, and only four preanal pores in males; it occurs in the eastern part of the range, from Mozambique and N. Kruger National Park. *C.l. occidentalis* is smaller (av. 125 mm TL), with fewer body annuli (242-262), but more segments (usually 33-34) per annulus and six preanal pores in males; it is found in N. Province, west of Kruger National Park.

## Swynnerton's Round-headed Worm Lizard
*Chirindia swynnertoni* (Pl. 42)
*SVL 110-130 mm; max. SVL 141 mm.*

This short, elongate worm lizard has a rounded head and two upper labials (the nasal, first and second upper labials, prefrontal and ocular are all fused). There are 235-265 body annuli, with 24-28 segments per annulus. Males have six preanal pores. The tail tapers to a rounded tip, and has 19-26 caudal annuli. The body is uniform unpigmented flesh-pink, with a purple sheen. **Biology and breeding:** This species is similar in habits and behaviour to Lang's round-headed worm lizard, *C. langi* (page 122). Predators include the dwarf wolf snake, which is a specialist feeder on this worm lizard. The first specimen was found in the stomach of a kingfisher. Its breeding is poorly known; a single egg (22 x 3 mm) was found in a female in December. **Habitat:** Thicket and grassland on alluvial soils. **Range:** Mozambique Plain and adjacent Zimbabwe.

## Purple Round-headed Worm Lizards    *Zygaspis*
These small, stoutish worm lizards have a rounded head, and distinct nasal, prefrontal and ocular scales.
There are seven species distributed from NW Democratic Republic of Congo to N. Cape. Isolated from other members of the genus, *Z. dolichomenta* inhabits lowland forest in NW Democratic Republic of Congo. *Zygaspis kufuensis* is restricted to the Kafue Flats of Central Zambia, whilst the remaining five species occur on the subcontinent; three are endemic.

## Ferocious Round-headed Worm Lizard    *Zygaspis ferox*
*(Endemic) SVL 170-210 mm; max. SVL 247 mm.*
A medium-sized worm lizard with a robust head and rounded snout. The preocular is not fused with the prefrontals. It has three upper labials. There are 193-203 body annuli, with 18-21 (usually 18) dorsals and 16-20 (usually 16) ventrals per midbody annulus. The tail is longish, tapering

122

slightly, and has 35-40 caudal annuli. The back is uniform dark brown above, darkening towards the tail, and paler below. **Biology:** This is an aggressive species that will bite and then spin like a crocodile, tearing off a piece of flesh. This is a feeding technique used by the very large S. American species, but no other African worm lizard. Only termites have been found in their diet. **Habitat:** Clayey soils in remnant forest. **Range:** Restricted to vicinity of Chirinda Forest, SE Zimbabwe escarpment.

### Van Dam's Round-headed Worm Lizard
*Zygaspis vandami* (Pl. 100)
*(Endemic) SVL 130-170 mm; max. SVL 185 mm.*
A small, stout worm lizard with a rounded snout. The preocular is fused with the prefrontals. It has three upper labials. There are 181-211 body annuli, with 12-22 (usually 14-16) dorsals and 12-20 (usually 14-16) ventrals per midbody annulus. The tail is longish, tapering slightly, and has 44-50 caudal annuli. The back is uniform dark purple-brown, the belly is light purple, sometimes with the pigment restricted to the scale edges, and the chin and cloacal region are white. **Biology and breeding:** Usually found under stones on sandy or humic soils. It feeds on termites. Predators include Bibron's burrowing asp. Females lay 2-3 elongate eggs (23 x 4 mm) in early summer. **Habitat:** Alluvial sands with mesic savannah. **Range:** SE Mpumalanga, extending onto Mozambique plain, south into N. Zululand as far as Mapalane. **Subspecies:** Two races recognized and both occur in the region. *Z.v. vandami* has two postoculars, two temporals and two posterior upper labials; it is restricted to N. Province and Mpumalanga. *Z.v. arenicola* usually has only a single large temporal and sometimes only a single posterior upper labial (in KwaZulu-Natal); it occurs on the Mozambique plain, into SE Zimbabwe and south to Zululand.

*Z.v. arenicola*
*Z.v. vandami*

### Violet Round-headed Worm Lizard
*Zygaspis violacea* (Pl. 42)
*(Endemic) SVL 130-170 mm; max. SVL 185 mm.*
A small, stout worm lizard with a rounded snout and few head shields due to fusion. The preocular is fused with the prefrontals and the parietals with the frontals; there is a single large temporal due to fusion with the labials. It has three upper labials. There are 174-182 body annuli, with 18-22 dorsals and 16-20 ventrals per midbody annulus. The tail is longish, tapering slightly, and has 50-59 caudal annuli. The back is uniform dark purple-brown, the belly is light purple, sometimes with the pigment restricted to the scale edges, and the chin and cloacal region are white. **Biology:** This worm lizard is probably restricted to humic soils in dune thicket, much of which has now been cleared for agriculture. **Habitat:** Dune thicket. **Range:** Narrow coastal strip along Mozambique Plain, from Bazaruto Archipelago to Maputo (more restricted than previously thought).

### Kalahari Round-headed Worm Lizard
*Zygaspis quadrifrons* (Pl. 42)
*SVL 170-210 mm; max. SVL 245 mm.*
Moderate-sized with a rounded snout and discrete preoculars that are not fused with the prefrontals. The third upper labial is bordered by a temporal shield above a smaller post-upper labial. There are 195-242 body annuli, with 12-23 dorsals and 10-22 ventrals per midbody annulus. Males have four preanal pores. The tail is longish, with 32-50 caudal annuli. The body is uniform purple-brown above, with a lighter belly; it is often darker

towards the tail. **Biology:** Common under stones in suitable habitat. It feeds on small insects and their larvae, particularly termites. Females lay 3-4 elongate eggs (3,5-4 x 17-19 mm) in summer. **Habitat:** Varied: sandy scrub and bushveld. **Range:** Through Kalahari, from N. Cape to Democratic Republic of Congo and along Limpopo River to Mozambique.

### Black Round-headed Worm Lizard          *Zygaspis nigra* **(Pl. 42)**
*SVL 200-250 mm; max. SVL 280 mm.*
A large worm lizard with a rounded snout and elongate preoculars. The latter are fused with the prefrontals. The third upper labial is bordered by a large temporal shield. There are 183-205 body annuli, with 14-24 dorsals and 12-16 ventrals per midbody annulus. Males have four preanal pores. The tail is longish, with 40-54 caudal annuli. The back is ivory, with a black base to each scale (90% on dorsals, 50% on ventrals), giving a speckled effect. The chin and scattered areas are ivory. **Biology:** Similar in habits and behaviour to the Kalahari round-headed worm lizard, *Z. quadrifrons* (page 123). **Habitat:** Miombo and Baikiaea woodland on sandy soils. **Range:** SW Zambia and adjacent Angola, just entering Caprivi Strip.

## Spade-snouted Worm Lizards   *Monopeltis*
These are large worm lizards with a broad, horizontal, spade-shaped snout that is covered with 1-2 large, horny shields. The nasal shields are always separated by the rostral. The pectoral region usually has very enlarged, long, smooth shields. The body is cylindrical, with fewer than 300 annuli (counted along the belly, as extra half-annuli are often inserted on the dorsal surface). The tail is usually short (4-24 caudal annuli, extralimitally 61 in *M. adercae* from Democratic Republic of Congo), with a rounded tip. Preanal pores may number up to 13 (but there are usually two in southern African species), and sometimes there are none.

Capable of burrowing in hard soils, these worm lizards are found in a wide variety of habitats, although they rarely enter forest. Most are exposed during earth moving, either in road construction or ploughing. Floods and attacks by carnivorous ants also force them to the surface. In suitable habitat they may be common. Reproduction is poorly known, but at least one species gives birth to live babies. The tail may be shed in long-tailed species. They feed almost exclusively on termites, although adult and larval insects are also taken. Predators include snakes, particularly quill-snouted snakes, but when forced to the surface they are also eaten by small carnivores and even birds of prey.

There are 19 species in central and southern Africa, with eight species occurring on the subcontinent, three of which are endemic.

### Anchieta's Spade-snouted Worm Lizard
*Monopeltis anchietae* **(Pl. 41)**
*SVL 200-300 mm; max. SVL 345 mm.*
This robust species has two shields that form a 'spade'. There are four pectorals. It has 170-198 body annuli, with 6-28 extra dorsal half-annuli. The tail is short (5-9 caudal annuli), with a rounded tip that cannot be shed. There are two preanal pores. The back, from the snout to the tail tip, is reddish-brown, being darkest behind the head and over the tail and lighter on the flanks. The belly is unpigmented. **Habitat:** Moist savannah, entering drier regions. **Range:** N. Namibia and Caprivi Strip, and into adjacent Angola and Botswana.

# Kalahari Spade-snouted Worm Lizard
### Monopeltis leonhardi (Pl. 41)

*(Endemic) SVL 200-250 mm; max. SVL 290 mm.*
A medium-sized species with two shields that form a 'spade'. It has six pectorals. There are 170-213 body annuli with 2-22 extra dorsal half-annuli. The tail is short (5-9 caudal annuli), with a rounded tip that cannot be shed. There are no preanal pores. Coloration is similar to that of the Anchieta's spade-snouted worm lizard, *M. anchietae* (page 124); juveniles are less strongly pigmented. **Biology:** Prefers to burrow in shallow sands. Predators include jackals and yellow-billed kites. **Habitat:** Kalahari sands. **Range:** Central Botswana, into adjacent Namibia, N. Cape and SW Zimbabwe, extending along Limpopo River to Kruger National Park.

# Zambezi Spade-snouted Worm Lizard   Monopeltis zambezensis

*SVL 150-200 mm; max. SVL 237 mm.*
This very small slender species resembles the Cape spade-snouted worm lizard, *M. capensis* (below). It has one shield forming a 'spade'. It has six pectorals. There are 239-263 body annuli, with 18-20 dorsals and 13-16 ventrals, and few extra dorsal half-annuli. The tail is short (6-8 caudal annuli), with a rounded tip that cannot be shed. There are two preanal pores. The back is unpigmented anteriorly, but is suffused with pigment over the rear, particularly on the tail. **Habitat:** Mopane woodland on red soils. **Range:** Both banks of the Zambezi River valley around Kariba Dam.

# Cape Spade-snouted Worm Lizard   Monopeltis capensis (Pl. 41)

*(Endemic) SVL 200-300 mm; max. SVL 340 mm.*
This robust, medium-sized species has one shield forming a 'spade'. There are 4-6 pectorals. It has 172-221 body annuli, with 18-30 dorsals and 16-29 ventrals, and numerous extra dorsal half-annuli. The tail is short (7-11 caudal annuli), with a rounded tip that cannot be shed. There are two preanal pores. The body is uniform pink-white. **Biology and breeding:** Very common in suitable habitat. It burrows in red soils and feeds on termites, beetle larvae, etc. For many predators it must be as tasty as the worms it resembles; enemies include birds (the yellow-billed kite, bateleur and hornbill), jackals, and particularly certain snakes (burrowing asps and quill-snouted snakes, among others). Floods drown many, as well as pushing them to the surface where predators wait. One to three babies (90-100 mm TL) are born in summer. **Habitat:** Kalahari sandveld and alluvial plains. **Range:** SE Botswana and central regions of South Africa, extending through NW Province into Limpopo basin. **Subspecies:** None; all previous races and forms have been raised to species status.

# Zimbabwe Spade-snouted Worm Lizard
### Monopeltis rhodesiana (Pl. 41)

*SVL 200-250 mm; max. SVL 285 mm.*
This medium-sized species has one shield forming a 'spade'. There are 4-6 pectorals. It has 172-221 body annuli, with usually fewer than 40 segments in a midbody annulus (13-26 dorsals and 10-22 ventrals), and numerous extra dorsal half-annuli. The tail is short (5-9 caudal annuli), with a rounded tip that cannot be shed. There are two preanal pores. The body is uniform pink-white, with pigment restricted to the back and rear of the body and the tail. **Biology:** Predators include quill-snouted snakes, jackals, hornbills and yellow-billed kites. **Habitat:** Mesic savannah on

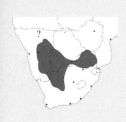

alluvial soils. **Range:** SE and NW Zimbabwe, extending into middle Zambezi Valley, with isolated records from NE Zimbabwe, S. Zambia, Central Mozambique and S. Malawi.

### Dusky Spade-snouted Worm Lizard
*Monopeltis infuscata* **(Pl. 100)**

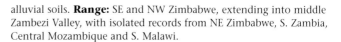

*SVL 200-250 mm; max. SVL 280 mm in east, 340 mm in west.*
This medium-sized species has one shield (usually with lateral clefts) forming a 'spade' in adults. This is divided transversely in juveniles. There are 4-6 pectorals. It has 179-209 body annuli, with usually more than 40 segments in a midbody annulus (19-32 dorsals and 18-27 ventrals), and numerous extra dorsal half-annuli. The tail is short (6-11 caudal annuli), with a rounded tip that cannot be shed. There is usually one, rarely two, preanal pores. The body is uniform pink-white, with extensive grey-brown blotches on the back. **Biology and breeding:** Similar to the Cape spade-snouted worm lizard (above). **Habitat:** Dry and moist savannah on sandy soils. **Range:** Two isolated populations; in the west from N. Cape and SW Botswana, through Namibia to SW Angola; in the east restricted to N. Province and Gauteng, and across Limpopo River into SW Zimbabwe.

### De Coster's Spade-snouted Worm Lizard
*Monopeltis decosteri*

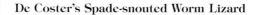

*(Endemic) SVL 200-250 mm; max. SVL 290 mm.*
This medium-sized species has one shield forming a 'spade'. There are usually 6 elongate pectorals. It has 188-221 body annuli, with usually more than 40 segments in a midbody annulus (17-31 dorsals and 12-23 ventrals), and numerous extra dorsal half-annuli. The tail is short (6-11 caudal annuli), with a rounded tip that cannot be shed. There are two preanal pores. The body is uniform pink-white, with light pigmentation on the back, darkening towards the tail but fading at the tip. **Biology and breeding:** Similar to that of the Cape spade-snouted worm lizard (above). **Habitat:** Moist savannah on sandy soils. **Range:** S. Mozambique, into SE Zimbabwe and NE corner of Kruger National Park.

### Slender Spade-snouted Worm Lizard
*Monopeltis sphenorhynchus* **(Pl. 41)**

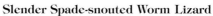

*SVL 200-300 mm; max. SVL 326 mm.*
A medium-sized, slender species with one shield forming a 'spade'. It has six pectorals. There are 228-316 body annuli (see Subspecies), with 20-45 dorsals and 16-29 ventrals, and few or no extra dorsal half-annuli. The tail is short (7-11 caudal annuli), with a rounded tip that cannot be shed. There are two preanal pores. The body is pale pink to whitish all over. **Habitat:** Deep Kalahari sand or coastal alluvium. **Range:** Northern part of subcontinent. **Subspecies:** Two races: *M.s. sphenorhynchus* has its ocular separated from the nasal, and 228-284 body annuli; found on S. Mozambique Plain including Bazaruto Archipelago, into N. Zululand and along Limpopo River to N. Province. *M.s. mauricei* has its ocular touching the nasal and 275-316 body annuli; occurs in Botswana, into adjacent regions.

■ *M.s. mauricei*

□ *M.s. sphenorhynchus*

## Blunt-tailed Worm Lizards  *Dalophia*
These are large worm lizards, very similar in appearance to the spade-snouted worm lizards, *Monopeltis* (page 124), having a broad horizontal, spade-shaped snout, usually with a single large, horny shield. The nasal

shields are usually in contact with each other, or are only narrowly separated. The pectoral region has 4-6 enlarged, smooth, long shields. The body is slender, usually with more than 300 body annuli (counted along the belly). There are no preanal pores. The tail is slender (17-46 caudal annuli) and always truncated with a characteristic flattened terminal pad.

Although they are similar in most respects of their behaviour and habits to spade-snouted worm lizards, they feed more heavily on beetles and their larvae, rather than termites. Reproduction is poorly known, but some species are known to lay eggs. Three species (none of which occurs on the subcontinent) can shed their tail in defence.

Seven species occur in Africa south of the Democratic Republic of Congo, with only two entering the subcontinent, neither being endemic.

### Blunt-tailed Worm Lizard          *Dalophia pistillum* (Pl. 41)
*SVL 380-480 mm; max. SVL 560 mm.*

By far the largest local worm lizard with a broad, horizontal 'spade' that is covered with a single horny shield, partially divided by lateral sutures. The nasals are in contact. There are six pectorals, and 280-352 body annuli. The tail is blunt-ended, with 19-33 caudal annuli but without 'herringbone' segmentation on the dorsal surface. There are no preanal pores. The body is uniform flesh-coloured, with light grey speckles on the back and tail, that may rarely extend onto the lower flanks. **Biology and breeding:** Preyed on by quill-snouted snakes, ratels and polecats. (SA RDB, Peripheral.) Lays four eggs (32-35 x 8-10 mm) in September. **Habitat:** Varied; includes Kalahari sand and coastal alluvium. **Range:** Northern border of the region, south to N. Cape and Free State. Elsewhere, to Zambia and along Zambezi River to mid-Mozambique Plain.

### Long-tailed Worm Lizard          *Dalophia longicauda*
*SVL 250-350 mm; max. SVL 365 mm.*

A large species; resembles blunt-tailed worm lizard, *D. pistillum* (above). Has a broad, roundly-pointed, horizontal 'spade' covered with a single horny shield, partially divided by lateral sutures. Nasals are in contact. Six pectorals, and 307-338 body annuli present. Tail is long and blunt-ended, with 33-42 caudal annuli, and with 'herringbone' segmentation on dorsal surface. No preanal pores. Body is uniform flesh-pink anteriorly, with light grey speckles on rest of body and tail, that may rarely extend onto lower flanks; the belly is unpigmented. **Habitat:** Moist alluvial soils along permanent river courses. **Range:** Caprivi Strip and adjacent regions.

# LIZARDS
## SUBORDER SAURIA (LACERTILIA)

Lizards are the most familiar reptiles, although many are highly specialized, and the legless species are often confused with snakes. Typically, they have well-developed limbs, but even in the most highly specialized legless forms, internal vestiges of limb girdles are nearly always present. The body is covered with scales that are usually overlapping, but may be granular and juxtaposed. They usually have external ears and movable eyelids, although in most geckos and some skinks the eyelids are transparent and fused, forming a 'spectacle' over the eye. The halves of the lower jaw are fused. The tongue cannot be withdrawn into a sheath, although in some families (for example monitors) it is retractile.

Most lizards, including geckos, skinks, lacertids, girdle and plated lizards, can shed their tail and regenerate a new one. A lost tail cannot be replaced in chameleons, agamas and monitors
Lizards have radiated into many environments, and are particularly common and diverse in deserts and arid regions. There are not many aquatic species, with only the marine iguanas of the Galapagos Islands, some freshwater monitors, and a few other species, being at home in water. Most feed on insects and other invertebrates, but a number of species are herbivorous, while some large species often eat small mammals. The Komodo dragon may even kill and eat humans, albeit rarely. The only venomous lizards are the two species of Gila monster restricted to the south of North America. Most lizards are egg-laying, and a number of American species brood their eggs after laying. Viviparity is common in some families, particularly the skinks, girdled lizards and dwarf chameleons.
Lizards occur throughout the world; some species have even reached the small oceanic islands of the Indo-Pacific. They form the largest group of living reptiles, with over 4 000 species in nearly 400 genera. At least 20 families are recognized and these are sometimes grouped into four infraorders, all of which are represented in southern Africa. The eight local families are placed in the Anguimorpha (Varanidae), Gekkota (Gekkonidae), Iguania (Agamidae and Chamaeleonidae) and Scincomorpha (Scincidae, Lacertidae, Gerrhosauridae and Cordylidae). There is still some debate as to the relationships of these groups.

KEY TO THE LIZARD FAMILIES IN SOUTHERN AFRICA
1 - Top of head covered with granules or small, irregularly arranged scales:
                                                                    go to 2
  - Top of head covered with large, symmetrical shields:           go to 5
2 - Toes bound in opposed bundles for grasping; tongue extensile, with club-shaped tip; eyes set in independently movable turrets:
                              Chamaeleonidae (Chameleons, page 219)
  - Toes separate; tongue not extensile; eyes normal:              go to 3
3 - Dorsal scales overlapping and strongly keeled:
                                       Agamidae (Agamas, page 211)
  - Dorsal scales juxtaposed, smooth or granular, sometimes with scattered tubercles:                                          go to 4
4 - Eyelids usually not or hardly movable, cannot close over eye; tongue short and broad, covered with soft papillae; tail easily shed:
                                      Gekkonidae (Geckos, page 229)
  - Eyelids movable, can close over eye; tongue forked at tip; tail cannot be shed:                        Varanidae (Monitors, page 209)
5 - Dorsal scales overlapping, cycloid, smooth or with 3 or more keels; femoral pores absent:                 Scincidae (Skinks, page 130)
  - Dorsal scales small and granular or juxtaposed and with a strong keel; with femoral pores or a row of glandular scales on posterior face of thigh:                                                   go to 6
6 - Lateral granular fold present, and/or limbs vestigial:
                                                                    go to 7
  - Lateral granular fold absent; limbs well developed:
                              Lacertidae (Old World lizards, page 160)
7 - Tongue long; body shields with underlying bony plates (osteoderms); tail covered with rectangular, non-spiny scales:
                         Gerrhosauridae (Plated lizards & seps, page 176)

– Tongue short; body shields without osteoderms; tail covered with
  whorls of spiny or strongly keeled scale:
  Cordylidae (Girdled lizards & their relatives, page 183)

## Lizard scales

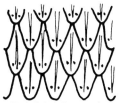

Keeled, imbricate scales
with pores

Mucronate scales

Cycloid scales (tricarinate
and smooth)

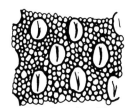

Granular scales with
enlarged tubercles

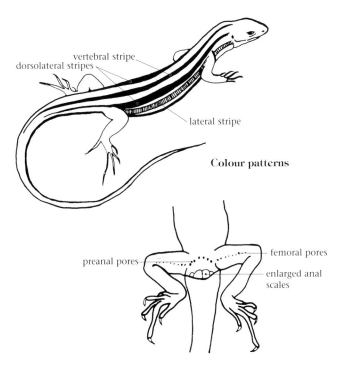

vertebral stripe
dorsolateral stripes

lateral stripe

### Colour patterns

preanal pores
femoral pores
enlarged anal
scales

### Pores

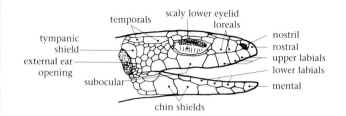

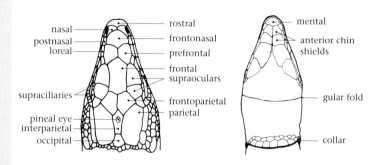

**The head scales of a scincomorph lizard**

# Skinks
## FAMILY SCINCIDAE

Although most of these diverse lizards have well-developed limbs, some have either no limbs or only vestiges of limbs. The dorsal scales are usually smooth, flat and highly polished, often appearing iridescent. They overlap strongly and are underlaid by osteoderms. This gives skinks a highly flexible but rigid and strong coat, ideal for burrowing or living in rock cracks. The head is relatively small and usually lacks an obvious neck. It is covered with large, symmetrical head shields. Ear holes are usually present, and often protected by scales. The eyes are often small (and absent in some burrowing forms) and the pupils are round. Functional eyelids are usually present, but in some species the lower eyelids have transparent windows and are immovable (like those of snakes). Femoral pores are absent. The tail is smooth, easily shed and quickly regenerated.

Most skinks may be called 'typical' lizards. They are usually terrestrial, although many climb trees and rocks, and are active during the day. Most are of medium size, with very few growing large. They feed almost exclusively on small insects, which are actively pursued. Most maintain a high body temperature by shuttling between sunny spots and shade. Some territorial species, which are mainly rock-living, are brightly coloured and develop dominance hierarchies, with brilliant, tyrant males. However, most species are solitary and drably patterned in browns and greys, and forage among loose leaves and wooded litter. Many of these have elongate bodies and reduced limbs, and in some burrowing genera the limbs are lost. In southern Africa the dwarf burrowing skinks, *Scelotes* show a clear evolutionary progression towards limb loss, and demonstrate how snakes must have evolved. Most skinks lay small clutches of soft-shelled eggs underground. Viviparity has evolved on many occasions. Individuals in some local species may lay eggs or give birth to live young.

This family is found throughout the tropical and temperate regions of the world. Despite this diversity, it has a very poor fossil history, and only two genera are known prior to the Pleistocene epoch (two million years ago). One of these dates from the late Cretaceous period (about 80 million years ago), and the other from the Oligocene epoch onwards (38 million years ago). The family is divided into three subfamilies, all of which occur in southern Africa. Approximately 80 genera with over 700 species occur worldwide. This is the second most diverse group of lizards in southern Africa (exceeded only by the geckos) with 69 species in 11 genera; 41 species and one genus are endemic.

### Key to the southern African genera in the Scincidae

1 - Each nostril pierced between the rostral and a very small nasal shield; prefrontals and frontoparietals (if present) very small; scales smooth; limbs reduced or absent: go to 2
   - Each nostril pierced in a small nasal shield and well-separated from the rostral; prefrontals and frontoparietal(s) present: go to 4
   - Each nostril pierced in front of a very large rostral and with a groove running to rear border of rostral; scales smooth; limbs absent: go to 7

2 - Interparietal scale not touching supraocular scales: go to 3
   - Interparietal touching supraocular scales: *Scelotes* (Dwarf burrowing skinks, page 139)

3 - Five toes on each forelimb and hind limb: *Proscelotes* (Slender skinks, page 139)
   - Three or four toes on each forelimb and hind limb: *Sepsina* (Savannah burrowing skinks, page 145)

4 - Eyelids immovable; each eye covered with a transparent spectacle; scales smooth; limbs present but small: go to 5
   - Eyelids movable: go to 6

5 - Three supraoculars; 24-26 scale rows at midbody; terrestrial: *Panaspis* (Snake-eyed skinks, page 159)
   - Five supraoculars; 26-29 scale rows at midbody; inhabiting intertidal zone: *Cryptoblepharus* (Coastal skinks page 149)

6 - Transparent window in each lower eyelid; limbs well-developed; scales with fine keels: *Mabuya* (Typical skinks, page 150)
   - Lower eyelids scaly, but may be translucent; limbs short; scales smooth or weakly striated: *Lygosoma* (Writhing skinks page 149)

7 - Eyes completely exposed, without eyelids; no enlarged preanal plate; three enlarged, transverse scales on front of head: *Typhlacontias* (Western legless skinks, page 146)
   - Eyes with eyelids or situated under head shields; an enlarged preanal plate; two enlarged, transverse scales on front of head: go to 8

8 - No eyelids present; eyes appearing as dark spots below head shields: *Typhlosaurus* (Blind legless skinks, page 135)
   - Lower eyelids movable and elongate; 3-4 supraciliaries: *Acontias* (Greater legless skinks, page 132)
   - Lower eyelids immovable, oval and transparent; two supraciliaries: *Acontophiops* (Woodbush legless skink, page 135)

# African Legless Skinks
## SUBFAMILY ACONTIINAE

These specialized, legless, burrowing skinks are characterized by a divided frontal bone in the skull. They lack all traces of external limbs and have a short, stubby tail (less than 22% of the total length). The body scales are smooth, tightly fitting and not enlarged on the belly. There is a single enlarged anal plate. The front scales on the head (rostral and mental) are enlarged, and each nostril is placed in the front of the rostral and in most species is connected to its rear border by a long groove. There are no external ear openings. Coloration is varied, and many have a striped pattern.

All African legless skinks burrow, most being restricted to loose sandy soil or leaf litter. A few of the larger, more robust species are able to burrow in harder, clayey soils. Most feed on earthworms, beetle larvae and termites. All species whose reproduction is known are viviparous; the larger species giving birth to up to 14 babies. Some small, thin species have only a single baby.

This subfamily is restricted mainly to southern Africa, with a few species extending into adjacent countries. There are three genera with 18 species, and all but two are endemic to the subcontinent.

## Greater Legless Skinks    *Acontias*

This is a group of medium-sized to large legless skinks that have elongate, movable lower eyelids and three to four supraciliary scales above each eye. Greater legless skinks do not have external ear openings. The tail is short and stubby.

All are burrowing and are normally found under stones or dead logs on loose soil. They feed on small invertebrates, but the bigger species may take other burrowing reptiles. They rarely drink from standing water and appear to obtain most of their moisture from the surrounding soil and their food. It is possible that the long groove on the rostral may funnel soil water to the nostril. They are viviparous, giving birth to a single brood of young in late summer. They are often eaten by burrowing snakes (for example the burrowing asp and harlequin snake) and small carnivores.

There are eight species in the genus, and all occur in the region; seven are endemic, the remaining species having an isolated, relict population in SE Kenya.

### Short-headed Legless Skink    *Acontias breviceps* (Pl. 100)
*(Endemic) SVL 130-170 mm; max. SVL 199 mm.*
A medium-sized legless skink, similar in appearance to the thin-tailed legless skink, *A. gracilicauda* (page 133), but has a thicker tail and a spotted belly. It has a broad head, a rounded snout, and a slender body. The lower eyelids are opaque, and each usually has three suboculars. The tail is cylindrical, and has a middle row of enlarged subcaudals. The body is olive to olive-brown in colour, with the scales spotted with dark brown to black. The belly is light olive-yellow, with spotted scales. Juveniles have a creamy-coloured, plain belly. **Biology and breeding:** A rare species that may be endangered by afforestation by pine plantations. Two Mpumalanga females contained two embryos each (measuring up to 64 mm TL) in January. **Habitat:** Prefers montane grassland. **Range:** Two isolated populations are found in the E. Cape and Mpumalanga escarpment.

### Thin-tailed Legless Skink

*Acontias gracilicauda* **(Pl. 44)**

*(Endemic) SVL 200-230 mm; max. SVL 260 mm.*

A medium-sized skink with a broad head, a rounded snout, a slender body and a thin, tapering tail. The lower eyelids are opaque, and each has three suboculars. The second upper labial usually enters the eye. There are 16-20 scale rows at midbody. The body ranges in colour from pale golden-olive to olive to grey-brown, but the body scales are always dark-edged, giving a speckled appearance. The belly is plain pale golden-yellow. **Biology and breeding:** These skinks show a preference for compact, moist soils. A large female (275 mm TL) gave birth to two babies (96-102 mm TL, 1,1-1,4 g) in February. **Habitat:** Mesic thicket, grassland, and entering sandy regions including KwaZulu-Natal. **Range:** Two isolated populations in Little Namaqualand, and E. Cape, Free State and adjacent NW Province, Gauteng and Mpumalanga. **Subspecies:** Two races are recognized. *A.g. gracilicauda* has 149-171 ventrals, and its body is olive to olive-grey; it occurs in E. Cape and highveld of Free State and adjacent regions. *A.g. namaquensis* has 158-179 ventrals, and its body is pale olive-brown, with dark scale margins; it is found in Little Namaqualand.

*A.g. namaquensis*

*A.g. gracilicauda*

### Striped Legless Skink

*Acontias lineatus* **(Pl. 45)**

*(Endemic) SVL 130-145 mm; max. SVL 148 mm.*

A small legless skink with a flattened snout that has a horizontal, spade-like edge. The lower eyelids are transparent. The tail is flattened below. There are a number of colour variations (see Subspecies); in addition, some specimens are uniform black above and below, while others are black-backed but have a pale belly or a few pale spots around the head or vent. **Biology and breeding:** These skinks are common in sandy flats, burrowing in loose soil at the base of vegetation. They possibly have only a single baby. **Habitat:** Sandy, arid soils. **Range:** W. and N. Cape, and into Little and Great Namaqualand. **Subspecies:** Three races are recognized. *A.l. lineatus* usually has five upper labials, and a yellow back with 4-10 dark stripes or rows of spots, and a plain, flesh-coloured belly; it occurs in Great Namaqualand, N. Cape and inland regions of W. Cape. *A.l. tristis* has similar coloration to the typical race, but has only four upper labials; it is found in Little Namaqualand. In *A.l. grayi* there are usually five upper labials, and each scale on the back has a dark, transverse mark; it occurs in the vicinity of Graafwater in SW Cape.

*A.l. grayi*

*A.l. tristis*

*A.l. lineatus*

### Coastal Legless Skink

*Acontias litoralis* **(Pls. 43 and 44)**

*(Endemic) SVL 110-115 mm; max. SVL 119 mm.*

A small legless skink with a flattened snout that has a horizontal, spade-like edge. The lower eyelids are transparent. There are four upper labials. Ventrals number 145-160. The tail is flattened below. The head and body are yellow, with a broad, dark purple-brown stripe down the back. Some specimens are all yellow-orange except for a dark eye stripe. **Habitat:** Sparsely vegetated coastal sands. **Range:** W. Cape coastal strip from Daberas, south to Elandsbaai

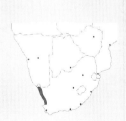

### Cape Legless Skink

*Acontias meleagris* **(Pl. 45)**

*(Endemic) SVL 200-230 mm; max. SVL 250 mm.*

A medium-sized legless skink with a slender head and body, a rounded snout and a blunt tail that tapers only slightly. The lower eyelids are opaque. There are three suboculars. The second upper labial does not

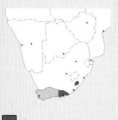

A.m. orientalis

A.m. meleagris

enter the eye. There are 14-16 scale rows at midbody. **Biology and breeding:** These skinks are found in dry sandy soils, often below stones or dead trees. They usually give birth to 2-4 babies (up to 80 mm TL) in late summer. **Habitat:** Coastal and fynbos vegetation, and richer soils associated with dry river courses and inland escarpment. **Range:** W. and E. Cape. with isolated populations extending inland along Karoo escarpment. **Subspecies:** Two races recognized: In *A.m. meleagris*, the tail is not tapered, and the back is plain or has a series of dark spots that may form ragged stripes; it occurs in W. Cape, through Cape fold mountains and escarpment mountains of Karoo, to Cradock and Tsitsikamma. *A.m. orientalis* has a slightly tapered tail, is thinner, and the back has six distinct black stripes; it is found in E. Cape.

### Giant Legless Skink
*Acontias plumbeus* (Pl. 44)
*(Endemic) SVL 250-350 mm; max. SVL 490 mm.*
The world's largest legless skink, with a stout body, elongate snout and broad head, and a cylindrical tail. The lower eyelids are opaque. There are two, sometimes 3, suboculars. The body is blue-black to black, often with a steel-grey snout. The belly is paler. **Biology and breeding:** This skink prefers accumulated leaf litter and humic soils in damp situations. It has been observed to flatten the neck when disturbed. It usually eats large invertebrates (worms, centipedes and larvae), but will also take frogs and other small vertebrates. The female gives birth to 2-14 babies (106-127 mm TL) in March-April. They grow slowly, and settle well in captivity, eating minced meat and pet food. **Habitat:** Forested areas. **Range:** From N. Province, through Mpumalanga and Swaziland to coastal N. KwaZulu-Natal and S. Mozambique. Isolated relict populations occur on eastern escarpment of Zimbabwe and around East London.

### Variable Legless Skink
*Acontias poecilus*
*(Endemic) SVL 200-300 mm; max. SVL 382 mm.*
The second largest legless skink, with a stout body, elongate snout and broad head, and a cylindrical tail. The groove between the nostril and the rostral may be absent or vague. The lower eyelids are opaque, there are two or three suboculars, and 5-7 scales bordering the mental. Body colour is variable (hence the common and scientific name). In juveniles the body scales are grey-brown with pale grey edges, giving the effect of broad stripes along the body. These fade in adults, which become mottled or plain dark brown. The belly is mottled grey-brown in juveniles to yellow-ish brown in adults. **Biology and breeding:** They have been found in accumulated leaf litter and humic soils in damp situations. They come to the surface occasionally as one was found in the stomach of a large sand snake. **Habitat:** Coastal Forest. **Range:** S. KwaZulu-Natal and E. Cape.

### Percival's Legless Skink
*Acontias percivali* (Pl. 44)
*SVL 180-220 mm; max. SVL 239 mm male, 257 mm female.*
A medium-sized legless skink with a slender head and body and a rounded snout. The lower eyelids are opaque. There are three suboculars. The second upper labial is well separated from the eye. There are 14-16 scale rows at midbody. The tail is cylindrical and moderately tapered. Coloration is varied (see Subspecies). **Biology and breeding:** This skink prefers to burrow in loose leaf litter and soil around the base of trees. It is often found under dead logs, where it hunts for grubs and earthworms.

A.p. occidentalis

A.p. tasmani

134

A single brood of 1-3 babies is born in summer. **Habitat:** Mesic coastal thicket and savannah. **Range:** Three widely separated populations occur (see Subspecies). **Subspecies:** Three races are recognized, two of which occur in the region. In *A.p. tasmani*, the interparietal is an equilateral triangle, and the body is diffuse red-brown above and yellowish below; it is found in E. Cape. *A.p. occidentalis* has a long, narrow, triangular interparietal, and the body is diffuse olive to grey-brown (and occasionally all-black); it occurs in N. Province and Zimbabwe, west to Namibia and into S. Angola. The typical race, *A.p. percivali*, is uniform blackish-brown, it is restricted to Voi in SE Kenya.

# Woodbush Legless Skink   *Acontophiops*

This is an unusual legless burrowing skink that seems to be an inter-mediate stage between the greater legless skinks (page 132), and the blind legless skinks (page 135). The only species in the genus is endemic to eastern N. Province.

**Woodbush Legless Skink**   *Acontophiops lineatus* **(Pl. 46)**
*(Endemic) SVL 140-170 mm; max. SVL 185 mm.*
A small, stout-bodied skink with immovable lower eyelids that each have an oval, semi-transparent window. Two supraciliaries are present. The external ear openings are hidden. There is a single enlarged anal plate. The tail is short and blunt. The body is yellow-white to creamy white, with thin, dark brown to black stripes on the back and belly. The head and tail are usually darker than the body. **Biology and breeding:** Usually found singly under stones on rocky hillsides. May eat termites. Much of their habitat has been destroyed by pine plantations at Wood-bush, but there are healthy populations on the Wolkberg (SA RDB, Restricted). Two young born in December-January. **Habitat:** Montane grassland. **Range:** Found in N. Province, from Woodbush to Wolkberg.

# Blind Legless Skinks   *Typhlosaurus*

These small legless skinks show many adaptations to life underground. Their eyes are almost lost and remain only as dark spots under the head shields. The rostral is very large and oval-shaped and is pierced at the front by the nostril, from which a long groove extends to the back of the rostral. The nostril can be sealed by a plug that protrudes from its rear wall. The external ear openings are hidden. The body is thin and covered with large, smooth close-fitting scales. There is a single enlarged preanal plate. Like the greater legless skinks, *Acontias* (page 132), they have varied colour patterns, both within and between species. They show an interest-ing evolutionary progression, the more specialized species that live in the western deserts having developed thinner bodies and fewer head shields. All are burrowing, most living in sandy regions. They are usually found under stones or among dead bark and fallen branches beneath trees. Others may be forced to the surface when pans flood or during ploughing and road construction. They feed mainly on beetle larvae and termites. Their reproduction is poorly known; 1-2 large babies have been reported for a few species. Their major predators include burrowing snakes (burrowing asps, quill-snouted snakes and garter snakes).

This genus contains nine species; eight are endemic (a single species reaches Zambia). Most species are found along the deserts and coastal sands of the west coast.

■ *T.a. aurantiacus*

□ *T.a. parietalis* (p)

□ *T.a. bazarutoensis* (b)

□ *T.a. carolinensis* (c)

## Golden Blind Legless Skink

*Typhlosaurus aurantiacus* (Pls. 46 and 100)
*(Endemic) SVL 150-200 mm; max. SVL 213 mm.*

A robust skink with a rounded (southern populations) to slightly flattened (northern populations) snout. The head shields are reduced in number; there are only two unpaired head shields behind the rostral. The frontal is pentagonal in shape; the prefrontal is separated from the loreals by the frontonasals. There are 12 scale rows at midbody. The tail is of medium length (26-36 subcaudals). Typically, the body is uniform pale orange or yellow, and paler below, sometimes with scattered spots below the tail. Some populations develop dorsal stripes on the back (see Subspecies), and all-black specimens also occur. **Biology:** Has been found under logs and in the roots of a Cassava plant. **Habitat:** Coastal sands and sandveld. **Range:** Eastern coastal plain of Mozambique and N. Zululand, extreme SE Zimbabwe and NE Mpumalanga. **Subspecies:** Five races: all occur on the subcontinent. *T.a. aurantiacus* is usually plain golden-pink in colour and has two temporals; it occurs on coastal plain of Maputaland and S. Mozambique, extending into extreme SE Zimbabwe. FitzSimons' blind legless skink, *T.a. fitzsimonsi*, is usually striped, has a single temporal, and the first supraciliary is fused with the prefrontal; restricted to NE Kruger NP and adjacent NE Mpumalanga. Three recently described races are endemic to Mozambique offshore islands. *T.a. parietalis* is distinguished by the fusion of the posterior supraocular and the parietal. It is golden-pink except for traces of black stripes on the tail of adults; restricted to Inhaca Island, Mozambique. *T.a. bazarutoensis* has low ventral counts (141-154) and a similar coloration to previous race; restricted to Bazaruto and Benguerua islands, Mozambique. *T.a. carolinensis* has low ventral counts (142-155) and fusion of head shields like *T.a. fitzsimonsi*. It is pale orange with two lines of spots along the backbone and 4-6 rows on tail; restricted to Santa Carolina Island, Mozambique.

## Brain's Blind Legless Skink

*Typhlosaurus braini* (Pl. 43)
*(Endemic) SVL 150-200 mm; max. SVL 200 mm.*

The thinnest of all the blind legless skinks. All the head shields between the rostral and parietals have fused into a single large shield. The first 8-10 scales behind the head are wider than the other body scales. There are 12-14 scale rows at midbody and more than 250 ventrals. The tail is relatively long (51-57 subcaudals). The whole body is light pink, with only a few faint brown marks on the forehead. **Biology:** This skink is active in the early evening during winter, but forages later in the evening during summer. Its tracks are very conspicuous, but it quickly disappears deep into the sand when disturbed. It feeds on termites and insect larvae. The Namib golden mole is a major predator. **Habitat:** Semi-stable sand dunes. **Range:** Central Namib Desert from Kuiseb River to Koichab River.

## Cuvier's Blind Legless Skink

*Typhlosaurus caecus* (Pl. 44)
*(Endemic) SVL 150-200 mm; max. SVL 213 mm.*

A small blind legless skink with a slightly flattened but rounded snout. There are few head shields, with only two undivided shields behind the large rostral, which is more than twice as long as the other head shields together. The frontal is reduced to a transverse band and is smaller than the prefrontal. The loreal is in contact with the prefrontal and there is a small preocular. The mental is heart-shaped with a posterior groove. There are 12-14 scale rows at midbody, and 207-230 ventrals. The body is light yellow-orange with a light pink band behind the head. The belly is orange-pink. **Habitat:** Sparsely vegetated coastal dunes. **Range:** N. and W. Cape coastal areas, from Alexander Bay to near Cape Town.

### Cregoi's Blind Legless Skink     *Typhlosaurus cregoi* (Pl. 46)
*(Endemic) SVL 150-200 mm; max. SVL 207 mm.*
This primitive blind legless skink has a rounded snout, and numerous head shields that include three unpaired head shields behind the rostral, and separate frontonasals and loreals. There are 16-20 scale rows at mid-body, and 170-192 ventrals. The tail is relatively long (31-43 subcaudals). The body is golden, with 6-10 thin black stripes extending to the tail tip. The belly is usually plain or faintly spotted in northern populations, but striped in those from N. Province (where all-black specimens are also common). **Biology:** These skinks are found under rocks in montane grassland, and occasionally in evergreen forest. **Habitat:** Montane rocky hillsides. **Range:** Two isolated populations, one in N. Province and the other in Zimbabwe highlands. **Subspecies:** Two races are recognized. *T.c. cregoi* usually has two supraoculars, the frontal as wide as the prefrontal, and 35-43 subcaudals; it is found on Soutpansberg and in the northwest corner of Kruger National Park. *T.c. bicolor* has three supra-oculars, the frontal wider than the prefrontal, and 31-37 subcaudals; it is restricted to the eastern highlands of Zimbabwe.

### Gariep Blind Legless Skink     *Typhlosaurus gariepensis* (Pl. 100)
*(Endemic) SVL 100-120 mm; max. SVL 123 mm.*
A small blind legless skink that resembles the striped blind legless skink, *T. lineatus* (below). It has two unpaired head shields behind the rostral. The frontal is pentagonal in shape, and is much larger than the prefrontal. The rostral is bordered by five shields, while the prefrontal touches the loreals. There are three upper labials, a single supraciliary, and no sub-ocular. There are 12 scale rows at midbody. The back is yellow, with four rows of dark streaks that form stripes on the tail. The belly is plain light yellow. **Biology and breeding:** These skinks live mainly among the roots of bunch grass, feeding almost exclusively on termites. Their tracks (thin, wavy, humped lines) can often be seen early in the morning on the dune surface. Mating probably occurs in August-September. In late summer, after a five-month gestation period, the female gives birth to a single baby (58-60 mm TL). The young grow rapidly during their first year and may reach sexual maturity in less than two years. **Habitat:** Vegetated sand ridges in Kalahari sand. **Range:** Kalahari Gemsbok National Park and adjacent Namibia, Botswana and N. Cape.

### Striped Blind Legless Skink     *Typhlosaurus lineatus* (Pl. 46)
*SVL 100-150 mm; max. SVL 180 mm.*
A small lizard that is very similar to the Gariep blind legless skink, *T. gariepensis* (above), but differs in having four upper labials, a subocular, and usually two supraciliaries. There are 14 scale rows at midbody. Coloration is varied (see Subspecies), and all-black specimens occur frequently. **Biology and breeding:** These skinks are common in heaps of wind-blown sand at the base of grass tufts and bushes, and desert dune streets and sand ridges. The diet consists mainly of termites. One or two large babies (56-74 mm TL) are born in mid-January through early March, after a five-month gestation period. The young grow rapidly during the

T.c. cregoi

T.c. bicolor

T.l. richardi

T.l. subtaeniatus

T.l. lineatus

first year, and reach sexual maturity in 2-3 years (exceptionally in less than two years). **Habitat:** Kalahari sands. **Range:** Kalahari region, extending from N. Cape through most of Botswana and adjacent Namibia, with isolated races in W. Zambia and N. Province. **Subspecies:** Four races are recognized, three of which occur on the subcontinent. *T.l. lineatus* has a yellow-golden back with 4-8 thin dark stripes, and a pure white belly; this race is found throughout the Kalahari region, reaching Kimberley in the south. *T.l. subtaeniatus* is striped above and below; this race is restricted to the Great Saltpan in Waterpoort in N. Province. *T.l. richardi* has a white belly, a single supraciliary, and few (160-168) ventrals; this race is restricted to sandveld in eastern N. Province. *T.l. jappi* has only two broad dorsal stripes and a plain belly; this race is restricted to the western border of Zambia.

### Lomi's Blind Legless Skink     *Typhlosaurus lomii* (Pl. 43)

*(Endemic) SVL 100-110 mm; max. SVL 114 mm.*
A small, slender blind legless skink with an elongate and flattened snout. The head shields are reduced in number, with only two unpaired shields behind the large rostral, and three upper labials and two lower labials. There are 12 scale rows at midbody, and 160-167 ventrals. The body is bright pink above, with a golden infusion on the front quarter that on the rear of the body is confined to a vertebral line. The belly is unpigmented and almost translucent. **Habitat:** Sandy soils in succulent veld. **Range:** Poorly-known from a small area in Little Namaqualand.

### Meyer's Blind Legless Skink     *Typhlosaurus meyeri* (Pl. 43)

*(Endemic) SVL 120-160 mm; max. SVL 188 mm.*
A small blind legless skink with a snout that has a sharp, horizontal edge and a rostral that is flattened below. The head shields are reduced in number with only two undivided shields behind the large rostral, which is longer than the other head shields together. The posterior supraciliary is fused with the postocular, and five chin shields border the mental. There are 12-14 scale rows at midbody, and 207-225 ventrals. The body has a broad yellow vertebral band, and a dark stripe on each flank. There is a dark band from the eye to the nostril, the tail has a black tip, and the lateral stripes often fuse. In some specimens the lateral stripes break into spots, while others lack all coloration except the dark streak on the head. **Habitat:** Sparsely vegetated coastal dunes. **Range:** Spencer Bay in Namibia, south to Orange River and into W. Richtersveld.

### Boulenger's Blind Legless Skink     *Typhlosaurus vermis* (Pl. 43)

*(Endemic) SVL 200-250 mm; max. SVL 278 mm.*
A long, thin blind legless skink with a slightly flattened, but rounded snout. There are few head shields, with only two undivided shields behind the large rostral, which is more than twice as long as the other head shields together. The frontal is reduced to a transverse band and is smaller than the prefrontal. The loreal is separated from the prefrontal and there is no preocular. There are 12-14 scale rows at midbody, and 215-244 ventrals. The body is unpigmented, flesh-pink in colour. **Breeding:** Three elongate eggs (17 x 5 mm) were present in a female from Port Nolloth. It is likely that the species is viviparous. **Habitat:** Sparsely vegetated coastal dunes. **Range:** Orange River to Spoeg River in Little Namaqualand. An unconfirmed report exists from near Prieska in N. Cape.

## Old World Skinks
### SUBFAMILY SCINCINAE

These are primitive skinks that usually have a smooth, cylindrical body and small, often vestigial legs. The frontal bones and nasal bones are separate. The body scales are generally smooth and overlapping, and there are two or more preanal scales. The tail is often long (always more than 30% of the total length), and in the species with reduced legs is sometimes used for food storage. It is readily shed and quickly regenerated. Coloration is usually drab, although a few species develop bright blue tails.

Many are either burrowing or secretive species, hunting among loose leaves and dead branches. Limb reduction is common in the subfamily, although only about 28 species totally lack external limbs. Reproduction is varied, with approximately half of the species being viviparous. A number of American species brood their eggs, protecting them from predators.

This subfamily is restricted to the Old World, except for a few species which enter North America, and with a relict distribution in south-central and E. Asia. They form an important part of the skink fauna in sub-Saharan Africa and on the islands of the Indian Ocean. There are approximately 180 species in 25 genera, with only four genera and 26 species occurring in southern Africa, of which 22 species are endemic.

## Slender Skinks  *Proscelotes*

This is a group of small skinks with reduced limbs that each bear five toes. External ear openings are present. The interparietal is usually small and does not touch the supraoculars. The supranasals touch behind the rostral.

There are four species in the genus, distributed in isolated populations in E. and SE Africa, with only one reaching the subcontinent.

### Arnold's Skink                           *Proscelotes arnoldi* (Pl. 51)
*(Endemic) SVL 60-80 mm; max. SVL 95 mm.*

A small skink with small, five-toed feet and a tail that is much longer than the body. Each nostril is bordered by the rostral and a small, ring-like nasal. There are only 6-8 lamellae under the fourth toe. The body scales are smooth and in 22-24 rows at midbody. The body is brown, often with a dark spot on each scale, forming long lines. There is a distinct, grey dorsolateral stripe, and the belly is salmon-pink. Juveniles have a bright blue tail. **Biology and breeding:** This skink lives under stones and logs, foraging during the day among vegetation and feeding on small insects. Both eggs (4-5) and embryos (5-6) have been found in different females. Four eggs (8,7 x 6,5 mm) found under a stone hatched in mid-December, the hatchlings measuring 34 mm TL. Predators include wolf snakes and the slender mongoose. **Habitat:** Montane grassland and evergreen forest. **Range:** Restricted to the eastern escarpment of Zimbabwe. **Subspecies:** No races are now recognized; *P. mlanjensis*, now treated as a full species, has smaller limbs, with 11-12 lamellae under the fourth toe, and is found on Mulanje Plateau in Malawi.

## Dwarf Burrowing Skinks   *Scelotes*

This is a diverse genus of small burrowing skinks that show a clear evolutionary progression towards limb loss. It includes species with front and hind limbs, each with five toes, as well as those without any vestiges of external limbs. The body is covered with small, smooth scales. The tail is longer than the body in those species with fully developed feet, and often slightly shorter in the legless species. The interparietal is large and touches the supraoculars, and the paired supranasals are in contact behind the rostral. External ear openings may be present or absent.

All dwarf burrowing skinks either burrow in sandy soil or forage in loose leaf litter or grassland. The mode of reproduction is known for a number of species; these are viviparous and give birth to only 1-4 babies.

There are 20 species in the genus, and all but one are endemic to southern Africa. *S. uluguruensis* is restricted to the Uluguru Mountains in Tanzania.

### Algoa Dwarf Burrowing Skink    *Scelotes anguineus* (Pl. 47)
*(Endemic) SVL 50-70 mm; max. SVL female 83 mm.*

A small burrowing skink that lacks all traces of external limbs and has a tail that is slightly shorter than the body. The lower eyelids are scaly and the ear openings are hidden. The frontal is short. Each nostril is pierced between the rostral and a small, ring-like nasal. There are four supraoculars. The back is silvery, sometimes with a bluish tinge, and with a dark band along the backbone. The flanks are dark brown. The belly is much paler and is often spotted. **Biology and breeding:** Common in the extensive vegetated sand dunes of Algoa Bay, this skink burrows in the upper layers of dry, sandy soil beneath the cover of stones or rotting spekboom bushes, etc. It feeds on small insect larvae and termites. Two to four babies are born in February-March. Predators include the harlequin snake and small carnivores. **Habitat:** Coastal dunes and thicket. **Range:** Restricted to vicinity of Algoa Basin in E. Cape.

### Zululand Dwarf Burrowing Skink    *Scelotes arenicolus* (Pl. 47)
*(Endemic) SVL 60-80 mm; max. SVL 88 mm.*

This small skink lacks all traces of external limbs and has a tail that is slightly shorter than the body. The lower eyelids are scaly, and the ear openings are absent. The frontal is short. Each nostril is pierced between the rostral and a small, elongate, oval nasal. There are three supraoculars, 95-117 ventrals, and 18 scale rows at midbody. The body is pale brown above, with a dark stripe along the backbone that becomes a double row of dark spots towards the rear. There are numerous similar stripes on the flanks. The belly is yellowish-white, with vague blotches. The tail is tinged with blue-violet. Juveniles are darker, and have a bluer tail. **Biology and breeding:** Lives in sandy soils in exposed and shaded grassland, and in humus and under logs in coastal dune forest. Two to four babies (43-52 mm TL) are born in February-March. **Habitat:** Vegetated coastal dunes. **Range:** Inhambane in S. Mozambique, to Lake Sibaya in KwaZulu-Natal.

### Lowveld Dwarf Burrowing Skink    *Scelotes bidigittatus* (Pl. 48)
*(Endemic) SVL 60-80 mm; max. SVL 83 mm.*

A small burrowing skink that lacks forelimbs. The small hind limbs each have two toes, with 2-3 lamellae beneath. The head is rounded, with scaly lower eyelids and minute ear openings. There are four supraoculars, all touching the frontal, no postnasal, and five supraciliaries. There are 20-22 scale rows at midbody. The tail is about the same length as the body. It is brown to greyish-brown on the back, each scale having a dark spot that together form almost continuous stripes. There is a well-defined, pale dorsolateral stripe that is straw-yellow on the head and body. The flanks are darker, and the belly is greyish. The tail is bluish, and sometimes bright metallic blue. **Biology and breeding:** Very common in suitable habitat, this skink is found among dead leaves and rotting logs. One or two young are born in December-January. **Habitat:** Lowveld bush. **Range:** Mpumalanga lowveld, south to Swaziland and N. KwaZulu-Natal, as far south as St Lucia Estuary.

### Silvery Dwarf Burrowing Skink      *Scelotes bipes* (Pl. 48)
*(Endemic) SVL 50-70 mm; max. SVL 79 mm.*

A small skink that lacks forelimbs. Each minute hind limb has two toes. The head is flattened with minute ear openings. The lower eyelid has a small transparent window. There are three supraoculars, two of which touch the frontal, and four supraciliaries. There are 18 scale rows at mid-body. The tail is shorter than the body, which is silvery-grey above, tinged with pale buff, the scales having dark centres that give a faint stippled or striped pattern. The belly is paler with faint spots. **Biology and breeding:** Found under stones or burrowing in sandy soils. Feeds on small invertebrates. Two young (60-65 mm TL) born in March. **Habitat:** Coastal strandveld. **Range:** SW Cape, from Mossel Bay to near Saldanha Bay.

### Striped Dwarf Burrowing Skink      *Scelotes sexlineatus* (Pl. 48)
*(Endemic) SVL 75-90 mm; max. SVL 98 mm.*

Very similar to the silvery dwarf burrowing skink, *S. bipes* (above), but grows larger, has slightly longer hind limbs and toes, a shorter frontal, the tail longer than the body, and a different colour pattern. The body is pale silvery-grey, often tinged with rich buff. All the scales are spotted with brown, giving a finely striped appearance; the dorsolateral stripes are particularly prominent. The tail is bright pinkish-blue, and the belly is greyish-white. **Biology and breeding:** Similar in habits and behaviour to the silvery dwarf burrowing skink. **Habitat:** Succulent veld. **Range:** Little Namaqualand, from Port Nolloth to Clanwilliam.

### Mozambique Dwarf Burrowing Skink
                         *Scelotes mossambicus* (Pls. 47 and 48)
*(Endemic) SVL 50-70 mm; max. SVL 75 mm.*

A small burrowing skink that lacks forelimbs. Each of the minute hind limbs has a single toe. The snout is rounded, the lower eyelids are scaly and the ear openings are minute. The postnasal is absent, and there are four supraoculars, three of which touch the frontal, and four supraciliaries. There are 18-20 scale rows at midbody, and 90-112 ventrals. The tail is as long as or slightly longer than the body. The body is pale bronze above, with each scale dark-centred, fading to slate-grey on the flanks and gun-metal-blue on the tail. The belly is grey-white. **Biology and breeding:** This skink is found under stones on mountain slopes, or logs on alluvial sand or loamy soils. Two or three young are born in late summer. **Habitat:** Prefers rocky grassland and alluvial sand. **Range:** Found from S. Mpumalanga and Swaziland, south through KwaZulu-Natal to Durban and north through S. Mozambique to Inhambane.

### Cape Dwarf Burrowing Skink      *Scelotes caffer* (Pl. 48)
*(Endemic) SVL 40-50 mm; max. SVL 55 mm.*
A small skink with well-developed forelimbs and hind limbs, each limb having three toes. There are 20 scale rows at midbody. The lower eyelid

has a transparent window and the ear openings are hidden. The tail is cylindrical and longer than the body. The back is drab silver with a tinge of olive, and each scale is dark-centred. The flanks are darker. A pale, buff-coloured lateral stripe may be present. The tail is bluish-grey at its base and blue at the tip. The belly is bluish-grey. **Biology and breeding:** In the east, this skink is usually found under stones and among dead plants, particularly the rotting, hollow stems of 'noors' (*Euphorbia* sp.). On the west coast it is found under litter on flat, sandy spots. When exposed, it wriggles rapidly into cover and is very difficult to catch. The tail is readily shed. Females give birth to 1-2 young in December-January. **Habitat:** Varied. Dry Fish River bush in E. Cape; karroid, stony veld in W. Cape; strandveld on W. Cape coast; restioid fynbos in Little Karro; succulent karroid veld in Namaqualand. **Range:** Scattered populations in E. Cape, Little Karoo, on the west coast (Elands Bay), Little Namaqualand (Garies) and the western Karoo (Calvinia).

### Western Dwarf Burrowing Skink      *Scelotes capensis* (Pl. 49)
*(Endemic) SVL 40-50 mm; max. SVL 57 mm.*

A small skink with small but well-developed front and hind limbs that each have five toes. The head is distinctly flattened and the lower eyelids each have a transparent disc. There is a small postnasal. The ear openings are round and minute. There are 22 scale rows at midbody. The tail is a little longer than the body. The body is light olive to olive-brown with a distinct coppery sheen, merging to dark brown to black on the tail. A pale olive-yellow to yellowish-brown dorsolateral stripe extends from the snout to the tail, where it is often blue to bluish-grey (white and more distinct in juveniles). The belly is greenish-yellow to pale yellowish-brown, with a paler chin and throat. The tail is bright blue in juveniles, often blue-grey in adults or when regenerated. **Biology:** Usually found under stones, on sandy soil or among rotting succulent aloes, etc. Wriggles rapidly into cover, the blue tail distracting attack away from the fragile head. **Habitat:** Rocky, succulent veld. **Range:** Little Namaqualand to central Namibia.

### Gronovi's Dwarf Burrowing Skink      *Scelotes gronovii* (Pl. 47)
*(Endemic) SVL 50-60 mm; max. SVL 70 mm.*

A small burrowing skink that lacks forelimbs, and has a single toe on each hind limb. The snout is flattened. The lower eyelid has a transparent window and the ear openings are minute. There are three supraoculars, two of which touch the frontal, and four supraciliaries. There are 18 scale rows at midbody. The tail is slightly shorter than the body, which is silvery-grey above, with the four middle scale rows spotted in brown and appearing as thin stripes. The flanks also appear faintly striped due to spots on the scales. The belly is yellowish-white to greyish-white, and is often heavily speckled. **Biology and breeding:** It is usually found under litter among sand dunes, often close to the high-water mark. (SA RDB, Restricted.) One or two young (45-50 mm TL) are born in March-April. **Habitat:** Sparsely vegetated coastal dunes. **Range:** W. Cape coast, from Doringbaai to Graafwater; also on Dassen and Robben islands.

### Günther's Dwarf Burrowing Skink      *Scelotes guentheri*
*(Endemic) SVL 100 mm.*

A medium-sized burrowing skink which lacks forelimbs and has very small, clawless hind limb buds. The head is rounded with scaly lower

eyelids. It has four supraoculars and a postnasal, but no ear openings. There are 20 scale rows at midbody and 119 ventrals. The back is pale brown with the centre of each scale darker, the dark spots becoming smaller on the flanks. Four central scale rows on the belly are uniform cream, but the lower surface of the tail is finely spotted. **Biology:** This very rare species (SA RDB, Rare) is most probably extinct. **Habitat:** Unknown. **Range:** The only known specimen was collected in Durban, KwaZulu-Natal, in 1886.

### Smith's Dwarf Burrowing Skink     *Scelotes inornatus* (Pl. 47)
*(Endemic) SVL 65-85 mm; max. SVL 90 mm.*
This small skink lacks all traces of external limbs. The tail is slightly shorter than the body. The lower eyelids are scaly, and there are no ear openings. There are four supraoculars. The anterior chin shields are in contact. There are 20-22 scale rows at midbody and 102-108 ventrals. The back has a pale buff stripe that is four scales wide, flanked by rows of dark purplish-brown spots. The belly is paler than the back and each scale has a small, dark spot, except on the chin and throat, which are plain. **Biology:** It is found in humus and sandy soils. **Habitat:** Prefers coastal thicket and grassland. **Range:** Restricted to a small area around Durban, from Umgeni Mouth to Amanzimtoti. **Subspecies:** None recognized. *S. mossambicus* is now treated as a full species (previously *S. brevipes*).

### Bazaruto Dwarf Burrowing Skink     *Scelotes insularis*
*(Endemic) SVL 40-60 mm; max. SVL 64 mm.*
This small skink is limbless, with a scaly lower eyelid, three supraoculars, and no ear opening. The first upper labial contacts the rostral behind the nasal, which may be absent. There are only 84-89 ventrals, and 18 midbody scale rows. The back bears a pale brown dorsal band, 5 scales wide, with a flecked dark stripe down the centre of each scale row. The head and sides of the body are dark brown. The belly and underside of the tail are lighter due to pale scale margins. **Biology:** Burrows in leaf litter at the base of dune thicket. Most specimens have regenerated tails. **Habitat:** Coastal thicket and dune forest. **Range:** Restricted to the islands of the Bazaruto Archipelago, Mozambique.

### Coastal Dwarf Burrowing Skink     *Scelotes vestigifer*
*(Endemic) SVL 50-70 mm; max. SVL 76 mm.*
This small skink is very similar to the Zululand dwarf burrowing skink, *S. arenicolus* (page 140), but has minute hind limb buds, a larger nasal shield, and only 95-99 ventrals. A broad, pale band which is 5 scales wide runs down the backbone, with a pair of fine lines or rows of dots on the central scales. It is bordered by 3-4 lateral scale rows with rows of confluent spots forming stripes. The belly is dusky pale brown. **Biology:** Burrows in sandy soils in dune forest. **Habitat:** Sandy coastal dunes. **Range:** Extreme S. Mozambique, along coast to St Lucia Estuary, KwaZulu-Natal.

### Bourquin's Dwarf Burrowing Skink     *Scelotes bourquini* (Pl. 101)
*(Endemic) SVL 75-90 mm; max. SVL 108 mm.*
This medium-sized skink is almost limbless, the clawless hindlimb buds being very small. There are 4 supraoculars, no postnasal, and 20 midbody scale rows. The lower eyelid is scaly and ear openings are absent. The back is brown above, paler on the sides, becoming uniform cream midbelly.

The top of the head is darker grey-brown. **Biology and breeding:** Lives beneath rocks and logs in damp soil near water. A female had five small, developing embryos in June. **Habitat:** Primary and secondary grasslands. **Range:** KwaZulu-Natal midlands between Howick and Nottingham Road.

### FitzSimons' Dwarf Burrowing Skink     *Scelotes fitzsimonsi*
*(Endemic) SVL 45-60 mm; max. SVL 65 mm.*
A small skink that lacks forelimbs and hind limbs. The snout is rounded, the lower eyelids are scaly and the ear openings are minute. The postnasal is absent, and there are four supraoculars, three of which touch the frontal, and four supraciliaries. There are 18-20 scale rows at midbody, and 89-97 ventrals. The tail is as long as or slightly longer than the body. The body is pale bronze above, with each scale dark-centred, fading to slate-grey on the flanks and gunmetal-blue on the tail. The belly is grey-white. **Biology:** Burrows in humus and sandy soils. **Habitat:** Coastal dune forest. **Range:** N. KwaZulu-Natal, in a narrow coastal strip from Kosi Bay to Mission Rocks. Isolated specimens from Durban and Vernon Crookes Nature Reserve may represent a new species.

### Dutton's Dwarf Burrowing Skink     *Scelotes duttoni*
*(Endemic) SVL 50-60 mm; max. SVL 64 mm.*
In this small skink the forelimbs are reduced to minute, clawless buds, and the hind limbs have only two toes, the inner much larger than the outer, and with 6-7 scales beneath. The snout is rounded, the lower eyelids are scaly and the ear openings are minute. The postnasal is absent, and there are four supraoculars and 5-6 supraciliaries. There are 18 scale rows at midbody, and 83-90 ventrals. The tail is as long as or slightly shorter than the body (short in juveniles). The body is dark brown above with a pair of thin golden lines running either side of the backbone. The chin and throat are white, rest of belly finely mottled in brown and white. The tail is blue-black, but bright blue at the tip in juveniles. **Biology and breeding:** Burrows in loose sand beneath leaf litter. Gives birth to 2-3 babies (45-50 mm TL) in December. **Habitat:** Coastal thicket. **Range:** Restricted to Benguerua Island in Bazaruto Archipelago, Mozambique.

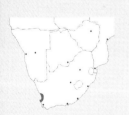

### Kasner's Dwarf Burrowing Skink     *Scelotes kasneri* **(Pl. 48)**
*(Endemic) SVL 80-105 mm; max. SVL 129 mm.*
This large skink lacks forelimbs. Its small hind limbs each have two clawed toes. The head is flattened, with well-developed eyes and opaque but not scaly lower eyelids. The ear openings are very small. There are three supraoculars, two of which touch the frontal, and four supraciliaries. There are 22 scale rows at midbody. The back has a pale buff to straw-coloured dorsal stripe, bordered by three rows of scales that bear dark purple-brown spots giving the impression of three thin, dark stripes. The belly is yellowish-white to greyish-white and dark-spotted beneath the tail. **Biology:** Common under stones and litter on coastal dunes (SA RDB, Restricted). **Habitat:** Sparsely vegetated coastal dunes. **Range:** W. Cape coast, from Lambert's Bay to Vredenburg.

### Limpopo Dwarf Burrowing Skink   *Scelotes limpopoensis* **(Pl. 47)**
*(Endemic) SVL 60-80 mm; max. SVL 85 mm.*
A small burrowing skink with a slightly flattened head. There are 2-3 toes on each forelimb (see Subspecies), and four toes on each hind limb.

The eyes are well developed, and there is a large, semi-transparent scale in each lower eyelid. The ear openings are small but distinct. There are 20-22 scale rows at midbody. The tail is as long as or slightly longer than the body. The back has a broad, dark brown stripe, bordered by a buff dorso-lateral streak, that in turn is flanked by a broad, dark brown stripe. The tail is tinged with blue, and the belly may be plain or spotted, particularly under the tail (see Subspecies). **Biology and breeding:** Forages among rocks and dead logs on sandy soil. Two young are born in November-December. **Habitat:** Alluvial sand with mesic savannah. **Range:** Limpopo River valley and adjacent regions. **Subspecies:** Two races; both occur on subcontinent. *S.l. limpopoensis* has spotted belly scales, five supraciliaries, and three toes on each forelimb; it is found in N. Province and adjacent Zimbabwe and Botswana. *S.l. albiventris* has an unspotted belly, six supra-ciliaries, and two toes on each forelimb; it is restricted to the vicinity of Langjan Nature Reserve in the Soutpansberg District of N. Province.

S.l. *albiventris*

S.l. *limpopoensis*

### Montane Dwarf Burrowing Skink        *Sceloites mirus* (Pl. 49)
*(Endemic) SVL 60-80 mm; max. SVL 85 mm.*
A small skink with well-developed but small fore- and hind limbs, each with five toes. The head is slightly flattened, with well-developed eyes that each have a scaly lower eyelid. The ear openings are small, vertical and oval. There is no postnasal, and the supranasal touches the first upper labial. There are 20-24 scale rows at midbody. The tail is longer than the body. The back varies from light brown to greyish-brown, and all the scales are dark-centred, particularly on the tail, which has a steel-blue tinge. The belly is dirty white to yellowish-brown, usually with feeble spotting. **Biology and breeding:** Lives in grass among rocks on upper mountain slopes and summits. Usually 2-4 young (50-60 mm TL) are born in late summer. **Habitat:** Rocky montane grassland. **Range:** Mpumalanga escarpment, with isolated populations on Wolkberg and Steenkampsberg, south to N. KwaZulu-Natal midlands.

## Savannah Burrowing Skinks   *Sepsina*
These small skinks have reduced limbs. The presence of 3-4 toes on each limb is the only external feature that distinguishes this genus from Arnold's Skink, *Proscelotes arnoldi* (page 139). The interparietal is small, and does not touch the supranasal scales, which are in contact behind the rostral. External ear openings are present. Nothing is known of the repro-duction habitat preferences or biology of these rare and secretive skinks. The genus contains four or five species which are distributed through central Africa to Tanzania and Namibia. Two species are found in the northern parts of southern Africa; one of these is endemic.

### Albert's Burrowing Skink        *Sepsina alberti* (Pl. 49)
*(Endemic) SVL 40-50 mm; max. SVL 55 mm.*
A beautiful, small skink with short legs, each with four small, clawed toes. The blunt head has largish eyes with scaly lower eyelids. The preocular is much smaller than the loreal. There are 22 scale rows at midbody. The back is pale greenish with a golden-yellow tinge, and each scale has a dark brown to black edge. The tail is bright blue at the tip, and the belly is grey-white. **Biology:** Forages among leaf litter around rock outcrops. The bright blue tail distracts attention from the vulnerable head and body. **Habitat:** Rocky, arid savannah. **Range:** Restricted to Kaokoveld, Namibia.

**Angola Burrowing Skink**     *Sepsina angolensis* **(Pl. 101)**
*SVL 70-80 mm; max. SVL 91 mm.*
A small, stout-bodied skink that has small limbs, each with three toes.
The head has a rounded snout, and small but distinct ear openings, and
the lower eyelids are transparent and divided into septae. There are 22-24
scale rows at midbody. The long fat tail has a rounded tip that mimics the
head. The back is yellow-brown, with dark-centred scales that give a
reticulated appearance. The belly is creamy to yellowish-white. **Biology:**
Wriggling among leaf litter, this small skink is difficult to catch. The fat
tail is easily shed. **Habitat:** Mesic savannah on sandy soils. **Range:** From
lower Congo, through Angola and W. Zambia to N. Namibia.

# Western Burrowing Skinks    *Typhlacontias*
This small genus of burrowing skinks lacks external limbs, except for
minute hind limbs in one species. The head has a flattened snout, and the
large rostral is pierced by the nostril, from which a long groove extends
backwards. There are three large, unpaired plates on top of the head,
between the rostral and interparietal. The eyes are small and lack eyelids,
and there are no external ear openings. The body scales are smooth and
overlapping. There are no femoral or preanal pores. They burrow in sandy
soils under leaf litter and rotting vegetable matter. Little is known of their
reproduction. A few, and perhaps all, species are viviparous. There are six
species, four of which occur in the southern African subregion, one of
which is endemic. *T. gracilis* occurs in Western Zambia, whilst the recently
described (1997) *T. rudebecki* is known from a single specimen from
Namibé district, Angola.

**Johnson's Burrowing Skink**    *Typhlacontias johnsonii* **(Pl. 101)**
*SVL 80-100 mm; max. SVL 117 mm.*
A small, slender skink that lacks external limbs or ear openings, and a
postnasal scale. The tail is short (about 25% of SVL). The eye is small,
lacks eyelids and, although it is partly overlain by the edges of the loreal
and supraocular, is not covered by head shields. The second upper labial is
about twice as long as it is tall and is in contact with the eye. There are 18
scale rows at midbody. Juveniles are pinkish pale yellow above, with small
dark spots on the head, a faint paired line along the backbone, and a pale
blue tail. With age black lines become more prominent and old individuals
may become very dark. **Biology and breeding:** Active during evenings
at the base of leeward slipfaces of windblown dunes, where debris accu-
mulates. They move just below the surface, leaving a regular undulating
track. If disturbed they dive deeper into the sand and become inaccessible.
Young (about 40 mm SVL) are born during late summer, i.e. February to
March. **Habitat:** Sparsely vegetated desert, avoiding coastal dunes.
**Range:** N. Namib Desert from Kunene sand-sea to SW Angola.

**Speckled Burrowing Skink** *Typhlacontias punctatissimus* **(Pl. 101)**
*SVL 60-80 mm; max. SVL 86 mm.*
The smallest and most slender of the burrowing skinks, with an enlarged
second lower labial and a prominent notch in the side of the rostral. The
large frontal is nearly semicircular with a straight posterior edge. Rudimentary hind limbs may occur. The eye lacks eyelids and is not covered
by the head shields. There are no external ear openings. There are 18 scale
rows at midbody. A black spot on some scale rows gives the body a striped

appearance. A broad, 4-scale dorsal band may be rich golden brown, or vary from straw yellow to pinkish grey with two vertebral lines of brownish specks. Two well-defined black lines start near the nostril, pass through the eye and extend along the flanks to the tail tip. Additional speckled scale rows may be present on the belly and the underside of the tail. The latter is silvery blue with two vertebral dark lines that are more prominent than on the body. The top and sides of the head may be marbled with brown or have a few dark spots or an arrow-head brown mark. **Biology and breeding:** This species is often found in small patches of sand on stony hillsides and may shelter under stones. Others have been found in sand at the base of trees and under stones and the leaves of *Welwitschia* plants. A female contained a few well-developed embryos. **Habitat:** Sparsely vegetated desert. **Range:** N. Namib Desert, from NW Kaokoveld to SW Angola. **Subspecies:** Three races are now recognized, two of which enter the region. In the typical race only the third upper labial enters the eye; it occurs along the inland edge of the Kunene Sand Sea into the Marienfluss Valley and as far south as the Munutum River. *T.p. brainei* has only five upper labials and the large second upper labial is in contact with the eye; it is found from the Sechomib to the Hoanib River valleys, just inland of the eastern border of the Skeleton Coast Park. *T.p. bogerti* has the second and third upper labial in contact with the eye; it is restricted to SW Angola.

### FitzSimons' Burrowing Skink — *Typhlacontias brevipes* (Pl. 45)
*(Endemic) SVL 80-100 mm; max. SVL 113 mm.*

A small, slender burrowing skink that has minute rudimentary hind limbs and a small postnasal scale. The eyes have no eyelids and are not covered by the head shields and there are no external ear openings. There are 18 scale rows at midbody. The tail is 32-44% of the total length. In colour, the body is various shades of light buff to sulphur-yellow. The scales along the back and upper flanks are often dark-centred, sometimes forming vague stripes. These stripes, when present, are usually restricted to the front of the body and particularly the tail, which is often blue-grey between the dark lines. **Biology and breeding:** These skinks forage at night and during the twilight hours when the sand is of a suitable temperature. They inhabit semi-stable sand, usually at the base of the leeward side of a dune, around the roots of grass tufts. They leave characteristic wavy tracks. They are easy to catch by watching for signs of activity, and then making a sudden grab in the sand. Very sensitive to movement, they disappear quickly into deep sand. They eat small insects, including termites, ants, beetles and ant-lions. Up to three babies (40 mm SVL) are born during late summer (February-March). **Habitat:** Sparsely vegetated desert. **Range:** Coastal Namib Desert, in two populations; in the south from near Lüderitz to the Omaruru River, then from the southern tip of the northern sand-sea to the mouth of the Kunene River.

### Kalahari Burrowing Skink — *Typhlacontias rohani* (Pl. 45)
*SVL 65-80 mm; max. SVL 90 mm.*

A slender burrowing skink that lacks external limbs. The eyes have no eyelids and are not covered by the head shields, and there are no external ear openings. There is no postnasal scale or enlarged lower labial scales. The second of the five upper labials enters the eye. The frontoparietal and prefrontal are in contact. There are 18 scale rows at midbody. The body is buff-coloured, with a vague, dark stripe along the backbone. A broad, grey-brown lateral stripe extends from the eye along the flanks to the tail. The belly is white at the edges and darker in the centre. In some areas (Kwando River, Caprivi Strip) the body sides are dark brown and the head, especially the snout, is also very dark. **Biology and breeding:** These skinks are common under logs and piles of vegetable debris. They are often drowned when flat pans flood after heavy rains. They are active sandswimmers, foraging just below the surface at night, leaving thin undulating tracks. Their diet comprises small insects, including beetle larvae and termites. They are viviparous and females contain three to four young. Few specimens are found with their original tail, indicating heavy predation. Enemies most probably include the burrowing purple gloss and quill-snout snakes. **Habitat:** Prefers Kalahari sand with an average rainfall above 400 mm p.a. **Range:** Found in the northern parts of the region, from NW Zimbabwe, through N. Botswana and Caprivi Strip to adjacent NE Namibia, and W. Zambia as far as the Zambezi Valley. **Subspecies:** No subspecies are recognized at present. *T. gracilis* is a separate Zambian species.

# Advanced Skinks
## SUBFAMILY LYGOSOMATIINAE

Members of this diverse group of skinks are all relatively similar in southern Africa but have undergone a tremendous radiation in Australia. There they have developed varied body shapes, with legless and obese species, that may have smooth or rough, almost spiny scales. The head is short, and rarely has a distinct neck. It is always covered with large, symmetrical shields which, in some species, may be fragmented or reduced due to fusion. The eyes are always well developed; some species have a transparent window in the lower eyelid, and in others the eyelid may be completely transparent and permanently shut, for example in some snake-eyed skinks, *Panaspis* (page 159). Ear openings may be absent, or protected by lobes, and each nostril pierces a single, discrete nasal scale. The limbs are almost always present (and are well developed in all southern African species), although limb reduction has evolved many times in the subfamily. The body scales are cycloid and overlapping, and either smooth or finely keeled (carinate). There is usually at least one pair of enlarged preanal scales (none in writhing skinks, *Lygosoma*). The tail is usually longer than the head-body length in local species.

Although a few species have reduced limbs, and scuttle around in leaf litter, most of our local species are active, diurnal lizards that live in trees, on rock outcrops and on the ground. The rock-living forms often occur in colonies, and consequently develop territorial behaviour and different colour patterns in the sexes. Most species, however, are drably-coloured in browns, greys and blacks. Viviparity has evolved on numerous occasions.

The subfamily is widespread but is particularly common in sub-Saharan Africa and the Australasian region. There is much controversy over the number of genera within the subfamily and numerous new species are still being discovered, particularly in Australia. It contains about 40-60 genera with over 600 species. Of this bewildering array, only four genera containing 25 species occur in southern Africa; only three species are endemic (this scarcity of endemics in the region indicates a relatively recent 'colonization' of the subcontinent by the subfamily).

# Coastal Skinks   *Cryptoblepharus*

These are small skinks with well-developed limbs, each with five toes, and immovable lower eyelids, each with a transparent window. They are mainly terrestrial, with some semi-arboreal species. They lay small clutches of 1-2 soft-shelled eggs.

The genus is found throughout much of the Indo-Pacific region. It was once considered to contain a single species, with numerous races, but 7-9 of the Australian races, and those from Society and Europa islands at least, are now thought to be full species. A single species reaches the subcontinent.

### Bouton's Skink   *Cryptoblepharus boutonii* (Pl. 51)

*SVL 30-40 mm; max. SVL 42 mm.*

A small, slender skink with well-developed limbs, each with five long, clawed toes. The distinct head has large eyes with immovable eyelids, each with a transparent spectacle. The body is covered with smooth, close-fitting scales, in 26-29 rows at midbody. The tail is cylindrical, tapers to a fine point and is longer than the body. The back has a black-ish-bronze hue, often with a bluish metallic sheen, with indistinct lateral bands and numerous pale spots on the flanks and legs. The tail bears large spots on the sides that give a finely banded appearance. **Biology and breeding:** This diurnal skink forages on intertidal rocks among the breaking waves. It feeds on insects, crustaceans and even small fish that it catches on the rocks and in tidal pools. It is often caught by breaking waves, but is an adept swimmer. It may dive into pools to escape predators, which include sea birds and crabs. Its ability to withstand salt water has allowed it to disperse throughout the Indo-Pacific by clinging to floating logs, etc., and drifting on the ocean currents. (SA RDB, Vulnerable.) One or two soft-shelled eggs are laid in rock cracks in moist sand above the high-tide mark. **Habitat:** Coastal rock outcrops. **Range:** Widely distrib-uted throughout Indian Ocean, Australia and through Pacific Ocean to Easter Island. On the African mainland it occurs in isolated populations along the east coast, reaching as far north as Mogadishu in Somalia. In southern Africa it is known from a single colony of only 200-300 lizards at Black Rock in Maputaland, and from three populations in the vicinity of Inhambane in Mozambique. **Subspecies:** More than 36 subspecies have been proposed for the many isolated populations on oceanic islands, some of which have recently been elevated to full species. The populations in southern Africa have been provisionally referred to *C.b. africanus*, which occurs along the east coast of Africa.

# Writhing Skinks   *Lygosoma*

These small to large skinks usually have well-developed, five-toed limbs, and scaly, movable lower eyelids (in most African species). There are no enlarged preanal scales.

They live in varied habitats, from arid savannah to tropical evergreen forest. They are cryptic inhabitants of leaf litter or burrowers in loose soil, and feed on small insects and their larvae. Many lay small clutches of soft-shelled eggs, but a number of specialized species, adapted to the arid regions of Somalia and N. Kenya, are viviparous.

The genus contains about 35 species, which are distributed through sub-Saharan Africa and the Indian subcontinent, with 18 African species. Three of these enter southern Africa; one is an island endemic.

## Mozambique Writhing Skink

*Lygosoma afrum* (Pl. 49)

*SVL 100-120 mm; max. SVL 140 mm.*

A medium-sized, stout, burrowing skink with small but well-developed, five-toed limbs, and a thick smooth tail that is rarely longer than the body. Each eye has a scaly, movable eyelid, and the ear openings are small and deeply sunk. The prefrontals are small and widely separated. Each nostril, which is pierced between 2-3 nasals, is well separated from the rostral. The body is covered with almost smooth scales, in 26-28 rows at midbody. It is pale to dark brown, heavily marked with irregular dark brown and white spots and streaks. Some specimens have uniform brown bodies, but usually have spotted tails. The belly is creamy white, sometimes with brown spotting. **Biology and breeding:** Common in sandy soil underneath logs and piles of vegetable debris. They eat small invertebrates, including ants, termites, beetles, cockroaches and millipedes. They lay 4-7 eggs (16-19 x 9-11 mm) in an underground cavity. **Habitat:** Eastern coastal plain. **Range:** E. Africa, from the Sudan south to Mozambique, reaching southern limit at Inhambane.

L.s. sundevalli

## Sundevall's Writhing Skink

*Lygosoma sundevallii* (Pl. 49)

*SVL 60-80 mm; max. SVL 88 mm.*

The body of this small burrowing skink is light brown to grey, usually with a dark spot at the base of each scale, that gives a finely speckled appearance. The belly is uniform creamy white, although it may be speckled beneath the tail. **Biology and breeding:** These skinks burrow in the surface layers of sandy soil, beneath stones and rotting logs, feeding on small invertebrates. In summer they lay 2-6 white, oval, soft-shelled eggs (18-19 x 9-11 mm) underground, particularly in old termitaria. The hatchlings measure 50-55 mm TL. Many are eaten by small carnivores (genets, Cape foxes and African wild cats) and snakes (Cape wolf snakes and black file snakes). The tail was once prized by Bushmen as a cure for snakebite. **Habitat:** Arid sandy areas and well-drained hillsides. **Range:** Northern part of the subcontinent, reaching southern limit in Kalahari Gemsbok National Park, north to S. Angola and Somalia. **Subspecies:** Two races; only the typical race is found in southern Africa. *L.s. somalica*, which is restricted to Somalia, is distinguished by its long fifth toe.

## Bazaruto Writhing Skink

*Lygosoma lanceolatum*

*(Endemic) SVL 50-80 mm; max. SVL 100 mm.*

This small burrowing skink is very similar to the Mozambique writhing skink, *L. afrum* (page 150), but is distinguishable from that species by both its smaller size and different coloration. The ear opening is partly covered by lance-like keeled scale. The body scales are smooth in adults, but each bears three fine keels in juveniles. The body is light grey-brown above, with the lateral scales slightly dark-tipped. The head is darker and the belly is white tinged with pale brown. **Biology:** They burrow in the surface layers of sandy soil, beneath leaf litter and fallen palm leaves. **Habitat:** Sandy soils in coastal thicket. **Range:** Restricted to the islands of the Bazaruto Archipelago, Mozambique.

# Typical Skinks *Mabuya*

This is a large genus of small to large skinks that have well-developed limbs, each with five toes, and long, tapering tails. The eyes are large, each with a movable eyelid that may have a transparent window. The ear openings are distinct, but are often deeply sunk. Each nostril pierces a single nasal. Supranasals and prefrontals are present. The body is covered with cycloid, overlapping scales that are usually keeled (they are smooth in only one species from southern Africa). Preanal and femoral pores are absent. The species all look very similar, although some are fatter, some have longer tails, etc. Their colour pattern and habitat are useful field guides; otherwise, details of scalation and foot structure distinguish them.

These active, diurnal skinks live in varied habitats and are common in all parts of the subcontinent, foraging on rocks, in trees and on the ground. They feed mainly on insects, which they actively search, moving through vegetation or under rock overhangs, etc. Prey is seized after a short dash. The primitive species lay eggs, but many species are viviparous, and some southern African species are reported to be either live-bearing or egg-laying within different parts of their range.

A cosmopolitan genus containing about 90 species, it is distributed throughout sub-Saharan Africa and the Indian Ocean (more than 65 species), the lowlands of South America and the Caribbean (about ten species) and SE Asia and the Pacific (about 15 species). Of the 19 species that occur in southern Africa, only two are endemic.

### Wedge-snouted Skink — *Mabuya acutilabris* (Pl. 53)

*SVL 40-55 mm; max. SVL 60 mm.*
A small skink with a flattened snout and a sharp edge to the upper lip. The ear openings are covered with long, sharp lobes. The subocular is narrowed below and does not reach the lip. The dorsal scales have three keels, and are in 28-32 rows at midbody. The scales on the soles are keeled, and those under the long toes have a single keel. The body is light brown above, with dark brown or black spots and white flecks that form short bands; there is usually a pale dorsal stripe and one (sometimes two) well-marked pale stripe on each side. The flanks may be barred in black. The belly is white. **Biology:** Terrestrial, catching beetles, ant-lions and wasps in sandy areas. Shelters in short burrows dug in accumulated sand at the base of grass tufts or small scrub. Juveniles often raise their tails, possibly as a signal to other lizards. **Habitat:** Desert and Karoo-Namib scrubland. **Range:** Little Namaqualand, through S. Namibia to S. Angola and the Democratic Republic of Congo. An old Little Namaqualand record needs confirmation.

### Ovambo Tree Skink — *Mabuya binotata* (Pl. 55)

*SVL 80-120 mm; max. SVL 127 mm.*
A large, stout skink with a transparent window in each lower eyelid. Each ear opening is partially covered with three lobes. The subocular is narrowed below and reaches the lip. The dorsal scales have three keels and are in 36-38 rows at midbody. The relatively long forelimbs and hind limbs overlap when pressed against the body. The scales on the soles are tubercular, and those under the long toes are smooth. The back is uniform olive-grey, tinged with buff, with a broad, black band on the side of the neck. The belly is grey-white, spotted with dull brown on the throat. Juveniles have scattered dark spots on the back that may form irregular bands. **Biology:** Usually found in hollow trunks of mopane trees, although it may enter rock cracks where available. Catches beetles and grasshoppers from surrounding area. Shy and difficult to approach. **Habitat:** Arid savannah. **Range:** Found in N. Namibia, from Etosha to S. Angola.

### Boulenger's Skink
*Mabuya boulengeri* (Pl. 53)

*SVL 60-80 mm; max. SVL 93 mm.*

A large, slender skink with a tail that is more than twice the body length. There are four supraciliaries. Adults usually have 7-9 keels on the dorsal scales, but this may range from three to 11, depending on the size of the skink. There are 28-32 scale rows at midbody. The back is grey-brown, sometimes with a few scattered black flecks. There is a black streak on the side of the head. The tail is flecked with dark brown and the belly is yellow. **Biology:** Although most are arboreal, southern populations rarely occur on vertical tree trunks preferring to forage on logs and in leaf litter; they also climb reeds alongside streams and long grass (where they may even sleep). The diet includes insects and spiders. **Habitat:** Coastal bush and dry woodland. **Range:** Save River in Mozambique, north to Tanzania and just entering E. Zimbabwe.

### Cape Skink
*Mabuya capensis* (Pl. 52)

*SVL 80-120 mm; max. SVL 135 mm.*

A large, fat (often obese) skink with a large window in each lower eyelid. The subocular reaches the upper lip. The ear openings are crescent-shaped and have small lobes. There are feeble spiny scales on the soles of the feet and a keel on the lamellae beneath the toes. The dorsal and lateral scales have three keels (these are strongest on the back), and there are 32-36 scale rows at midbody. There are 15-20 lamellae under the fourth toe. The body is light brown to olive greyish-brown, with three pale stripes. Between the stripes and extending onto the flanks are series of dark brown to black spots or short bars. The belly is uniform yellowish-white to grey. Occasional specimens are uniform grey-brown above, sometimes with vague stripes. **Biology and breeding:** This common, gentle skink lives on the ground hunting large insects in clearings and open sandy spots. It digs tunnels in loose sand at the base of bushes or boulders, and also favours dead trees and fallen aloe stems. Throughout most of its extensive range it gives birth to 5-18 babies (60-75 mm TL) in late summer. However, females from some regions (for example Pretoria and Port Elizabeth) have also laid clutches of eggs (see also the variable skink, *M. varia*, page 157). It tames easily, and would be much more common in gardens if it were not hunted by domestic cats. **Habitat:** Very varied; arid karroid veld, moist coastal bush, montane grassland, etc. **Range:** Throughout the subcontinent (except in Namib Desert, extreme northern regions and lowveld). North of Limpopo River, there are relict populations on Inyanga Mountains in Zimbabwe, and Liuwa Plain in Zambia.

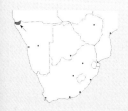

### Chimba Skink
*Mabuya chimbana* (Pl. 102)

*SVL 50-55 mm; max. SVL 60 mm.*

This small, slender skink is similar to the variegated skink, *M. variegata* (page 158). It has a window in each lower eyelid. The subocular reaches the upper lip. The ear openings are lobed. There are spiny scales on the soles of the feet and a keel on the lamellae beneath the toes. The dorsal scales have 5-7 weak keels and are in 34-40 rows at midbody. The body is olive-brown to bronze above, sometimes with black flecks on the scales and a ragged, pale dorsolateral stripe that is more distinct on the tail. The flanks are mottled in black and white and the belly is white. **Biology:** Rock-living; favours granite outcrops. It is poorly known. **Habitat:** Mixed mesic savannah. **Range:** SW Angola, extending into N. Namibia.

## Hoesch's Skink
*Mabuya hoeschi* (Pl. 52)

*SVL 50-80 mm; max. SVL 100 mm.*

A medium-sized, slender skink with a window in each lower eyelid and smooth scales on the soles of the feet. The subocular reaches the upper lip. The ear openings have distinct lobes. The dorsal scales have 2-3 weak keels and are in 32 rows at midbody. The tail is approximately twice as long as the body. In colour, it is brown-grey above with four rows of dark brown blotches that form transverse bands. There is a pale lateral stripe. The belly is white with a yellowish throat. **Biology:** It lives among rock outcrops and boulders, feeding on wasps, beetles and moths. **Habitat:** Arid savannah. **Range:** N. Namibia to S. Angola.

## Red-sided Skink
*Mabuya homalocephala* (Pl. 52)

*(Endemic) SVL 60-75 mm; max. SVL 79 mm.*

A medium-sized, elegant skink with a small, transparent window in each lower eyelid. Each ear opening is partially covered with 2-3 lobes. The subocular reaches the lip, but is not narrowed below. The dorsal scales have three strong keels and are in 28-30 rows at midbody. The relatively short forelimbs and hind limbs hardly overlap when pressed against the body. The scales on the soles are tubercular, and those under the long toes are smooth. Coloration varies sexually. The back is usually olive to olive-brown or pale brown, bordered by a pale dorsolateral stripe and then a dark brown to black lateral band, which itself is bordered by a conspicuous pale lateral stripe. In breeding males the latter becomes suffused with bright red. The belly is yellowish to blue-white, reddish in breeding males. **Biology and breeding:** Mainly terrestrial, foraging in leaf litter around the base of thicket. Inland they are fond of basking on rounded boulders in vegetation beside dry riverbeds. Difficult to approach and quickly dives into cover. Up to 10 eggs (8-9 x 13-15 mm) are laid in November-December in a small chamber dug in sandy soil under a boulder or dead log. Hatchlings (60-70 mm TL) emerge in February-March. **Habitat:** Varied; usually in moist situations. In the Cape, in coastal bushy fynbos, and riverine vegetation in montane grassland. **Range:** Throughout coastal regions of S. and E. Cape. Relict populations occur on the Cape and Mpumalanga escarpment mountains, reaching as far north as the Wolkberg, N. Province. There is an old, possibly mistaken, record from Little Namaqualand. **Subspecies:** No races are now recognized. Previous Cape races were poorly defined; *M. depressa* is treated as a separate species.

## Eastern Coastal Skink
*Mabuya depressa* (Pls. 52 and 102)

*(Endemic) SVL 60-75 mm; max. SVL 83 mm.*

A medium-sized, elegant skink with a flattened head and body. There is a small, transparent window in each lower eyelid, and the frontonasals are in contact. Each ear opening is partially covered with 2-3 lobes. The subocular reaches the lip, but is not narrowed below. The dorsal scales have 5-7 faint keels. The scales on the soles are tubercular, and those under the long toes are smooth. The back is either plain grey-brown to red-brown in colour, or has scattered black spots, or the tip of the scales are dark forming narrow stripes along the body. A dark lateral band, often broken by pale flecks, extends from the eye to the groin. It is bordered below by a yellow stripe which begins on the upper lip and is bordered below by another dark stripe. The belly is plain lemon-yellow. **Biology and breeding:** Mainly terrestrial, foraging on sandy soil around the base of thicket. Regularly climbs onto trunks and into foliage. At night, and if disturbed, hides by shuffling into loose sand. Up to seven eggs (18 x 9 mm) laid in early summer. **Habitat:** Coastal thicket on sandy soils. **Range:** Coastal regions of KwaZulu-Natal to Central Mozambique, inland along Limpopo Valley to NE Kruger National Park and SE Zimbabwe.

### Five-lined or Rainbow Skink   *Mabuya quinquetaeniata* (Pl. 55)
*SVL 85-110 mm; max. SVL 120 mm.*

*M.q. margaritifer*

A large, beautifully coloured skink with a small, transparent window in each lower eyelid. The ear openings are oval, and each is bordered by 2-5 lobes. The subocular reaches the lip but is not narrowed below. The dorsal scales have three strong keels, and are in 42-44 rows at midbody. The relatively long forelimbs and hind limbs overlap when pressed against the body. The scales on the soles are tubercular, and those under the long toes are smooth. Coloration is varied, depending on sex and age. Juveniles and subadult males are dark olive-brown to black above, with three distinct bluish-white stripes that are brilliant electric-blue on the tail. Adult females retain this coloration, although the stripe may become subdivided and faint. Adult males become buffy-olive to olive-brown above, each scale bearing a pearly white spot. The pale stripes become indistinct. The tail changes from yellowish to orange-brown, and the belly is creamy white. **Biology and breeding:** Active and rock-living, it runs around on exposed granite domes and other hard rock faces (paragneiss and some sandstones), feeding on insects. It is territorial; the status of the large breeding males, which become sexually mature in 15-18 months, is displayed by their different colours. They do not attack young males or females that retain the juvenile colour pattern. The female lays 6-10 eggs (10-15 x 17-21 mm) in summer. The young (73-80 mm TL) hatch after 61-62 days. It is possible that two clutches are laid per season, particularly in northern populations. **Habitat:** Mesic and arid savannah. **Range:** KwaZulu-Natal, through lowveld and Zimbabwe to Algeria and Senegal. **Subspecies:** Three races are recognized, with only *M.q. margaritifer* entering southern Africa. It is replaced by the typical race, *M.q. quinquetaeniata*, in N. and E. Africa, and by *M.q. scharica* in W. and central Africa.

### Bronze Rock Skink   *Mabuya lacertiformis*
*SVL 45-50 mm; max. SVL 54 mm.*

This small, slender skink is similar to the variegated skink, *M. variegata* (page 158). It has a window in each lower eyelid. The subocular reaches the upper lip. The ear openings are lobed. There are spiny scales on the soles of the feet and a keel on the lamellae beneath the toes. The dorsal scales have five strong keels, and are in 36-40 rows at midbody. The body is grey-brown to bronze above, with a few scattered, dark spots. The tail has a faint pale stripe above. The belly is white, with vague, dark marks on the chin and throat. **Biology and breeding:** These skinks are active in the early morning and evening. They are found mainly on hard rock outcrops (granite, paragneiss and some sandstones), living under exfoliating flakes, although they may also shelter in hollow trees. They hunt for insects among the accumulated leaves around rock bases, and prefer boulder-strewn slopes rather than open rock faces. They lay a small clutch of 3-4 eggs (8,5 x 6 mm). **Habitat:** Arid and mesic savannah. **Range:** Lower Zambezi River valley and adjacent regions, extending along eastern escarpment of Zimbabwe, and with an isolated population in SW Angola.

## Angolan Blue-tailed Skink
*Mabuya laevis* (Pl. 55)

*SVL 45-60 mm; max. SVL 63 mm.*

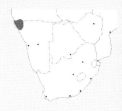

A small, slender, flattened skink with a conspicuous colour pattern and smooth body scales. There is a window in each lower eyelid. The subocular reaches the upper lip. The ear openings are lobed. The scales on the soles of the feet and on the lamellae beneath the toes are smooth. There are 29-33 scale rows at midbody. The body is brilliantly coloured in both sexes, in adults and juveniles. The back is shiny black, with a sky-blue stripe on each side. Scattered sky-blue spots occur on the back between the stripes, and on the flanks. The head is golden carrot-orange, with each head shield black-edged. The tail is sky-blue, and the chest and belly are blue-grey. **Biology:** These shy skinks forage in the early morning in large rock cracks of granite outcrops, feeding on small beetles. **Habitat:** Arid rocky savannah. **Range:** Kaokoveld of N. Namibia and S. Angola.

## Speckled-lipped Skink
*Mabuya maculilabris* (Pl. 102)

*SVL 65-75 mm; max. SVL 82 mm.*

This large skink is very similar to Boulenger's skink, *M. boulengeri* (page 152) but is stouter, and has five supraciliaries and 30-38 scale rows at midbody. It has different coloration, although this may be variable. Usually the back is pale brown, with distinctly darker flanks that are speckled with dark brown and white. The belly is yellow, and sometimes has brown speckles. Males are often more heavily spotted than females. Some specimens are uniform brown above. **Biology and breeding:** These skinks are found on tree trunks and in hollow logs. They climb on to thatched huts and are common in forest clearings. The diet consists of insects and other invertebrates. Over much of its range, the species does not have a definite breeding season, and may lay 5-6 clutches, each of 6-8 eggs (8 x 14 mm), a year. They are laid in moist soil under logs. **Habitat:** Evergreen forest, dry deciduous woodland and coastal bush. **Range:** Liberia in W. Africa, to Angola and Mozambique, just crossing Zambezi River to Inhamitanga; also on a number of Indian Ocean islands. **Subspecies:** Five races are recognized, with only the typical race entering the subcontinent. The other four races are restricted to offshore islands: *M.m. infralineata* occurs on Europa Island; *M.m. albotaeniata* is found on Pemba Island; *M.m. comorensis* is restricted to the Comores Islands, and *M.m. casuarinae* occurs on Casuarina Island.

*M.m. maculilabris*

## Grass Skink
*Mabuya megalura* (Pl. 102)

*SVL 50-70 mm; max. SVL 73 mm.*

A large, sleek skink that resembles the Cape skink, *M. capensis* (page 152), but has an exceptionally long tail (well over twice the body length). The subocular reaches the upper lip. The ear openings lack lobes. The scales on the soles of the feet are smooth. The dorsal scales have three weak keels (but may be smooth in old females), and are in 24-26 rows at midbody. The body is light orange-brown to grey-brown, with a pale, dark-edged stripe along the backbone (which may be absent), and a white stripe on the flanks. The belly is white. **Biology and breeding:** This species' long tail enables it to move, snakelike through long grass. It forages beside clearings, dashing out to grab large grasshoppers, crickets, mantids, etc. It gives birth to 4-8 babies. **Habitat:** Savannah and montane grassland. **Range:** Ethiopia, through Uganda and Katanga, to Mozambique, just south of Zambezi River.

### Western Three-striped Skink
*Mabuya occidentalis* (Pl. 52)

*SVL 70-90 mm; max. SVL 95 mm.*

This large skink is similar in appearance to the Cape skink, *M. capensis* (page 152), but does not get as obese. It also has 30-32 scale rows at midbody, smooth scales on the flanks, 2-3 enlarged ear lobes, and 21-24 lamellae under the fourth toe. Its coloration is more distinct. The back is rich red-brown to olive-brown with three pale, dark-edged stripes. The flanks, which are darker, are broken by a white stripe that runs from the lips to the groin. The belly is uniform white. **Biology and breeding:** A terrestrial species, it runs in open, sandy veld, sheltering at night in a short burrow that it digs in loose soil at the base of scrub bush. It hibernates during winter. Its reproduction is poorly known; females collected from the Namib Desert (February) and Free State (November) each contained seven foetuses, while Kalahari females lay 5-7 eggs. **Habitat:** Arid savannah, karroid veld and desert. **Range:** Karroid areas of the Cape, including western Little Karoo valleys, through Namibia and SW Botswana, to S. Angola.

### Kalahari Tree Skink
*Mabuya spilogaster* (Pl. 54)

*SVL 60-80 mm; max. SVL 83 mm.*

This medium-sized skink has a window in each of the lower eyelids. The subocular is narrowed below and reaches the upper lip. The ear openings each have two short lobes. There are spiny scales on the soles of the feet and a keel on the lamellae beneath the toes. The dorsal scales have three keels, and are in 32-36 rows at midbody. The body is dark brown, with a pair of broad, pale dorsolateral stripes. There are numerous scattered, small, pale spots between the stripes and on the flanks. The white belly with its irregular dark speckles distinguishes this species from the sympatric striped skink, *M. striata* (below). **Biology and breeding:** An aboreal species, it is common on *Acacia* trees along dry river courses. It gives birth to 3-5 babies. **Habitat:** Found in arid savannah. **Range:** Kimberley and Lower Orange River in N. Cape Province, through Botswana and Namibia to S. Angola.

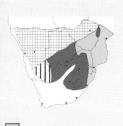

### Striped Skink
*Mabuya striata* (Pl. 54)

*SVL 60-90 mm; max. SVL 110 mm (to 113 mm in Dem. Rep. of Congo).*

This medium-sized skink has a window in each of the lower eyelids. The subocular is narrowed below and usually reaches the upper lip (see Subspecies). The ear openings are lobed. There are spiny scales on the soles of the feet and a keel on the lamellae beneath the toes. There are 32-43 scale rows at midbody. Coloration differs between the subspecies. In northern populations the head of breeding males is orange-brown, with a yellow-orange throat. **Biology and breeding:** Feeds on small insects (beetles, moths, etc.) and other small invertebrates. Common around towns and tames readily. An active climber, forages on rock outcrops and houses as well as trees. Southern populations give birth to a single litter of 3-9 babies (63-76 mm TL) in summer. Reproduction may occur throughout the year in northern populations. Growth is relatively fast, sexual maturity is reached in 15-18 months. **Habitat:** Varied; from mangrove swamp to arid savannah. **Range:** E. Africa, south to former Transkei and NE Cape extending along the Orange River to the Richtersveld, and west through Zambia to Angola and S. Namibia. **Subspecies:** All four occur on the subcontinent. *M.s. striata* adults are large (80-108 mm SVL) and the

☐ *M.s. striata*

■ *M.s. punctatissima*

▦ *M.s. wahlbergii*

▥ *M.s. sparsa*

156

subocular is separated from the lip; the back is red-brown, with distinct yellow dorsolateral stripes, and the belly is white although the chin and throat may be speckled with grey, black or orange. It occurs in KwaZulu-Natal, north through the lowveld and Limpopo Valley and SE Zimbabwe to Ethiopia. *M.s. sparsa* adults rarely exceed 80 mm SVL, the subocular does not reach the lip and the prefrontals are in contact; the back is dark brown to black, with numerous small, pale spots and the belly is white, sometimes with a black or orange throat. Found in S. Namibia and adjacent N. Cape and Botswana. *M.s. punctatissima* adults rarely exceed 80 mm SVL and the prefrontals are well separated; the back is dark brown to black, speckled with pale spots and with a pair of pale dorsolateral stripes, and the belly is yellow, usually with black spots and streaks on the chin and throat. It occurs in NE Cape, through former Transkei, W. KwaZulu-Natal, Free State, S. Botswana and N. provinces, with relict populations in eastern highlands of Zimbabwe and Malawi. *M.s. wahlbergii* adults are large (80-110 mm SVL) and the subocular usually reaches the lip. The back is pale grey, sometimes with faint dorsolateral stripes; a black band extends from the eye above the shoulder; the belly is white. Found in N. Namibia, Botswana, into Angola, NW Zimbabwe and W. Mozambique.

### Western Rock Skink

*Mabuya sulcata* (Pl. 54)

*SVL 60-75 mm; max. SVL 81 mm.*

A medium-sized slender, flattened skink with a window in each lower eyelid. The subocular does not reach the upper lip. Each ear opening has 3-4 small lobes. There are spiny scales on the soles of the feet, and three keels on the lamellae beneath the toes. The dorsal scales have 3-5 strong keels, and are in 34-40 rows at midbody. Coloration varies between the sexes. In juveniles and adult females the body is pale olive to olive-brown, with six dirty-gold stripes. The chin and throat region may be infused with yellow-orange. The belly is dirty white, and usually heavily spotted with black on the throat. Sexually mature males become suffused with black, and throughout the Karoo, Free State and around Lüderitz Bay males may become completely jet-black above and below. In Little Namaqualand and the rest of Namibia males are usually dirty bronze on the hind body and black elsewhere, and sometimes all-bronze. **Biology and breeding:** Very active, these rock-living skinks can be seen chasing over rock outcrops, feeding on beetles, grasshoppers and other invertebrates. They shelter at night in rock cracks, often in pairs. Three to five babies (58-65 mm TL) are born from November-March, and females may have two broods per season. There are informal reports that they may also occasionally lay eggs. Sexual maturity is reached around 63 mm SVL. **Habitat:** Karroid veld, desert and arid savannah. **Range:** Karroid areas of the Cape and adjacent Free State, through Namibia to S. Angola. **Subspecies:** In addition to the typical race, two poorly defined races are sometimes recognized. *M.s. nigra* is all-black, even in juveniles; it is restricted to the vicinity of Lüderitz Bay in Namibia. *M.s. ansorgii* grows larger (up to 100 mm SVL) and has a bigger head; it occurs in Kaokoveld of N. Namibia and S. Angola.

■ *M.s. sulcata*

□ *M.s. ansorgii*

◪ *M.s. nigra*

### Variable Skink

*Mabuya varia* (Pl. 53)

*SVL 50-60 mm; max. SVL 65 mm.*

A medium-sized skink with a rounded snout and a window in each lower eyelid. The subocular reaches the upper lip. The ear openings are oval and

have short lobes. There are spiny scales on the soles of the feet, and three keels on the lamellae beneath the toes. The dorsal scales have three strong keels, and are in 30-36 rows at midbody. Coloration is variable; the back may be blackish, olive, pale brown or red-brown, with or without black spots. There is always a distinct, white lateral stripe and sometimes other pale stripes down the backbone and on the upper flanks. The belly is bluish-white. **Biology and breeding:** Forages on broken ground, climbing on rocks and tree bases. The diet consists of insects (grasshoppers, caterpillars and termites), spiders and, in exceptional cases, of other lizards. Prey is grabbed after a short dash from cover. Over most of its range it is viviparous, and embryos have been recorded from the Free State and Tete in the lower Zambezi Valley (where small broods of 2-4 young are usual). A large female from the Suurberg in E. Cape gave birth to 10 small babies (60-76 mm TL) in mid-February. Mpumalanga and KwaZulu-Natal females also give birth to 4-9 babies. However, in N. Province a single clutch of 6-12 eggs is laid in November-December; they hatch after a two-month incubation period. Hatchlings measure 40-50 mm TL. Growth is rapid; both sexes reach maturity in only eight months. They may live for two years, but males usually die earlier (after 15-16 months) than females (16-17 months). **Habitat:** Varied: grassland to arid and mesic savannah. **Range:** SE Cape, through E. Africa to Sudan and Somalia, west to Namibia, Angola and Congo. **Subspecies:** A poorly-defined race, *M.v. nyikae*, is sometimes recognized from the Nyika Plateau in Malawi.

### Variegated Skink
*Mabuya variegata* **(Pl. 53)**
*SVL 35-50 mm; max. SVL 57 mm.*
A small, slender skink with a window in each lower eyelid. It grows larger in the western arid regions. The subocular reaches the upper lip. The ear openings are lobed. There are spiny scales on the soles of the feet, and a keel on the lamellae beneath the toes. The dorsal scales are in 30-36 rows at midbody. Coloration is very varied, particularly in the west. The body is light grey to dark brown above, usually with a pair of pale stripes on the sides. There is sometimes an extra pale stripe along the backbone, with or without a series of paired black spots (see Subspecies). In Namaqualand and S. Namibia the pale stripes may be obscured or absent, and the back heavily flecked with black. Plain pale grey-brown specimens also occur. The belly is plain white. Breeding males develop a reddish-brown blush below the hind legs and on the tail base. **Biology and breeding:** The two races differ considerably in ecology, and possibly represent cryptic species. The typical race is active on small rocky outcrops, sheltering in burrows under rocks and logs, and occasionally in soil-filled rock cracks. The diet includes spiders and beetles. It is viviparous, having small litters, each of 2-4 babies (48-57 mm TL), usually in January-March. Births have also occurred in August in the Namib Desert. The eastern race lives on sandy soils, sheltering in a hole at the base of bush clumps. **Habitat:** Extremely varied: desert, karroid veld, montane grassland, savannah, coastal bush, mesic thicket. **Range:** Through most of the subcontinent and extending into S. Angola. Absent from S. Cape, KwaZulu-Natal and Mpumalanga. **Subspecies:** There are two races, and both occur in the region. *M.v. variegata* grows larger (up to 53 mm SVL) and has three keels on the dorsal scales; it is found in E. Cape, through karroid areas to Great Namaqualand and Namib Desert. *M.v. punctulata* does not exceed 48 mm SVL and has 5-7 (but three in juveniles) keels on the dorsal scales, and a

■ *M.v. punctulata*
□ *M.v. variegata*

158

thin dorsal stripe bordered by a series of black spots or streaks that continue onto the tail; it occurs from central Mozambique, through the Limpopo Valley and adjacent regions, Botswana, N. Cape and E. Namibia, to S. Angola.

# Snake-eyed Skinks   *Panaspis*
These small to medium-sized skinks usually have small but well-developed, five-toed limbs. The lower eyelids may be movable or fixed and snake-like.

They are terrestrial or semi-burrowing, and occur in arid and mesic savannah. All lay small clutches of soft-shelled eggs.

Restricted to sub-Saharan Africa, the genus contains approximately 30 species, two of which reach southern Africa.

### Wahlberg's Snake-eyed Skink   *Panaspis wahlbergii* (Pl. 51)
*SVL 40-50 mm; max. SVL 64 mm.*

A small, burrowing skink with small but well-developed, five-toed limbs and an unblinking, snake-like eye. The nasals and prefrontals are well separated. The ear openings are visible. The body scales are smooth, in 22-28 rows at midbody, usually 24 in the south and 26 in the north. Scales on soles of feet are rounded. The tail is cylindrical and slightly longer than the body. Coloration is varied; the back may be light grey, brown or gold, and is sometimes plain but usually bears six dark lines. A pale dorsolateral stripe is usually present at least anteriorly, and a dark brown to blackish lateral band may be conspicuous or faint. The belly is white to greyish-blue, except in breeding males, which are pinkish-orange below. Males are more conspicuously striped. **Biology and breeding:** Diurnal, scuttles among grass roots and rotting logs, and around stones and old termitaria on broken ground. Eats termites and other small insects. Short-lived, males surviving 10-12 months and females a few months longer. Both reach sexual maturity in 8-9 months. Males grow larger than females. Mating takes places in August-October, and females lay 2-6 oval, white eggs (7-9 x 4-5 mm) in November-December, under stones or in logs. In good seasons they may produce another clutch in late summer. The eggs hatch in 40-50 days; hatchlings measure 30 mm TL. **Habitat:** Arid and mesic savannah. **Range:** Through KwaZulu-Natal, N. Free State, Gauteng, NW and N. provinces, and Mpumalanga, to central and E. Africa; just entering N. Botswana and Namibia.

### Spotted-neck Snake-eyed Skink   *Panaspis* sp. (Pl. 102)
*SVL 25-35 mm; max. SVL 43 mm.*

A small, slender burrowing skink with small but well-developed, five-toed limbs and an unblinking, snake-like eye. It is almost indistinguishable from Wahlberg's snake-eyed skink (above), but usually has a series of black and white spots along the side of the neck. It usually has 26 scale rows at midbody, and the scales on the soles of the feet are conical. In males a blackish patch extends from midneck to above the shoulder, and the pink breeding colour is restricted to the throat and neck. **Biology and breeding:** Found among vegetation, foraging actively for food among grass tussocks and leaf litter. Females usually lay up to 3 eggs (3-4 x 7-8 mm) in midsummer. Hatchlings appear in January and measure 39-42 mm TL. **Habitat:** Arid and mesic savannah. **Range:** N. Province and N. Mpumalanga, into Zimbabwe and adjacent regions.

# Old World Lizards or Lacertids
## FAMILY LACERTIDAE

These small to medium-sized lizards have a slender body, a long tail and well-developed legs. The dorsal scales are usually small, smooth and granular (although some genera have large, rough overlapping scales), but large and quadrangular on the belly. The head is covered with large, symmetrical scales that have osteoderms. Femoral pores are usually present. The tail has whorls of keeled scales, which may be spiny, and it can be shed and regenerated.

Active and diurnal, they live mainly on the ground, but some are rock-living or arboreal. There are no burrowing species, limb reduction is rare and is always associated with grass-living species. Many are brightly-coloured, particularly the breeding males. All except the European viviparous lizard (*Lacerta vivipara*) lay eggs, which is surprising as many live in temperate and montane environments where viviparity may be expected to evolve.

The family is restricted to the Old World, mainly Europe and Africa, but one genus (*Takydromus*) extends into the Far East. All look very similar. Although there are 24 genera and at least 160 species, no sub-families are recognized. There are eight genera in southern Africa, only two of which are endemic, although 26 of the 37 species are endemic.

### KEY TO THE SOUTHERN AFRICAN GENERA IN THE LACERTIDAE

1 - Tail flattened, with a lateral fringe of large, flat scales; arboreal:
*Holaspis* (Blue-tailed tree lizard, page 161)
- Tail cylindrical, without a lateral fringe; rock-living or terrestrial:
go to 2

2 - Toes without a serrated or fringed edge: go to 3
- Toes with a serrated or fringed edge; subocular not bordering lip:
*Meroles* (Desert lizards, page 164)

3 - Smooth or tubercular lamellae beneath toes; subocular bordering lip:
go to 4
- Keeled lamellae beneath the toes: go to 6

4 - A distinct collar present; dorsal scales small, granular or flattened and not overlapping: go to 5
- No distinct collar; dorsal scales large, strongly keeled and overlapping:
*Tropidosaura* (Mountain lizards, page 175)

5 - Nostril pierced between 2-3 nasals and well separated from first upper labial; temporal scale rounded; terrestrial:
*Nucras* (Sandveld lizards, page 167)
- Nostril pierced between 2-4 nasals and first upper labial; temporal scale elongate; rock-living:
*Australolacerta* (Southern rock lizards, page 163)

6 - A distinct collar present; dorsal scales small or granular; head shields smooth or slightly rough: go to 7
- No collar present; dorsal scales large, keeled and overlapping; head shields striated and keeled:
*Ichnotropis* (Rough-scaled lizards, page 162)

7 - Belly plates in 6 long rows; collar curved; an elongate temporal shield present: *Heliobolus* (Bushveld lizards, page 161)
- Belly plates in 10 or more rows; collar straight; no upper temporal shield present: *Pedioplanis* (Sand lizards, page 170)

# Bushveld Lizard   *Heliobolus*

This small genus of African lacertids is closely related to the sand lizards, *Pedioplanis* (page 170) and desert lizards, *Meroles* (page 164) but has only six longitudinal rows of large belly scales. All are terrestrial and oviparous. Five isolated species occur, widely distributed through Africa. *H. speckii* occurs in E. Africa, *H. quadrinasalis* in Chad, *H. nitida* in W. Africa and *H. neumanni* from Ethiopia to NE Tanzania. One species is found in southern Africa.

### Bushveld Lizard   *Heliobolus lugubris* (Pl. 57)

*SVL 50-60 mm; max SVL 65 mm.*

A medium-sized lacertid with a small, elongate temporal scale bordering each parietal, a crescent-shaped tympanic scale above each ear opening and a distinct collar. The subocular borders the lip. The lower eyelids are scaly. The dorsal scales are small and keeled. There are 12-18 femoral pores on each thigh. The toes are long and lack a fringe; there are 2-3 keels on the scales beneath the toes. Adults have a light grey-brown to red-brown back with vague, dark crossbars and three pale dorsal stripes, the middle one dividing on the neck and extending onto the tail. The legs have pale spots. The tail is usually pale brown. The belly is white. In contrast, hatchlings have a jet-black body, with broken, yellow-white lateral and dorsal stripes, and a sand-coloured tail. **Biology and breeding:** These diurnal, terrestrial lizards can be commonly seen on sparsely vegetated, compacted, sandy plains, darting from bush to bush. They eat small insects, particularly termites. The female lays 4-6 oval, soft-shelled eggs (6-7 x 11-12 mm) in a small chamber dug in loose sand. Eggs hatch from December to March and the hatchlings measure about 65 mm TL. They walk stiffly and jerkily and, with their very unusual colour pattern, resemble the distasteful oogpister ('eye squirter') beetle (*Anthia*) which can squirt an acidic, pungent fluid when threatened; it is probable that this mimicry protects the hatchlings from predators. They hibernate during winter. **Habitat:** Arid and mesic savannah. **Range:** Lowveld and SE Zimbabwe, through Botswana. N. Cape and E. and central Namibia to S. Angola.

## Tree Lizard   *Holaspis*

A unique and beautiful arboreal lizard. There is a single species in the genus and it just enters the subcontinent.

### Blue-tailed Tree Lizard   *Holaspis guentheri* (Pl. 61)

*SVL 45-48 mm; max. SVL 51 mm.*

*H.g. laevis*

A very small, beautifully coloured lacertid with a flattened body and tail that has an unusual fringe of flat scales. It has a well-developed collar. The lower eyelids are scaly and each has 3-5 enlarged, semi-transparent scales in the middle. The toes are long and have a fringe of flattened scales. A single large preanal plate is present. There are 17-25 femoral pores on each thigh. The back is black. There is a broad cream stripe on the top of the head. Two dorsolateral cream stripes arise on the head and extend over the back before merging on the tail base. Another cream stripe extends from the upper lip to the tail base. The tail is blue below and black above, with a middle row of bright blue spots and yellow lateral scales. The throat, limbs and anal region are cream, and the belly is orange. **Biology and breeding:** Hunts on vertical tree trunks feeding on spiders and ants. When threatened, it darts behind a trunk away from danger and climbs into the canopy, or shelters underneath dead bark; it is very difficult to catch. Jumps between trees and can glide quite long distances. Lays two relatively large eggs (5-6 x 9-11 mm) under loose bark or in leaf litter. **Habitat:** Lowland forest. **Range:** Through tropical and coastal forests of central, E. and W. Africa, just entering the subcontinent in central Mozambique (Amatongas and Dondo). **Subspecies:** Two races, with only *H.g. laevis* entering the subcontinent: restricted to E. Africa. Replaced in rest of Africa by typical race, which has six pale dorsal stripes.

## Rough-scaled Lizards  *Ichnotropis*

This small genus of lacertids lacks a collar, and has rough head shields and large spiny, overlapping scales on the back. The lower eyelids are scaly. The lamellae beneath the toes are strongly keeled. Femoral pores are present. The tail is long.

All are terrestrial and run around on sandy soil in savannah. They lay eggs and some species are 'annuals', maturing within 5-8 months of hatching, and dying soon after laying one (exceptionally two) clutch of eggs. When they occur together, the life cycles of the Cape and common rough-scaled lizards, *I. capensis* and *I. squamulosa* (below and page 163, respectively) are staggered, so that the juveniles and adults of both species are found at different times, and therefore do not compete for the same food resource.

The genus currently contains seven species which are distributed through the savannahs of S. and central Africa. Three species, one of which is endemic, occur on the subcontinent.

### Cape Rough-scaled Lizard  *Ichnotropis capensis* (Pl. 61)

*SVL 50-60 mm; max. SVL 62 mm.*

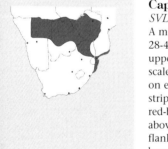

A medium-sized lizard with a narrow head. The large body scales are in 28-43 rows at midbody. The frontonasal is undivided. There are four upper labials in front of the subocular, which borders the lip. The dorsal scales are strongly keeled and overlapping. There are 9-14 femoral pores on each thigh. Juveniles have a pale grey-brown back, with a white lateral stripe. In adults, the back becomes uniform grey to yellowish-brown or red-brown with a narrow, white dorsolateral stripe that may be bordered above by a series of dark blotches. There is a broad, black stripe on the flank, bordered below by another white stripe. The belly is white. In breeding males, the white lateral stripe, chin and throat turn bright yellow, with an additional rust-red stripe on the anterior lower flank. **Biology and breeding:** These lizards are active hunters searching throughout the day for termites and other insects. Mating occurs in October-December and is followed almost immediately by egg-laying. The female digs an inclined burrow 100-200 mm long in soft soil, and lays 3-9 eggs (6,5 x 9,5 mm). Development is rapid, and they hatch in 56-77 days; the hatchlings (60-70 mm TL) emerging in January-March. Two clutches may be laid by a female before she dies. Growth is rapid, and sexual maturity is reached in 7-8 months (140-150 mm TL). By December adults begin to disappear, although some may be present until May; it is unusual for an individual to live for longer than 13-14 months. **Habitat:** Arid and mesic savannah. **Range:** Maputaland, Mpumalanga, N. Province and S. Mozambique, through Botswana, Zimbabwe and NE Namibia, to Angola and Zambia. **Subspecies:** A number of northern races have been described, but all are of doubtful validity.

**Caprivi Rough-scaled Lizard**     *Ichnotropis grandiceps*
*(Endemic) SVL 60-65 mm; max. SVL 70 mm.*

A medium-sized species, similar to the Cape rough-scaled lizard, *I. capensis* (above), but with a larger head, small body scales in 44-47 rows at mid-body, and without white borders to the dark dorsolateral stripe, which may also be absent or faint. The frontonasal is undivided. There are five upper labials in front of the subocular, which borders the lip. The dorsal scales are strongly keeled and overlapping. There are 13 femoral pores on each thigh. The back is pale grey-brown, with a few scattered, small, dark spots. A dark, broken dorsolateral band (which may be faint or absent) extends from the neck to the groin, where it breaks up into a line of lateral spots on the tail. The sides of the head and lower flanks are white, stippled with grey, and the belly is white. **Biology and breeding:** It is doubtful that this species is an 'annual' as adults and juveniles have been collected together. It lives together with both other species of rough-scaled lizards. It is rare and despite many searches has not been collected in recent years. It occurs in open woodland on hard limy soils or white sand. **Habitat:** Open mesic savannah. **Range:** Caprivi Strip and adjacent Botswana and NE Namibia.

**Common Rough-scaled Lizard**     *Ichnotropis squamulosa* **(Pl. 61)**
*SVL 60-70 mm; max. SVL 76 mm.*

A medium-sized lizard with a small head and small body scales in 42-58 rows at midbody. The frontonasal is divided. The subocular does not border the lip. The dorsal scales are strongly keeled and overlapping. There are 11-18 femoral pores on each thigh. The back is pale buff to dark grey-brown, usually with narrow, broken, dark crossbands or blotches, and six long rows of pale spots. The belly is white to grey. In adult males, the lower labials and chin shields are mottled with black. **Biology and breeding:** These lizards are active hunters on sandy flat clearings, feeding mainly on termites, but also catching grasshoppers, beetles, etc. They dig branching burrows in soft sand, usually at the base of *Acacia* trees, that are sometimes shared by several individuals. The female lays 8-12 eggs (7 x 10-12 mm) in April-May (exceptionally as late as July), and hatchlings (70-80 mm TL) appear in October-November. The long incubation period (5-6 months) is due to cold winter temperatures. Growth is rapid, and sexual maturity is reached in 4-5 months. Adults die off during July-October. **Habitat:** Arid and mesic savannah. **Range:** Maputaland, Mpumalanga, N. Cape (including Kalahari Gemsbok NP), extreme S. and central Mozambique, through Botswana, Zimbabwe and E. Namibia, to Angola and Tanzania.

## Rock Lizards   *Australolacerta*

Previously placed in the genus *Lacerta*, which includes the beautiful and common lizards of the Mediterranean region. These two primitive species have been placed in a new genus that is endemic to South Africa.

**Southern Rock Lizard**     *Australolacerta australis* **(Pl. 62)**
*(Endemic) SVL 50-65 mm; max. SVL 70 mm.*

A medium-sized, graceful lizard with a well-developed collar and a tail that is twice as long as the body. The subocular borders the lip. The lower eye-lids are scaly. The dorsal scales are very small, granular and smooth, in 67-68 rows at midbody. The ventral scales are in six long rows. The lamellae beneath the toes are smooth. There are 16-19 femoral pores. The back is dark olive-brown in adults (blue-green in juveniles) and has rows of small, pale yellow to white spots that fade on the rear of the body and are bright orange on the flanks. The top of the head is black, vermiculated with bright yellow spots. The throat and belly are bluish-white, with narrow black edges to the scales. The tail is grey-green, tinged with blue at the tip, and with numerous black flecks. **Biology and breeding:** For many years this was one of South Africa's rarest lizards; only one specimen was collected between 1926 and 1973. It lives in mountainous country, in rock cracks and under large rock slabs on rugged sandstone outcrops. (SA RB Restricted.) It often basks on the vertical faces and is locally common, but relatively shy. It lays up to seven oval, soft-shelled eggs. **Habitat:** Fynbos vegetation. **Range:** W. Cape fold mountains, from Cedarberg to Worcester.

### Soutpansberg Rock Lizard *Australolacerta rupicola* (Pl. 62)
*(Endemic) SVL 40-50 mm; max. SVL 52 mm.*

A small, graceful lizard with a well-developed collar. The subocular borders the lip. The lower eyelids are scaly, each with a few enlarged elongate central scales. The dorsal scales are granular and smooth, in about 36 rows at midbody. The ventral scales are in six long rows. The lamellae beneath the toes are smooth. There are 15 femoral pores. The back is dark brown, with a pair of rich reddish-brown, narrow vertebral stripes, and a white dorsolateral stripe that extends from the eye to the tail base. There may be a thin pale lateral band that in adults is often broken into scattered white spots. The top of the head is reddish brown, the tail is pale brown, and the belly is bluish with dark-blue to black speckles. **Biology and breeding:** This diurnal lizard forages on exposed bedrock and rocky mountain slopes. (SA RDB Restricted.) It allows observers to approach closely, but can retreat speedily into rock piles. Its reproduction is poorly known; a female contained two eggs. **Habitat:** Prefers sparsely vegetated mountain summits. **Range:** Endemic to the Soutpansberg in the N. Province from Waterpoort to Lake Funduzi.

## Desert Lizards *Meroles*

This is a small genus of lizards that have fine, granular dorsal scales and a well-developed collar. There is no window in the lower eyelid and the subocular does not reach the lip. The feet are well developed, with long, usually fringed toes. Femoral pores are present.

These active, diurnal, terrestrial lizards are well-adapted for desert life. Their reproduction is poorly known; all appear to be oviparous. They are camouflaged in pale colours and none develops bright breeding colours.

There are seven species in the genus, all occurring in the western arid regions of southern Africa; all but two are endemic.

### Shovel-snouted Lizard *Meroles anchietae* (Pl. 56)
*SVL 45-50 mm; max. SVL 55 mm.*

This is a small lacertid that is easily identified by its unusual, flattened snout, which has a sharp cutting edge. The nostrils are directed upwards and pierced between three nasals. The subocular does not border the lip. The lower eyelids are scaly. It lacks a collar and femoral pores. The dorsal scales are very small and granular. The hind legs are large and often splay outwards. The long toes have a conspicuous fringe of large scales. The tail has a broad base but tapers rapidly. The body is sand-coloured above, with a network of black marks that extends onto the flanks and limbs. The head is paler and has a silvery sheen. A broken black stripe may extend along the backbone and onto the tail base. The belly is white. The tail may have a few black crossbands. Males grow larger than females. **Biology and breeding:** These lizards race at high speed over the loose sand dunes of the Namib Desert. Although they can withstand high body temperatures (up to 44°C) they may overheat from the hot sand. To avoid this they have an amusing 'thermal dance' during which they lift the tail and two of the feet high in the air. When disturbed they dive into the dune slipface, swimming deep into the sand until they are out of danger. They also sleep beneath the sand. If they cannot escape, they raise the body high and will jump and bite. They are territorial, particularly during the reproductive peak when males establish and defend territories. These may contain up to 4-5 females. A prime site is an eddy in a dune slipface where seeds collect. Small beetles and other insects are eaten, as well as seeds during dry periods when insects are absent. All their moisture is obtained from their food. There is no fixed breeding season and eggs are laid at irregular intervals but with a peak during December-March. Females may mature in only 4-6 months and lay eggs 3-4 times per year at 30-40 day intervals. A single large egg (8-9 x 16-17 mm) is laid in a small chamber dug in firm sand in a dune slack. After good rains clutches of two eggs may be laid. Hatchlings are very large and measure about 25-27 mm SVL. **Habitat:** Sparsely vegetated, unstable desert dunes. **Range:** Endemic to Namib Desert from the Klinghardt mountains to S. Angola.

### Smith's Desert Lizard
*Meroles ctenodactylus* **(Pl. 56)**
*(Endemic) SVL 70-80 mm; max. SVL 90 mm.*

A large desert lizard with a flattened, wedge-shaped snout and toes that have a prominent, serrated fringe. Each ear opening is covered with a skin fold. The supranasals are in contact. There are 78-92 scale rows at mid-body, 22-26 long rows of ventral plates and 27-38 femoral pores on each thigh. The back varies in colour from greyish-fawn to orange-brown or russet-brown and is sometimes densely speckled with dark brown to black. A yellowish-white, dark-edged dorsolateral stripe runs from the ear to the tail base, with another broad, greyish to dark brown lateral stripe (that may have white and yellow spots) and a yellow lateral stripe, below. The limbs have large, yellow-white spots and the belly is white or pale yellow. Juveniles are orange-brown. **Biology and breeding:** Sit-and-wait hunters, these lizards shelter in the shade of sparse vegetation, dashing out to grab passing insects. They dive into loose sand to escape danger and to sleep at night. They lay approximately six eggs (9-10 x 13-14 mm). **Habitat:** Vegetated coastal dunes and adjacent sandy plains. **Range:** Little Namaqualand and coast of S. Namibia, extending into Sperrgebiet.

### Wedge-snouted Desert Lizard
*Meroles cuneirostris* **(Pl. 56)**
*(Endemic) SVL 45-55 mm; max. SVL 58 mm.*

A small lizard with a flattened, wedge-shaped snout and toes that have a prominent, serrated fringe. Each ear opening is covered with a skin fold. The nasals are swollen. The supranasals are not in contact. There are 90-110 scale rows at midbody, 24-30 long rows of ventral plates, and 18-24 femoral pores on each thigh. Coloration matches sand colour, and the back may be greyish, sand-coloured or reddish-brown with pale spots (that may be absent) and dark flecks. Males have a more reticulated dorsal pattern. A pale dorsolateral stripe extends from the eye to the tail. The lateral skin folds and upper lip may be yellow-orange. The belly is white. **Biology and breeding:** Very fast, sprinting between tufts of vegetation on sand hummocks. Their diet varies seasonally, depending on the availability of food. In summer they eat mainly adult beetles, but take termites and other small insects during winter. They forage in the cool morning and evening, and often sit next to ant paths, robbing the ants of their insect prey. They dive beneath loose sand to escape danger and to sleep at night. There is no distinct breeding season. The female lays 2-4 eggs (7-8 x 12-14 mm) in soft sand up to 600 mm below the surface. Hatchlings measure approximately 56 mm TL. **Habitat:** Prefers sparsely vegetated desert and coastal dunes. **Range:** Restricted to S. Namib Desert from Richtersveld to Walvis Bay.

### Knox's Desert Lizard

*Meroles knoxii* **(Pl. 57)**

*(Endemic) SVL 55-65 mm; max. SVL 68 mm.*

A medium-sized desert lizard with a rounded snout that lacks a sharp edge. Specimens from the Cape Peninsula are small (rarely longer than 180 mm TL). The lobed ear openings are visible. The supranasals are in contact. The dorsal scales may be smooth (in northern populations) or weakly keeled, and are in 54-78 rows at midbody. There are 10-12 long rows of ventral plates, and 13-22 femoral pores on each thigh. The toes have a small fringe. Coloration is varied. Juveniles are dark brown to black with five white stripes and scattered white spots. In adults, the back becomes red-brown (paler in coastal regions), with a dark dorsolateral stripe, that may be broken into a series of partially white-edged black spots. The flanks are grey, with a series of yellowish or brownish spots or circles. The limbs may have numerous pale spots. The belly is creamy white or bluish-grey. Adult breeding males are bright yellow on the lower head, throat and anal region. **Biology and breeding:** Active, diurnal lizards, commonly seen dashing between bushes in sandy areas. They feed on insects, mainly beetles and flies. They shelter in a burrow dug in compacted soil at the base of a succulent bush or under refuse. Clutch size varies; small lizards from the Cape Peninsula lay only 2-3 eggs, while larger lizards from Namaqualand may lay up to six eggs (7,8 x 12-13 mm). **Habitat:** Varied: coastal dunes and succulent karroid veld. **Range:** Along W. Cape coast from Cape Peninsula to coastal regions of S. Namibia, extending inland to Matjiesfontein, the Tankwa Karoo, and western valleys of the Little Karoo.

### Small-scaled Desert Lizard

*Meroles micropholidotus* **(Pl. 56)**

*(Endemic) SVL 55-65 mm; max. SVL 68 mm.*

A small desert lizard with a flattened wedge-shaped snout and toes that have a serrated fringe. Each ear opening is covered with a skin fold. The nasals are not swollen. The supranasals are in contact. The dorsal scales are smooth and minute, in 126-138 rows at midbody. There are 24-28 long rows of ventral plates, and 17-20 femoral pores on each thigh. The back is light grey above, with a vague network of dark blue-grey that extends onto the limbs. The belly is yellowish-white. **Biology:** When disturbed, these lizards dive into coarse sand, and wriggle until they are completely covered; they also sleep under the sand. **Habitat:** Sparsely vegetated desert. **Range:** S. coastal Namib Desert, between Lüderitz Bay and Walvis Bay.

### Reticulated Desert Lizard
*Meroles reticulatus* **(Pl. 56)**

*SVL 45-50 mm; max. SVL 55 mm.*
This small desert lizard has a pointed snout with a weak edge along the upper lip. The lobed ear openings are visible. The supranasals are in contact. There are 50-56 scale rows at midbody, 16-18 long rows of ventral plates, and 19-23 femoral pores on each thigh. The toes have a prominent serrated fringe. The back is grey to blue-grey, speckled with paler and darker grey tones that may form a dense network. The belly is white.
**Biology and breeding:** These lizards forage on mobile sand dunes, but may also run on granite bedrock and shelter under rock flakes. When disturbed, they run for some distance before diving just beneath the sand. Crows have been reported as major predators. They feed on small insects. A female contained four large eggs in October. **Habitat:** Sparsely vegetated coastal desert. **Range:** Coastal areas of N. Namib Desert, from near Walvis Bay to S. Angola.

### Spotted Desert Lizard
*Meroles suborbitalis* **(Pl. 57)**

*(Endemic) SVL 55-65 mm; max. SVL 71 mm.*
A medium-sized desert lizard with a rounded snout that lacks a sharp edge on the upper lip. The lobed ear openings are visible. The supranasals are not in contact. There are 60-75 scale rows at midbody, 12-14 long rows of ventral plates, and 14-20 femoral pores on each thigh. The toes have a feeble fringe. Juveniles are pale yellow-white above, with four black stripes, and a black network enclosing large, pale spots on the limbs. Adults are exceptionally variable in coloration; this is regional and matches ground cover. In southern specimens the dark stripes develop light brown centres with age, and the back becomes grey-brown and covered with large pale spots that may form rows. In the Namib Desert, adults are slate-coloured with a pinky sheen, and with irregular rows of dark, pale-edged spots. The belly is creamy white or bluish. The throat and hind limbs of males in some populations are yellow. **Biology and breeding:** These sit-and-wait hunters live on flat gravel or sandy plains with scattered bush. They dash from the shade of low vegetation to grab bees, beetles, grasshoppers and termites. In the central Namib Desert, breeding seems to be continuous and females may lay clutches of 3-7 eggs throughout the year. In the Kalahari, mating occurs in early winter and females may lay two clutches, each of 4-8 eggs (7,5 x 12,5 mm), per season. Growth is relatively slow and they may take up to three years to mature. **Habitat:** Varied; arid savannah to desert. **Range:** From the central Karoo to Little Namaqualand and S. Namibia, extending to the central parts of the Namib Desert.

## Sandveld Lizards  *Nucras*
This is a small genus of lacertids that have a rounded snout, a cylindrical body, and a very long tail. The subocular borders the lip, and the lower eyelids are scaly. Each nostril is pierced between 2-3 nasals and is well separated from the upper labials. A distinct collar is present. The dorsal scales are small, smooth and non-overlapping. There are smooth lamellae beneath the toes, which lack a fringe. Femoral pores are present.

These secretive, terrestrial lacertids may be locally common, but are rarely seen. They forage in the early morning and evening, and are only conspicuous when gorging themselves on flying termites. Some are specialist feeders on scorpions. Unlike other local lacertids they are foragers, actively searching out food rather than waiting to ambush it. They may store fat in the long, thick tail. All appear to be oviparous. Their predators include birds of prey and snakes, and some species have brightly coloured tails to deflect attacks away from the vulnerable head and body.

They are restricted mainly to arid and mesic savannah on sandy soils, although some species enter fynbos and montane grassland. Ten species are recognized from southern and E. Africa with eight entering the sub-continent; six of these are endemic. Identification is based mainly on coloration and distribution, as there is often a great overlap in scale counts between the species.

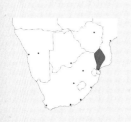

### Blue-tailed Sandveld Lizard
*Nucras caesicaudata* (Pl. 61)

*(Endemic) SVL 50-60 mm; max. SVL 65 mm.*
A small, slender sandveld lizard with a brilliant blue tail. It has a series of six enlarged plates under the forearm. There are 40-54 scale rows at mid-body, and 14-15 femoral pores on each thigh. The back is dark brown, with seven thin, cream stripes, three of which extend onto the back of the head. The limbs are light brown with cream blotches and the belly is pure white. **Biology:** Very little is known about these lizards (SA RDB, Peripheral). They live on deep sands and seem to emerge only when termites swarm. **Habitat:** Arid savannah on deep sand. **Range:** Restricted to Gazaland Plain of S. Mozambique, extending just into SE Zimbabwe and N. Kruger National Park.

### Spotted Sandveld Lizard
*Nucras intertexta* (Pl. 60)

*(Endemic) SVL 80-90 mm; max. SVL 94 mm.*
A large sandveld lizard, usually with a spotted back and an orange-brown tail. It has 4-7 enlarged plates under the forearm, and 34-56 scale rows at midbody. There are 11-15 femoral pores on each thigh. The back is light brown to reddish-brown, with a series of pale spots that may be black-edged, or fuse to form a mesh pattern or irregular, transverse bands. Sometimes a pale vertebral stripe is present. The belly is creamy white, with dark specks on the outer scale rows. Juveniles have darker backs, with rows of distinct cream spots; the sides of the neck are barred in pale yellow, and the tail is coral-red. **Biology and breeding:** Foraging widely in open dry savannah, these lizards search for slow-moving food such as spiders and scorpions, and even other lizards. They lay from 2-8 eggs (measuring 8 x 12-13 mm), that hatch in February-March. The hatchlings measure about 60 mm TL. **Habitat:** Arid savannah, usually on Kalahari sand. **Range:** S. Mozambique and extreme N. KwaZulu-Natal, through Kalahari region to Kaokoveld in N. Namibia.

### Delalande's Sandveld Lizard
*Nucras lalandii* (Pl. 61)

*(Endemic) SVL 75-95 mm; max. SVL 101 mm male, 110 mm female.*
A large, stout-bodied sandveld lizard that has a blunt snout and a thick, cylindrical tail. It lacks enlarged plates under the forearm. There are 34-42 scale rows at midbody. It has 10-15 femoral pores on each thigh. Juveniles are light red-brown, with 8-10 irregular rows of large, white, black-edged spots on the back, and black and white vertical bars on the sides of the head and neck. In adults, the back varies from grey-green to reddish-brown, and the black edges to the dorsal spots expand, often fusing and forming irregular black crossbands. The tail is olive-grey, heavily spotted in black, and the belly is creamy white, often with numerous black spots.

**Biology and breeding:** These attractive lizards are usually found under stones in open grassland. They move slowly, scratching in loose soil around the base of grass clumps and boulders for spiders, beetles and larvae. The female lays 3-9 eggs (9-13 x 14-21 mm) in a chamber, often dug under a stone, in early summer. Eggs hatch in late January to early February and the hatchlings measure 70-90 mm TL. They do well in captivity and make fine, long-lived pets. **Habitat:** Montane and temperate grassland. **Range:** Distributed through the grassy uplands of E. Cape to KwaZulu-Natal, Swaziland and adjacent Free State, with relict populations in S. Cape, Gauteng, Mpumalanga and N. Province.

### Striped Sandveld Lizard

*Nucras taeniolata* (Pl. 60)

*(Endemic) SVL 50-60 mm; max. SVL 70 mm.*
A small sandveld lizard with a finely striped colour pattern. It lacks a parietal foramen on the crown of its head. It has 6-7 enlarged plates under its forearm, 42-52 scale rows at midbody, 3-7 granules between the supraoculars and supraciliaries, and 12-15 femoral pores under each thigh. Juveniles are more distinctly patterned. Adults are dark brown above, with 8-11 fine, cream stripes that are fainter in the middle and of which 4-5 pale stripes extend onto the back of the head. **Biology and breeding:** A secretive lizard that may be locally common. None may be seen for 8-9 months, and then, following late summer rain when termite alates swarm, up to 20 may be found feeding avidly. The female lays 4-5 eggs. **Habitat:** Dry Kaffarian and Mesic Thicket. **Range:** Algoa Bay and Albany district of E. Cape. **Subspecies:** None; all races are now treated as full species.

### Holub's Sandveld Lizard

*Nucras holubi* (Pl. 60)

*SVL 60-70 mm; max. SVL 73 mm.*
A small sandveld lizard with a striped colour pattern. It has a parietal foramen on its crown, 5-9 enlarged plates under each forearm, 41-65 scale rows at midbody, and 3-7 granules between the supraoculars and supraciliaries. It has 10-21 femoral pores under each thigh. Juveniles are more distinctly patterned. Adults are grey or buff to reddish-brown above, with three well-marked, pale stripes along the back (that extend onto the back of the head), and 1-2 rows of spots on the flanks. The tail is light buff to coral-red, and the belly is creamy white. **Biology and breeding:** This species forages around grass tussocks and at the base of bushes, retreating into a small tunnel beneath a rock. It may climb into low bushes to thermoregulate. It preys on small insects, particularly beetles. From 1-7 (usually 4-5) eggs are laid in midsummer. Hatchlings measure 50-60 mm TL. **Habitat:** Broken rocky ground in mesic savannah. **Range:** N. Cape and KwaZulu-Natal, through Free State to NE Cape, Botswana, NW and N. provinces, and Zimbabwe to S. Malawi. There is an apparently isolated population in central and N. Namibia.

### Ornate Sandveld Lizard

*Nucras ornata* (Pl. 103)

*SVL 70-85 mm; max. SVL 94 mm.*
A large sandveld lizard with a bold blotched pattern in adults. It lacks a parietal foramen on the crown of its head. It has 8-10 enlarged plates under each forearm, 39-60 scale rows at midbody, 2-5 granules between the supraoculars and supraciliaries, and 12-19 femoral pores under each thigh. Juveniles are blackish-brown on the back with three white longitudinal stripes. Adults are brown dorsally with irregular black blotches.

Two thin stripes run along the back. The tail is heavily flecked with black and the belly is white. **Biology and breeding:** An agile terrestrial lizard that forages around grass tussocks, etc., and preys on large insects, including centipedes and grasshoppers. From 5-7 eggs are laid in midsummer. **Habitat:** Broken montane grassland and mesic savannah on sandy soils. **Range:** From the Lebombo Mountains, N. Zululand, through Swaziland, Mpumalanga, N. Gauteng, and Zimbabwe to S. Zambia, Malawi and Rondo Plateau in SE Tanzania.

### Western Sandveld Lizard

*Nucras tessellata* **(Pl. 60)**
*(Endemic) SVL 70-80 mm; max. SVL 92 mm.*
A slender, brilliantly coloured lizard with vertical bars on the flanks and a long tail. It has 5-7 enlarged plates under each forearm, 36-48 scale rows at midbody, and 11-18 femoral pores on each thigh. The black body has four thin cream stripes on the back and brilliant white bars on the flanks. The rear of the body, hind limbs and tail are rich red-brown. The belly is pure white. Some specimens are pale red-buff, with only two faint stripes on the back; Kalahari juveniles have pale blue forebodies. **Biology and breeding:** Forage widely and feed on scorpions and spiders which are dug from their daytime retreats. Grasshoppers, beetles and cockroaches also taken. Lays 3-4 eggs. **Habitat:** Rocky ground in arid savannah and karroid veld. **Range:** W. Little Karoo, Namaqualand to S. Namibia and Botswana.

### Karoo Sandveld Lizard

*Nucras livida* **(Pl. 60)**
*(Endemic) SVL 70-80 mm; max. SVL 85 mm.*
A slender, long-tailed lizard with fine, irregular bars on the sides of the neck and forebody. It has 5-7 enlarged plates under each forearm, 44-56 scale rows at midbody, and 11-18 femoral pores on each thigh. The dark brown body has six pale stripes on the back and extensive spots on the yellow flanks. The belly is cream. **Biology and breeding:** Forages widely on sandy flats. When disturbed it disappears quickly into its retreat, a deep burrow dug at the base of a bush. Lays 3-5 eggs in midsummer. Predators include the fiscal shrike. **Habitat:** Well-vegetated sandy flats in karroid veld. **Range:** Central and E. Karoo, from Cradock to Little Karoo.

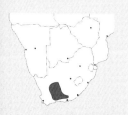

## Sand Lizards   *Pedioplanis*

This is a group of small lizards that have a cylindrical body and a long tail. The subocular borders the lip. The lower eyelid may be scaly or have a transparent window. A distinct collar is present. The dorsal scales are usually small, smooth and non-overlapping. There are keeled lamellae beneath the long toes, which lack a fringe. Femoral pores are present. These diurnal, terrestrial lizards are commonly seen dashing between sparse vegetation in the arid west. They are oviparous, laying small clutches of soft-shelled eggs. The genus contains at least 11 species which are restricted mainly to southern Africa, with several species entering S. Angola. All except three species are endemic to the subcontinent.

### Short-headed Sand Lizard

*Pedioplanis breviceps* **(Pl. 58)**
*(Endemic) SVL 35-45 mm; max. SVL 46 mm.*
A small, slender sand lizard with a short head, scaly lower eyelids, no enlarged tympanic shield, four upper labials in front of the subocular, and 12 long rows of scales on the belly. The scales on the lower leg are small and not keeled. There are 11 femoral pores on each thigh. Males and

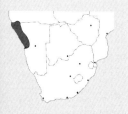

females have different coloration. Hatchlings and adult females have
five distinct dark stripes on the back, with those on the flanks darker and
more conspicuous. In young males the bands begin to fade and the backs
of adult males are uniform light brown, with many grey spots that may
form faint lines. The belly is white and the tail is light brown, with thin,
dark brown bands fading to red at the tip. **Biology and breeding:**
Active lizards; forage on open, sandy plains and in dry riverbeds. Eggs
begin to develop in December and 2-4 large eggs (6 x 11 mm) are laid in
March-May. Hatchlings (50-80 mm TL) appear in May-July. **Habitat:**
Desert flats. **Range:** Western areas of central and N. Namib Desert.

## Burchell's Sand Lizard

*Pedioplanis burchelli* **(Pl. 59)**

*(Endemic) SVL 45-55 mm; max. SVL 57 mm.*

A small sand lizard with a relatively short tail and a slightly flattened head
and body. It has no enlarged tympanic or temporal shields. The lower eyelids are opaque, each with 10-15 small scales across the middle. There is a
faint gular fold. The nasals are usually in contact behind the rostral. Four
to 13 small granules occur in front of the supraoculars. There are four
pairs of chin shields. There are no lobes at the front of the ear openings.
There are 62-75 scale rows at midbody, 14 (rarely 16) long rows of
ventrals, and 13-16 femoral pores on each thigh. Coloration is extremely
varied. Juveniles are black, with seven thin, pale cream to white stripes on
the body, large, white spots on the limbs, and a bluish tinge to the tail.
The belly is white, and the tail is orange below. This coloration may
continue in some adults, but usually the stripes fade or become broken
into rows of white spots, and the back becomes buff, grey-brown or red-
brown, usually with irregular black markings. **Biology and breeding:**
Inhabits exposed bedrock with sparse vegetation and scattered rock slabs.
Shelters in a small chamber excavated in soil under a flat rock. They are
sit-and-wait hunters, dashing from behind a rock to catch small insects.
In winter they lie dormant in their shelters. The female lays 4-6 oval eggs
(7.5-10 x 9-13 mm) in moist soil under a rock slab in December-January.
These hatch in 60-70 days (February-March); the hatchlings measure
66-78 mm TL and weigh 0,3-0,4 g. **Habitat:** Rocky montane grassland,
entering succulent karroid veld and coastal fynbos in the southwest.
**Range:** Cape Agulhas, through Cape fold mountains and inland Cape
escarpment to W. Free State, Lesotho and SE Mpumalanga.

## Cape Sand Lizard

*Pedioplanis laticeps* **(Pl. 59)**

*(Endemic) SVL 50-60 mm; max. SVL 63 mm.*

This medium-sized sand lizard is very similar to Burchell's sand lizard,
*P. burchelli* (page 171), but its nasals are not in contact behind the rostral
and there is no gular fold. There are 13-30 small granules in front of the
supraoculars, and five pairs of chin shields. It has 48-62 scale rows at
midbody, and 16-18 long rows of ventrals. There are 12-18 femoral pores
on each thigh. Coloration is extremely varied. Juveniles are similar to
young Burchell's sand lizards, but have only five pale stripes on the back.
In adults, the lateral stripes fade and become broken into spots, and the
back becomes brown with scattered pale spots, although three faint stripes
remain. **Biology and breeding:** These lizards are similar in behaviour
and habits to Burchell's sand lizards, except that they are found on
compacted, well-vegetated soils. **Habitat:** Montane grassland and
succulent karroid veld. **Range:** Central Karoo.

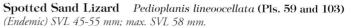

**Spotted Sand Lizard** *Pedioplanis lineoocellata* (Pls. 59 and 103)
*(Endemic) SVL 45-55 mm; max. SVL 58 mm.*
A small sand lizard with a relatively short tail and a slightly flattened head
and body. It has no enlarged tympanic or temporal shields, but has a
window, formed by two black-edged, transparent scales, in each lower eyelid. There are 3-4 lobes at the front of each ear opening. There are 12-14
long rows of ventrals, and 10-17 femoral pores on each thigh. Coloration
is extremely varied. The back ranges from buff to grey-brown or red-
brown, usually with 2-4 rows of small, pale dorsal spots that may fuse into
broken or continuous dorsolateral stripes. The flanks have a series of 4-7
large, pale blue-white spots that may be dark-edged. Namaqualand and S.
Namibia specimens are brightly coloured and have paired, black dorsolateral stripes. The hind limbs are usually spotted and the tail is flecked with
pale and dark dots. The belly is white and males may have a blue-grey
throat. **Biology and breeding:** These lizards prefer flat rocky veld. They
are sit-and-wait hunters, grabbing small insects after a short dash from
shaded cover. The diet varies with the season; they take mostly termites
during winter, and beetles and locusts during summer. They are active
during the day, even on warm winter days. They shelter in a small burrow
dug beneath a flat rock. When chased, they dash from stone to stone,
turning sharply. They are difficult to catch, unless pursued in the open,
where they tire quickly. The female lays 4-8 eggs (9-10 x 12-13 mm) in
November, in a small chamber dug in moist soil beneath a rock. The eggs
hatch after about 70-80 days (in February); hatchlings measure 50-55 mm
TL. Sexual maturity is reached in 15-18 months, and they may live for
4-5 years. **Habitat:** Very varied; karroid veld, mesic thicket and arid and
mesic savannah. **Range:** Western half of the subcontinent, but absent
from regions of deep sand (for example Namib Desert and central
Kalahari). **Subspecies:** Two races are recognized, and both occur in the
region. Typical *P.l. lineoocellata* has smaller scales on its back than it does
on its lower forelimbs, and they are slightly overlapping and keeled; it is
found in the northern part of the range, in NW Province, Botswana
(where it is restricted to hard soil around pans), Free State, N. Cape and
N. Namibia. *P.l. pulchella* has small scales on its back, which are not
overlapping and are almost smooth; it occurs in E. and W. Cape, through
Karoo to Namaqualand and S. Namibia, with an isolated population in
N. Province. Specimens from Lüderitz Bay have dull, dark grey bodies,
occasionally with four faint dorsal stripes, and lack the large flank spots;
they are sometimes treated as a separate race (*P.l. inocellata*).

Legend for map:
- *P.l. lineocellata*
- *P.l. pulchella*

**Namaqua Sand Lizard** *Pedioplanis namaquensis* (Pl. 57)
*SVL 40-50 mm; max. SVL 53 mm.*
A small, slender sand lizard with a long tail. It has an enlarged tympanic
shield. The lower eyelids are semi-transparent, each having 10-12 enlarged
scales across the middle. A small group of 3-8 granules occurs in front of
the supraoculars. There are no lobes at the front of the ear openings.
There are 47-65 scale rows at midbody, and 12-14 long rows of ventrals.
It has 10-16 femoral pores on each thigh. The juveniles are black, with
four thin, white stripes; they have brown legs with white spots, a white
belly and a pinkish-brown tail. This coloration may persist in adults in
the Karoo on dark soils, but the dorsal stripes of adults from the western
regions fade or become pale brown, and the flanks may be irregularly
barred. **Biology and breeding:** These amazingly fast lizards can be seen

172

in the heat of the day, dashing over open, sparsely vegetated sand and gravel flats. They forage widely, feeding on small insects. During the winter months they remain dormant in their burrows, which they dig in sand accumulated at the base of bushes. They lay 3-5 eggs in November. **Habitat:** Prefers karroid veld, arid savannah and semi-desert. **Range:** Found in the E. Cape, through the Karoo, Namaqualand, Namibia and Botswana, to S. Angola.

### Angolan Sand Lizard
*Pedioplanis benguellensis*

*SVL 40-50 mm; max. SVL 52 mm.*
This small, slender species is very similar to the Namaqua sand lizard, *P. namaquensis* (above), but has a black-edged window in each lower eyelid. There are 52-67 scale rows at midbody, 10 long and 25-30 transverse rows of ventrals, and 7-15 small granules in front of the supraoculars. There are 12-15 femoral pores on each thigh. The tail is long; almost twice the length of the head and body. The back is grey or pale reddish-brown with five distinct dark longitudinal stripes, those on the sides with whitish interspaces. The tail is yellowish-orange, and the belly white. **Biology:** A terrestrial species that forages around small bushes on sandy soils. **Habitat:** Prefers arid, sparsely-vegetated desert. **Range:** Found from S. Angola, into the Kaokoveld and adjacent N. Namibia.

### Western Sand Lizard
*Pedioplanis undata* (Pl. 58)

*SVL 45-50 mm; max. SVL 54 mm.*
This small, slender species is very similar to the Namaqua sand lizard, *P. namaquensis* (above), but the lower eyelid has a window composed of 2-4 large semi-transparent scales. In addition, there are 57-75 scale rows at midbody, usually 10 long rows of ventrals, and 6-15 small granules in front of the supraoculars. There are 8-15 femoral pores on each thigh. The tail is long; almost three times longer than head and body. The back is yellowish-tan with five distinct longitudinal stripes, that fade in northern populations. There is a series of yellow spots on the flanks. Juveniles have similar coloration to adults. **Biology and breeding:** They are active hunters of small insects on sandy flats around rocky areas. They mate in November-January, and the young (55-75 mm TL) hatch in January-March. **Habitat:** Sandy soils in arid savannah. **Range:** S. Angola to N. and central Namibia. **Subspecies:** None; all previous races are now recognized as full species.

### Waterberg Sand Lizard
*Pedioplanis rubens* (Pl. 58)

*(Endemic) SVL 40-50 mm; max. SVL 50 mm.*
A small species in which the tail is just over twice the length of the head and body. The lower eyelid has a window composed of 2-4 large semi-transparent scales. The head and forebody are red-brown, without dorsal markings or spots on the flanks. The hind body and tail are bright brick-red. The belly is lighter. Juveniles have similar coloration to adults. **Biology and breeding:** A terrestrial species that shelters in a small tunnel burrowed in soil beneath a rock slab or within a rock crack. It is a sit-and-wait predator, catching small insects with a short dash from cover. A female collected in February contained two eggs (9-11 x 5-6 mm). **Habitat:** Prefers red sandstone bedrock in Mopane savannah. **Range:** Normally restricted to the red sandstones of the Waterberg Plateau in N. Namibia.

### Plain Sand Lizard
*Pedioplanis inornata* **(Pl. 58)**
*(Endemic) SVL 45-50 mm; max. SVL 52 mm.*
A small species, similar to the Waterberg sand lizard (*P. rubens*). The tail is just over twice the length of the head and body. The lower eyelid has a window composed of 2-4 large semi-transparent scales. The uniform grey-brown back is patternless, becoming orange-brown on the tail. Unlike the Waterberg sand lizard, however, it has a series of pale greenish spots on the flanks. Juveniles have similar coloration to adults. **Biology:** Terrestrial; actively forages around succulent vegetation on exposed bedrock surfaces on the lower slopes of mountains. **Habitat:** Bedrock flats in semi-desert. **Range:** N. Cape, Richtersveld and Great Namaqualand, Namibia.

### Kaokoveld Sand Lizard
*Pedioplanis gaerdesi* **(Pl. 103)**
*(Endemic) SVL 45-50 mm; max. SVL 52 mm.*
A small species in which the tail is nearly three times the length of the head and body. The lower eyelid has a large, undivided, black-ringed transparent window. There are 60-67 scale rows at midbody and usually 10 long rows of ventrals. The red-brown body has a golden tinge and pale yellow spots on the flanks. Dorsal stripes are faint and sometimes absent. The belly is uniform cream. Juveniles have similar coloration to adults. **Biology:** A terrestrial species that runs among small basalt boulders on gravel plains, and shelters in a small tunnel in soil beneath a boulder or at the base of a bush. **Habitat:** Desert gravel plains. **Range:** N. Namibia, from Erongo to Kaokoland.

### Husab Sand Lizard
*Pedioplanis husabensis* **(Pl. 58)**
*(Endemic) SVL 45-55 mm; max. SVL 58 mm.*
This small species has a small tympanic shield, and eight opaque scales in each lower eyelid. The back is greyish in front and reddish-brown towards the rear. It bears dark dots and bars, but lacks stripes or lateral spots. Juveniles have similar coloration to adults. **Biology and breeding:** Terrestrial; prefers expanses of flat rock on exposed bedrock. More predatory than the Western sand lizard, *P. undata*, with which it lives; catches and eats small lizards. Hatchlings emerge in April-June, and are 40-50 mm TL. **Habitat:** Rocky desert. **Range:** Restricted to junction of the Khan and Swakop rivers in the Husab Mountains in central Namibia.

## Mountain Lizards   *Tropidosaura*
These small lacertids have a short head, a cylindrical body, and a long, cylindrical tail. They lack a collar, but usually have a faint gular fold. The body is covered with rough, spiny, overlapping scales. Femoral pores are present. The body is camouflaged in brown and olive, but breeding males develop bright colours on the flanks.

They are terrestrial. Most live among rocks and heather on mountain summits, basking and foraging on flat bedrock and sheltering in short tunnels that they dig under rock slabs, or in soil-filled cracks. They hibernate in their retreats during winter, when snow often blankets the mountains. The females lay a small clutch of 2-7 eggs.

The four species in the genus are endemic to southern Africa. Two are restricted to the montane grassland of KwaZulu-Natal and Cape Drakensberg, and another to the fynbos of the Cape fold mountains. The remaining species is more widely distributed through the southern coastal regions.

174

## Essex's Mountain Lizard                  *Tropidosaura essexi* (Pl. 103)
*(Endemic) SVL 40-50 mm; max. SVL 52 mm.*

This small species is very similar in appearance to the common mountain lizard, *T. montana* (page 176). The head is short, and there is a well-marked gular fold. The subocular borders the lip. The scales on the sides of the neck are small, smooth and granular. The body scales are large, spiny and overlapping. There is a single large preanal plate, and 7-11 femoral pores. The back is olive to olive-green, with a dark, pale-edged stripe along the backbone. The flanks have dark-edged dorsolateral and lateral stripes. The head is bluish-green, spotted with brown. The belly is bluish, usually with dark edges to the scales. The tail is green-blue.
**Biology and breeding:** Rarely forages far from thick vegetation along mountain streams and at the base of rock faces, and quickly disappears when danger threatens. Two eggs are laid in summer. **Habitat:** Rocky montane grassland. **Range:** Summit slopes of KwaZulu-Natal Drakensberg and adjacent Free State. Single specimen from NE Cape (Naude's Nek).

## Cottrell's Mountain Lizard              *Tropidosaura cottrelli* (Pl. 62)
*(Endemic) SVL 55-65 mm; max. SVL 66 mm.*

This large mountain lizard has a flattened head and a well-developed gular fold. The subocular borders the lip, and the first upper labial is well separated from the nostril. The scales on the side of the neck are small, smooth and granular, while the body scales are large, spiny, over-lapping and rhombic in shape. There are two large preanal plates and 11 femoral pores. Coloration is varied. Cape specimens have a brown back with scattered black and orange scales. There is a row of yellow or yellow-tipped scales on the flanks, and a black yellow-edged stripe on the neck that continues onto the lips. The tail is olive-brown above, with scattered, dark brown scales, and blue-white below. The belly is bluish, with large, black blotches on the scales. Natal specimens are brown-black above, with numerous green and blue spots that form crossbands on the rear half of the body and tail. The flanks are pale blue, with a black stripe.
**Biology and breeding:** This terrestrial species hunts small insects among clumps of grass and heather. It shelters in a tunnel that it digs in deep soil. A female had four eggs in her oviducts. **Habitat:** Montane grassland. **Range:** Drakensberg escarpment of KwaZulu-Natal and E. Cape.

## Cape Mountain Lizard                     *Tropidosaura gularis* (Pl. 62)
*(Endemic) SVL 50-60 mm; max. SVL 62 mm.*

A large mountain lizard that has a distinct gular fold across the throat. The subocular borders the lip, and the first upper labial enters the nostril. The scales on the sides of the neck are small, smooth and granular, while the body scales are large spiny and overlapping. There are two large preanal plates, and 9-12 femoral pores. The back is dark brown to olive-brown, usually with a pale olive-brown band along the backbone. The scales are black-edged, giving a speckled appearance. There are two white-yellow lateral stripes that may be faint and/or broken up into spots, with a row of yellow spots below. The tail is blue-grey in juveniles and females, and pale olive with black flecks in adult males. In breeding males, the dorsal band becomes bright green, the yellow flank spots turn bright orange, and the head becomes black with yellow spots. **Biology and breeding:** These lizards are common among the heather and proteas of mountain summits but are shy and difficult to catch. They readily climb onto rock faces and boulders, and feed on flies and bees attracted to the heather flowers. The female lays 4-8 eggs (7-8 x 11-12 mm) in November in a small chamber under a flat rock. **Habitat:** Fynbos-covered mountain summits. **Range:** Cape fold mountains, from Matroosberg to Lady's Slipper near Port Elizabeth.

### Common Mountain Lizard     *Tropidosaura montana* (Pl. 62)
*(Endemic) SVL 45-55 mm; max. SVL 58 mm.*
A small lizard with a short head, a faint gular fold and a long tail. The subocular borders the lip. The scales on the sides of the neck are keeled and the body scales are large, spiny and overlapping. There is a single large preanal plate, and 5-8 femoral pores (see Subspecies). The back is olive-brown to dark brown, with a dark streak along the backbone and a greenish-white to yellowish dorsolateral stripe. A broken white stripe extends from the upper lip onto the lower flank, with a series of large, pale yellow (bright orange in breeding season) spots below this. The belly is greenish-white, often with large, dark spots. The tail becomes faint blue-green in breeding season, and has black spots below. **Biology and breeding:** These shy and secretive lizards often bask on vegetation, where they are perfectly camouflaged. They are active in the early morning and late afternoon, and feed on small insects. The female lays 4-5 eggs (6-7 x 10-11 mm) in mid-November. They hatch in 33-34 days (at 28-30°C); hatchlings are 55-60 mm TL. **Habitat:** Fynbos and montane grassland. **Range:** Cape fold mountains through E. Cape and Amatola Mountains, to KwaZulu-Natal midlands and Drakensberg foothills. **Subspecies:** Three poorly defined races are recognized. *T.m. montana* usually has 7-8 femoral pores; it occurs in S. and W. Cape. In *T.m. rangeri* the gular fold is usually absent and there are 5-6 femoral pores; it is found in E. Cape. *T.m. natalensis* has a longer head and frontal scale, the body scales are smaller and there are only five femoral pores; it occurs in foothills of KwaZulu-Natal Drakensberg and adjacent midlands.

■ *T.m. rangeri*
□ *T.m. natalensis*
▦ *T.m. montana*

# Plated Lizards and Relatives
FAMILY GERRHOSAURIDAE

These lizards have longish tails and well-developed legs; some grass-land species have become snake-like with reduced limbs. The head has large, symmetrical head shields with osteoderms. Body scales are usually rectangular (plates), overlapping and often keeled; they possess osteo-derms and are arranged in regular rows. A granular lateral body fold is prominent. The clavicle (collar bone) is flattened and perforated. The eyes and eyelids are well developed, external ear openings are visible, and the tongue is moderately long and covered with scale-like papillae. The femoral glands have conspicuous pores in most species, particularly in males.

Previously treated as a subfamily of the Cordylidae, plated lizards evolved before the breakup of the southern supercontinent Gondwana-land and the separation of Madagascar from the African continent in the middle Cretaceous epoch (80-100 million years ago). They are diurnal, oviparous lizards, most having stout bodies and well-developed limbs. All are terrestrial, although some retreat into rock cracks at the base of outcrops. One species is adapted to desert dunes, whilst another genus contains snake-like species with reduced limbs.

There are six genera, with two occurring on Madagascar (*Tracheloptychus* and *Zonosaurus*) and four in sub-Saharan Africa, none of which is endemic to the subcontinent. The only known fossils are from the lower Miocene epoch (10 million years ago) of Mfangano Island, Lake Victoria in Kenya; they are referable to a living species (*Gerrhosaurus major*).

## KEY TO THE SOUTHERN AFRICAN GENERA IN THE GERRHOSAURIDAE
1 - Prefrontal shields present:                  go to 2
   - Prefrontal shields absent:                  go to 3
2 - Snout with sharp horizontal edge (spade-like); toes with lateral fringe:
          *Angolosaurus* (Desert plated lizard, page 177)
   - Snout not spade-like; toes without fringe:
          *Gerrhosaurus* (Plated lizards, page 178)
3 - Lower eyelids with transparent disc; small, and usually with bright
     blue tail:          *Cordylosaurus* (Dwarf plated lizard, page 178)
   - Lower eyelids scaly; limbs short or rudimentary (some with forelimbs
     absent); colour dark grey-olive:
         *Tetradactylus* (Seps and Plated snake-lizards, page 181)

# Desert Plated Lizard    *Angolosaurus*
This is a medium-sized plated lizard with a spade-like snout, a relatively short, cylindrical tail, a cylindrical body, and long limbs with lateral fringes to the toes. These are all adaptations to the desert regions in which it lives. There is a single species in the genus.

### Desert Plated Lizard        *Angolosaurus skoogi* (Pl. 64)
*SVL 110-150 mm; max. SVL 160 mm male, 148 mm female.*

A medium-sized plated lizard with a spade-like snout and a cylindrical body and tail. Prefrontals are present and each nostril is pierced between two nasals and the first labial. The tympanic shield is large, covering most or all of each ear opening. The dorsal scales are smooth and small, in 32-35 longitudinal and 62-65 transverse rows. The lateral scales bordering the fold are granular. Ventrals are in eight longitudinal rows. The tail is short, tapering to a fine point, and at its maximum is only slightly longer than the body. There are 12-13 femoral pores on each side (these are absent or rudimentary in females). The back is ivory, grey-white or light buff, often with numerous, scattered, small, rectangular, maroon-orange blotches. The flanks are paler and often have large light blotches. The chin throat and lower chest are speckled in black, becoming very black in breeding males. The belly is white. Juveniles are sand-coloured. **Breeding and biology:** These active, diurnal lizards are often found in small colonies (up to 3 000 per sq. km). They forage on loose wind-blown sand dunes, feeding on beetles and dry plant debris, including seeds, grass stems and the succulent Nara plant. When disturbed they dash into Nara clumps or dive into dunes, disappearing beneath the sand with a swimming motion. They can spend up to 24 hours under the sand, sheltering from both danger and temperature extremes. The female usually lays two, sometimes up to four, large eggs (20-24 x 11-13 mm). Hatchlings measure 101 mm TL and weigh 2-3 g. Females reach sexual maturity in their second year, males in their third year. Males grow larger and longevity in the wild may reach ten years. Crows and hawks are the main predators on adults. **Habitat:** Scrub-covered sand dunes. **Range:** N. Namib Desert of Namibia and S. Angola.

## Dwarf Plated Lizard  *Cordylosaurus*

This very small, brightly coloured lizard has well-developed limbs, a prominent lateral fold and a longish tail. There is a single species in the genus. It is restricted to the arid western region, from S. Angola to the Little Karoo.

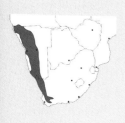

### Dwarf Plated Lizard  *Cordylosaurus subtessellatus* (Pl. 65)
*SVL 35-45 mm; max. SVL 55 mm.*

The head of this lizard is short, with large head shields and no prefrontals, and each nostril is pierced between two nasals and the first labial. Each lower eyelid has a transparent disc. The dorsal scales are smooth to distinctly keeled, in 15 longitudinal and 52-55 transverse rows. The ventrals are in eight longitudinal rows. There are 7-10 femoral pores on each side. The tail may be up to twice the length of the body. The back is dark brown to black, with distinct pale cream to light yellow dorsolateral stripes that become electric blue on the tail. The belly is off-white.
**Biology and breeding:** Forages among succulent vegetation on small rock outcrops searching for grasshoppers, flies, etc. Frequently stops to bask, resting on its belly and lifting its limbs off the hot sand. Often tolerates very close approach before slipping away between the rocks. If grabbed, it will readily shed its tail which continues to writhe for some time, attracting the predator's attention while its owner slips away to safety. Two eggs (12-13 x 5-6 mm) are laid in November. Hatchlings measure 20-30 mm TL and emerge in February-March. **Habitat:** Succulent and karroid veld. **Range:** S. Angola, through W. Namibia, Namaqualand and W. Cape, to Beaufort West in the Karoo and Rooiberg in the Little Karoo.

## Plated Lizards  *Gerrhosaurus*

These medium to large lizards have fully developed but relatively small limbs, and a long tail. The body has a prominent lateral fold. Each nostril is pierced between two nasals and the first labial. The lower eyelids are opaque. The scales beneath the toes are smooth or have tubercles. Femoral pores may be present in both sexes, but are more prominent in males.

Diurnal and terrestrial, most species live in savannah or sandveld although some are rock-living. They dig holes in loose sand around bushes or excavate leaf litter from rock cracks or under boulders. Slow-moving, they eat insects, snails, etc; larger species also eat plant material. Shy and usually solitary, they are rarely common, although the giant plated lizard may form loose colonies. When foraging, they scrape away loose soil or leaf litter looking for prey. They may toboggan slowly down gentle slopes on their smooth belly; this behaviour gives an indication of how the evolution of limb-loss in the gerrhosaurines (*Tetradactylus*) occurred. They bask resting on the belly with the limbs flexed upwards, off the ground. The thick tail base is used for fat storage, and is readily shed but can be fully regenerated. Oviparous, they lay a few soft-shelled eggs in moist sites.

There are six species, all occurring on the subcontinent, with some extending into central and E. Africa. One is endemic.

### Yellow-throated Plated Lizard  *Gerrhosaurus flavigularis* (Pls. 3, 65)
*SVL 110-130 mm; max. SVL 142 mm.*

This medium-sized, graceful lizard has a slender rounded body and a small head. The prefrontals are in narrow contact or are separated. The fronto-nasal and rostral are separated by the nasals. There are five supraciliaries.

The dorsal scales are strongly keeled, in 22-24 longitudinal and 54-64 transverse rows. There are eight rows of ventral plates. Males have 11-17 femoral pores; females have no femoral pores. The back is dark red-brown to olive in colour, with a pair of prominent, dark-edged, yellow dorsolateral stripes. The flanks are darker, often with faint yellowish bars. The belly is cream. In breeding season, the chin, throat, chest and sides of the head of the males turn bright yellow, red or, in some regions, light blue. **Biology and breeding:** Can be very common, even in urban areas. Lives in burrows, which it digs at the base of bushes, under boulders, etc, but is also found under rubbish. Moves surprisingly quickly, catching grasshoppers, termites and millipedes. Alert and difficult to catch without causing it to shed its tail, which is quickly regenerated. It bites readily when first captured, but tames easily and makes an interesting and long-lived (longer than 11 years) pet. The female buries her 4-8 oval, soft-shelled eggs (16-19 x 9-14 mm) in a small chamber dug in leaf litter or under a stone. Hatchlings, measuring 100 mm TL, emerge in late summer. **Habitat:** Varied; montane grassland, savannah, bushveld and low, open coastal forest. **Range:** Throughout the eastern part of the subcontinent, with a patchy distribution along the south coast to Cape Town; absent from karroid and western arid regions, but with a relict population near Gobabis in Namibia. Elsewhere, through E. Africa to Ethiopia and Sudan.

### Rough-scaled Plated Lizard    *Gerrhosaurus major* (Pl. 64)
*SVL 150-200 mm; max. SVL 219 mm.*

A large, stout lizard, with a short head and large eyes. The tympanic shields are long and narrow. The prefrontals touch each other, as do the frontonasal and the rostral. The dorsal scales are rough, in 14-18 longitudinal and 31-33 transverse rows. There are 10 rows of ventral plates. Both sexes have 9-13 femoral pores, but these are more prominent in males. The back is straw-coloured to light brown; each scale is often dark-centred, creating a speckled to striped effect. It has a pale dorsolateral stripe. The chin and throat are light straw to cream, and the belly is smoky-grey to light brown. In the breeding season males develop a pinkish throat (blue in males from Jos, N. Nigeria). Juveniles are more brightly coloured. **Biology and breeding:** Regularly eats soft fruits and flowers, in addition to insects and millipedes; a large wild specimen ate a gravid Kirk's agama, and captive specimens will eat any small lizard they can catch and swallow. Lives in cracks in small, well-vegetated rock outcrops and also in old termitaria. Tames easily and settles well in captivity. Males fight (biting legs and trying to overturn one another) and defend territories. Mating occurs in August and 2-6 large, oval eggs (45-58 x 23-26 mm; 25-30 g) are laid in October-November in moist soil beneath a log or in a rock crack. Incubation takes 70-81 days; hatchlings measure 120-173 mm TL. **Habitat:** Arid and mesic savannah. **Range:** Savannahs of Africa, from Togo in the west and Ethiopia in the north to Maputaland in the south-east. **Subspecies:** Two races are recognized; only the typical race occurs on the subcontinent. Replaced in N. Ethiopia, NW Somalia, W. Kenya and Ghana by *G.m. bottegoi.*

### Kalahari Plated Lizard    *Gerrhosaurus multilineatus* (Pl. 64)
*SVL 150-180 mm; max. SVL 215 mm.*

This large, thick-bodied, handsome lizard has a moderately sized head. The prefrontals are in broad contact, while the frontonasal and rostral are

*G.m. auritus*

separated by the nasals. There are four supraciliaries. The tympanic shields
are broad and crescent-shaped. The dorsal scales are strongly keeled, in
26 longitudinal and 51-54 transverse rows. There are eight rows of ventral
plates. Both sexes have 14-18 femoral pores. The body is pale brown to
sepia, often with dark brown flecks on the head. The scales on the back
and tail have a yellow spot on the inner edge, giving a flecked appearance. Sometimes there is a series of 3-4 narrow, dark-edged pale dorsolateral stripes. The flanks are lighter, with dark brown spots. The limbs
have dark-edged spots. The belly is creamy white. Breeding adults develop
a blue flush on the flanks, throat and upper lips. Juveniles are darker
above with more distinct spots. **Biology and breeding:** This lizard
lives in holes burrowed among the roots of shrubs. Its diet consists of
grasshoppers, beetles, termites and scorpions. Berries are also eaten.
About a dozen eggs are laid in summer. **Habitat:** Bushveld and Kalahari
sandveld. **Range:** N. Kalahari, north to Angola and the Democratic
Republic of Congo (former Zaïre). **Subspecies:** Two races are recognized,
with only one occurring in the region. *G.m. multilineatus* has mucronate
dorsal scales and spiny proximal caudals: this northern race occurs in
Angola, Democratic Republic of Congo and Zambia. *G.m. auritus* attains
440 mm TL, its dorsal scales are not mucronate, and its proximal caudals
are not spiny; this southern race is found in northern regions of Namibia
and Botswana, to Hwange, SW Zimbabwe.

### Black-lined Plated Lizard     *Gerrhosaurus nigrolineatus* **(Pl. 65)**
*SVL 140-175 mm; max. SVL 183 mm.*
A large, thick-bodied plated lizard with a large, robust head. The prefrontals
are in broad contact, while the frontonasal and rostral are separated by
the nasals. There are four supraciliaries. The tympanic shields are narrow.
The dorsal scales are strongly keeled, in 22-24 longitudinal and 54-64
transverse rows. There are eight rows of ventral plates. Both sexes have
16-18 femoral pores. The back is reddish-brown with well-defined, black-
edged, yellow dorsolateral stripes, and often with yellow streaks down the
backbone. The flanks are vermillion or chestnut-brown, usually with
irregular yellow spots. The belly is cream to yellow-white. Juveniles often
have irregular, dark transverse bars on the back. In the breeding season
males develop a blue flush to the throat. **Biology and breeding:** Similar
to the yellow-throated plated lizard, *G. flavigularis* (page 178), but prefers
more open bushveld and lives in rodent and meerkat burrows and old
termitaria. Shy and elusive, it dashes to its burrow at the first sign of danger. Its diet consists mainly of grasshoppers and beetles, but snails are also
taken. It has many predators, including snakes, birds of prey and small
carnivores. The female lays 4-9 eggs (22-30 x 12-18 mm) in an abandoned
rodent burrow, that may be reused subsequently. Incubation takes 70-80
days; hatchlings measure 160-180 mm TL. **Habitat:** Savannah and
bushveld. **Range:** N. Province and Mpumalanga, through Zimbabwe and
adjacent regions to N. Namibia, reaching Gabon and lower Congo.

### Namaqua Plated Lizard     *Gerrhosaurus typicus* **(Pl. 64)**
*(Endemic) SVL 75-100 mm; max. SVL 114 mm.*
This small plated lizard has a shortish head, large eyes and a rounded
body. The tympanic shields are large and crescent-shaped. The prefrontals
are separated (occasionally in short contact), while the frontonasal and
rostral touch. The dorsal scales are keeled, in 22-24 longitudinal and 56-58

transverse rows. There are 10 rows of ventral plates. Both sexes have 15-20 femoral pores. The back is fawn to light purple-brown in colour, some-times with a few scattered dark spots. A pair of dark-edged, white dorso-lateral stripes is present. The flanks are darker, with scattered white, elongate spots. The limbs are pale, pinky-brown. The tail is irregularly spotted and the belly is white. The undersurfaces of the limbs and the base of the tail are carrot-red in breeding males. **Biology:** Rarely seen (SA RDB Rare), and similar in habits to the black-lined plated lizard, *G. nigro-lineatus* (above), living in small burrows that it digs at the base of bushes. It is active in the early morning and evening. Its diet includes termites and blattids. **Habitat:** Karroid succulent veld and renosterveld. **Range:** Little Namaqualand to eastern Great Karoo and western Little Karoo.

### Giant Plated Lizard *Gerrhosaurus validus* (Pl. 64)
*SVL 200-250 mm; max. SVL 285 mm.*
A large lizard with a flattened head and body. The tympanic shields are large and triangular. The prefrontals are in contact, as are the frontonasal and rostral. The dorsal scales are small in 28-34 longitudinal and 52-55 transverse rows. There are 12-16 rows of ventral plates (see Subspecies), and 18-25 femoral pores in both sexes. In adults, the back is dark brown to black with each head shield and dorsal scale spotted yellow, giving a speckled appearance; a pair of broad dorsolateral stripes is sometimes present. The throat is dirty white, and the belly is light brown. Juveniles are black, with a distinct series of yellow spots on the back and bars on the flanks. In breeding season, the chin, throat and sides of the head of the males become tinged with pink-purple. **Biology and breeding:** Rock-living, these lizards prefer the upper slopes of large granite koppies. They may be common. They are shy and difficult to approach. They forage for invertebrates and vegetable matter (flowers, leaves, figs and other soft fruit), but will also eat small lizards, and even baby tortoises. They are very difficult to catch, and jam themselves into large cracks by inflating the body. The female lays 2-5 (usually four) large, oval eggs (44-46 x 24-26 mm) in soil-filled rock crevices in midsummer. Hatchlings measure 150-170 mm TL. **Habitat:** Arid and mesic savannah. **Range:** Northern regions of the subcontinent (see Subspecies). **Subspecies:** Two races are recognized with both occurring in the region. In *G.v. validus* the subocular does not border the lip and there are 14-16 ventral scale rows, and 18-24 lamellae under the fourth toe; this eastern race occurs from Maputaland, through lowveld, Zimbabwe and Mozambique, to Malawi and Zambia. *G.v. maltzahni* has its subocular bordering the lip, 12-14 ventral scale rows, and 15-17 lamellae under the fourth toe; this western race is found in central and NW Namibia, extending into S. Angola.

■ *G.v. maltzahni*

□ *G.v. validus*

# Seps or Plated Snake-lizards *Tetradactylus*
These are small plated lizards, with species that include those having small, but normal limbs, to snake-like forms lacking forelimbs and having only small spiky hind limbs. The body scales are arranged in straight, longitudinal and transverse rows. There is a prominent lateral fold. The head is small, with large head shields. The prefrontals are absent in southern African species. The lower eyelids are scaly. Femoral pores are present, except in the extralimital *T. ellenbergeri*. The tail is elongate.

Most of these lizards are snake-like and speedily hunt grasshoppers and other insects in grassland. They are diurnal, retreating at night into a grass tussock or beneath a stone. The vestigial hind limbs are minute, and are used to support the lizard when stationary and to assist small movements in long vegetation. The very long tail (up to three times the body length) is used for propulsion, rendering them almost impossible to catch when they 'swim' through grass. When startled they also 'spring' by flexing stiff coils against the ground. If grabbed, the tail is readily shed; regeneration is very rapid, as they are helpless without it. All are probably oviparous.

Five species exist; four of which are endemic to the subcontinent. Extralimitally, *T. ellenbergeri* is distributed through the grasslands of E. Angola to SE Tanzania.

### African and FitzSimons' Long-tailed Seps

*Tetradactylus africanus* (Pl. 50)
*(Endemic) SVL 50-75 mm; max. SVL 82 mm (TL 344 mm).*

This snake-like seps has minute, single-toed forelimbs and hind limbs (the forelimbs are sometimes absent; see Subspecies). Each nostril is pierced between two nasals and the first labial. The frontoparietals are just in contact. The dorsal scales are strongly keeled in 14 longitudinal and 69-72 transverse rows. Ventrals are in six longitudinal and 50-52 transverse rows. There are 2-3 femoral pores on each side. The tail is more than three times the length of the body. The back is olive, with dark brown stripes running down the middle of the scale rows. The head is irregularly spotted with dark brown. The sides of the neck have a series of short black bars. The belly is pale olive. **Breeding:** A very common species in the coastal grasslands of KwaZulu-Natal. A small clutch of 2-5 eggs (13-17 x 9-11 mm) is laid in midsummer, specifically in a live ant (*Anochetus faurei*) nest which may be used as an egg site by a number of females. They hatch between February and April; hatchlings measure approximately 115-135 mm TL. **Habitat:** This seps occurs in coastal grassland in the north and coastal fynbos in the south. **Range:** It is found in KwaZulu-Natal (from Pondoland to Maputaland) and in adjacent Swaziland, with an isolated population occurring in the E. Cape. **Subspecies:** Two races recognized, and both occur in the region. *T.a. africanus* has minute forelimbs, and occurs in KwaZulu-Natal. *T.a. fitzsimonsi* lacks forelimbs and is restricted to the Algoa Bay region, E. Cape (with an unconfirmed record from George). It is probably a separate species.

☐ *T.a. africanus*

■ *T.a. fitzsimonsi*

### Breyer's Long-tailed Seps

*Tetradactylus breyeri* (Pl. 51)
*(Endemic) SVL 40-65 mm; max. SVL 72 mm female, 64 mm male.*

A snake-like seps with two minute toes on each forelimb and one on each hind limb. The three supraoculars touch the frontal. Each nostril is pierced between two nasals. The frontoparietals are rarely in contact. The dorsal scales are strongly keeled, in 14 longitudinal and 70-80 transverse rows. The ventrals are in eight longitudinal and 53-63 transverse rows. There are two (rarely three) femoral pores on each side. The tail is more than three times the body length. The back is olive-brown, with faint, darker dorsolateral stripes. The head is dark-spotted. The sides of the neck have short, dark bars. The belly is pale olive in colour. **Biology and breeding:** Active in short grasslands, sheltering in old termite nests and under stones. The female lays a small clutch of 1-2 eggs in early summer. (SA RDB, Rare.) **Habitat:** Prefers montane and highveld grassland. **Range:** Found in SE Mpumalanga and adjacent KwaZulu-Natal and Free State.

### Eastwood's Long-tailed Seps
*Tetradactylus eastwoodae*

*(Endemic) SVL 40-50 mm; max. SVL 64 mm.*
This snake-like seps is similar in appearance to Breyer's long-tailed seps,
*T. breyeri* (above). It has three toes on each forelimb and two on each
hind limb. The two supraoculars touch the frontal. Each nostril is pierced
between two nasals. The frontoparietals are band-like and not in contact.
The dorsal scales are strongly keeled, in 12 longitudinal and 67-70
transverse rows. Ventrals are in 6-8 longitudinal and 50 transverse rows.
There are three femoral pores on each side. The tail is more than twice the
length of the body. The back has olive-brown, indistinct, dark longitudinal
stripes. The head is dark-spotted, and the belly is grey-brown. **Habitat:**
Unknown. **Range:** Woodbush Forest in N. Province. It has not been
rediscovered since its original description in 1913; it is probably extinct,
its habitat having been destroyed for pine plantations (SA RDB Extinct).

### Short-legged Seps
*Tetradactylus seps* **(Pls. 51 and 65)**

*(Endemic) SVL 60-50 mm; max. SVL 68 mm.*
A small long-tailed plated lizard with reduced but fully formed limbs. The
lower eyelids are scaly. The dorsal scales are in 13 longitudinal rows. The
tail is twice the body length. The body is uniform dark olive to blackish-
brown, with slightly fainter flanks. The head has dark brown spots on top
and dark-edged spots on the upper lip. The lower neck is white with short
bars. The belly is olive to bluish-grey. **Biology and breeding:** Rarely
seen, but is locally common. It basks among thick vegetation in moist
clearings. When alarmed it 'swims' through the grass, using its long tail.
It feeds on bees, grasshoppers, etc. The female lays 2-3 large, oval, creamy
white eggs (14 x 8 mm) among rotting logs or in leaf mould. **Habitat:**
Coastal forests or montane grassy plateaus. **Range:** S. and W. Cape, from
Cedarberg along Cape fold mountains, through Amatola Mountains to
KwaZulu-Natal midlands. **Subspecies:** None are now recognized.

### Common Long-tailed Seps
*Tetradactylus tetradactylus* **(Pl. 51)**

*(Endemic) SVL 50-60 mm; max. SVL 73,4 mm.*
This thin, snake-like seps has minute four-toed forelimbs and hind limbs.
The frontoparietals are in contact. The dorsal scales are keeled, in 14
longitudinal and 59-62 transverse rows. Ventrals are in six longitudinal
and 45-46 transverse rows. There are 4-5 femoral pores on each side.
The tail is three times the body length. The back is olive, with a pair of
dark brown dorsolateral stripes. The sides of the neck have short, black
and white bars. The belly is pale olive. **Biology and breeding:** This seps
is very quick and difficult to catch. It shelters at night in tufts of grass.
Two to four eggs are laid in summer. **Habitat:** Montane grassland and
fynbos. **Range:** W. and E. Cape, with relict populations in montane grassland of old escarpment (for example Beaufort West and Cradock), to SE
Free State. **Subspecies:** None are now recognized.

# Girdled Lizards and Relatives
#### FAMILY CORDYLIDAE

These lizards have a short tongue that is covered with long papillae. The
body scales lack osteoderms, except in *Cordylus*, and are arranged in regular girdles (although interspersed with granules, particularly on the flanks,
in some species). The scales on the tail are arranged in regular rings and

are spiny or strongly keeled. The body is often depressed, and in most species is box-like in cross-section, with a lateral fold. The tongue is stout, roundly pointed and sometimes has a shallow notch.

Grass lizard behaviour is poorly known, but cordylids are considered ambush predators, sitting on a suitable vantage point before making a short dash to capture prey. All species are viviparous except those belonging to the genus *Platysaurus*.

This is the only lizard family that is restricted to the African continent. No cordylid fossils are currently known. Plated lizards, previously included as a subfamily, are now treated as a separate family. Fossils (*Pseudolacerta* and *Palaeocordylus*) referred to the Cordyliformes (the group containing the families Cordylidae and Gerrhosauridae) are known from the Early Eocene to the Early Miocene of Europe. There are four genera in southern Africa of which one is endemic. The others are restricted to the subcontinent, except for a few species that extend into central and E. Africa, one reaching Ethiopia.

KEY TO THE SOUTHERN AFRICAN GENERA IN THE CORDYLIDAE
1   Legs very reduced; body snake-like with very long tail:
                    *Chamaesaura* (Grass lizards, page 148)
  - Legs well developed; head with an obvious neck; tail not more than
    twice body length:                                      go to 2
2   Back scales granular and mostly of the same size; tail without spines;
    body strongly flattened:        *Platysaurus* (Flat lizards, page 198)
  - Body scales large; tail with spines; body not strongly flattened:
                                                            go to 3
3   Dorsal scales large and with osteoderms; nasal shield pierced by nostril:
                              *Cordylus* (Girdled lizards, page 185)
  - Dorsal scales small and without osteoderms; nostril pierced between
    nasal and upper labial:
                           *Pseudocordylus* (Crag lizards, page 205)

## Grass Lizards   *Chamaesaura*

These very unusual lizards have extremely reduced limbs (often little more than spikes) and a very long tail (3-4 times longer than the SVL length). The body scales are very rough, strongly keeled and arranged in regular rows.

The elongate shape of grass lizards allows them to move freely in long grass, through which they 'swim' with the speed and agility of snakes (although the generic name translates more correctly as 'creeping lizards'). They are not as mobile on smooth or sandy surfaces. Although the minute limbs appear useless, they give stability when the lizard is at rest. The tail is proportionately shorter in hatchlings. Only the minimum needed for survival is shed, as without their tails they move very slowly and noisily, and thus succumb easily to predation or starvation. Regeneration of the lost segment is rapid. Their rustic colours camouflage them in dried grass. Small invertebrates, particularly grasshoppers, are actively chased and eaten. Viviparous, they give birth to 5-12 babies (up to 150 mm TL) in late summer. Parturition may take 2-3 days, and the young often escape by wriggling from their mother's body.

There are three species in the genus, all occurring in southern Africa. Two have northern races (possibly sibling species) in the savannahs of central and E. Africa, and the other is endemic.

184

**Transvaal Grass Lizard**     *Chamaesaura aenea* **(Pl. 50)**
*(Endemic) SVL 80-120 mm; max. SVL 137 mm (TL 455 mm).*
A slender grass lizard with five clawed digits on each of its four feet and small body scales (42-46 transverse body rows). Its coloration is drab, the head and back being dark brown, with three light yellow or grey-olive, black-edged stripes, the flanks straw-coloured, with 2-3 series of dark spots or a reddish-brown (the specific name means 'coppery') lateral stripe, and the belly off-white. **Breeding:** Up to 12 babies (about 100 mm TL) are born in early summer, and may develop during winter. **Habitat:** Grass-covered mountain slopes and plateaus. **Range:** Scattered populations in the eastern escarpment grasslands, from Mpumalanga, NE Free State, KwaZulu-Natal underberg, to the Amatola Mountains in E. Cape.

**Cape Grass Lizard**     *Chamaesaura anguina* **(Pl. 50)**
*SVL 80-120 mm; max. SVL 140 mm. (TL 570 mm).*
An elongate grass lizard with 1-2 clawed digits on each of its minute forelimbs and hind limbs. The body scales are in 26-30 longitudinal and 36-40 transverse rows. In colour, it is similar to the Transvaal grass lizard, *C. aenea* (above) but the vertebral stripe is broader and the dorsolateral stripes (if present) are black. The flanks are straw-coloured, sometimes with a narrow white lateral band. The belly is whitish or golden-yellow. **Breeding:** Gravid females have very swollen bellies, and give birth to 6-9 babies in summer. **Habitat:** Grassy or fynbos-covered, gentle slopes. **Range:** Cape Town, through Cape fold mountains, E. Cape and KwaZulu-Natal lowlands, and along the escarpment to Mpumalanga Drakensberg. **Subspecies:** Only the typical race, *C.a. anguina*, occurs on the subcontinent; isolated, relict populations occur in Angola (*C.a. oligopholis*), and in upland grasslands (900-2 500 m) of E. Democratic Republic of Congo (former Zaïre) and E. Africa (*C.a. tenuior*).

*C.a. anguina*

**Large-scaled Grass Lizard**     *Chamaesaura macrolepis* **(Pl. 50)**
*SVL 80-120 mm; max. SVL 130 mm male, 166 mm female. (TL 525 mm).*
Forelimbs are absent in this lizard and the hind limbs are vestigial spikes, each having only one claw. The scales are enlarged in 22 longitudinal and 38-40 transverse rows. It is light brown, with two dark brown stripes (often broken into a series of elongate spots). The flanks are straw-coloured and the belly is off-white. **Breeding:** Gives birth to 6-8 babies in March. **Habitat:** Grassveld and mountain plateaus. **Range:** KwaZulu-Natal, through Swaziland and Mpumalanga to Mokeetsi, N. Province, with an isolated population on Chimanimani Mountains in Zimbabwe. Elsewhere to Zambia. **Subspecies:** Only the typical race, *C.m. macrolepis*, occurs on the subcontinent; a relict race (*C.m. miopropus*) is found in N. and E. Zambia.

*C.m. macrolepis*

# Girdled Lizards     *Cordylus*
These are the most characteristic lizards of southern Africa. The body is stocky and the limbs are always well developed. The head is triangular and flattened on top, and covered with large shields that are fused to the skull. The eyes and eyelids are well developed. The eardrums are visible but are partly shielded by scales. The body scales have osteoderms and are overlapping, usually keeled, and sometimes spiny. They are arranged in regular rows (girdles), sometimes separated by granular interspaces. The tail, which has whorls of spiny scales, can be shed and regenerated, albeit slowly and poorly.

They are diurnal and mainly rock living (some species live on the ground or in trees). The thick scales, with their bony plates, protect them from abrasion against rough rock. To evade predators, many species jam themselves into rock cracks by inflating the body and shortening and thickening the skull, which has an unusual hinged structure. They eat a wide variety of large invertebrates, while some of the bigger species also eat small vertebrates and plant matter. All are viviparous, giving birth to a few (1-6) large babies each year. Some live in diffuse colonies, in which the males are territorial during the breeding season. Although they usually have drab coloration, adult males do have active femoral and glandular pores, and appear to use chemical clues to signal status and territorial boundaries. Sexual maturity is reached in 2-4 years, and they are long-lived (up to 25 years is known in captivity).

Their greatest diversity and probable origin is south of the Zambezi River, although a number of species extend into central and E. Africa (*Cordylus rivae* reaches Ethiopia). The taxonomy of many species has long been confused, as have generic boundaries between the girdled and crag lizards. Recent revision has raised the number of species now recognized to 31, all but two of which occur in the region (some with local races), and 26 of which are endemic.

### Campbell's Girdled Lizard      *Cordylus campbelli* (Pl. 104)
*(Endemic) SVL 60-75 mm; max. SVL 79 mm.*

A small girdled lizard, similar in appearance to the Herero girdled lizard, *C. pustulatus* (page 193). It has a flattened body. The nasals, which touch each other, are not or are only feebly tubular, and separate the rostral and the frontonasal. Each lower eyelid has a semi-transparent disc. There are 6-8 occipitals, the middle ones often being small. The dorsal scales are keeled on the back and moderately spiny on the flanks, in 27-31 rows. The ventrals are mostly smooth and in 16-18 longitudinal rows. There is a pair of enlarged preanal plates. Five large femoral pores are present on each thigh. The back and tail are chestnut to light brown, with irregular dark brown crossbars, and sometimes with a dark central band. There are numerous small yellow specks along the back and on the head. The belly is off-white, with rusty infusions on the chin and throat. **Biology:** This poorly-known lizard lives in rock cracks on arid mountain slopes, feeding on termites and beetles. **Habitat:** Rocky, arid savannah. **Range:** Vicinity of Helmeringshausen, Great Namaqualand in Namibia.

### Armadillo Girdled Lizard      *Cordylus cataphractus* (Pl. 68)
*(Endemic) SVL 75-90 mm; max. SVL 105 mm.*

This thick-set, flattened girdled lizard has a broad head. The scales on the sides of the neck have sharp spines. The nasals are in contact, separating the rostral and the frontonasal. It has six large, keeled occipitals. There are 15-17 broad, sometimes asymmetrical, bands of spiny scales around its body. The tail is ringed with large spines. Males have prominent femoral pores (13-16 on each side). The back is plain, dirty yellowish-brown. The upper lips are dark brown. The throat is yellow (especially in males) or violet, with dark brown blotches. The belly is yellow with darker infusions, particularly on the inner surfaces of the limbs. **Biology and breeding:** This heavily armoured, lovable lizard is too often illegally collected (SA RDB Vulnerable). It lives in large cracks in low rock outcrops, and feeds on the insects attracted by the floral splendour of Namaqualand.

In an unusual behaviour for a lizard, it forms family groups that inhabit the same rock cracks. There are even reports of captive adults feeding young. It is very wary and retreats at the first sign of danger. It is very difficult to extract from cracks because of its spiny scales, but if caught in the open, it will bite its tail and roll into a tight ball (hence its common name), making it too spiny for predators to eat. One or two large babies are born in late summer. **Habitat:** Dry, succulent, karroid veld. **Range:** Succulent Karoo, from S. Richtersveld to Matjiesfontein.

### Blue-spotted Girdled Lizard

*Cordylus coeruleopunctatus* (Pl. 71)
*(Endemic) SVL 50-75 mm; max. SVL 82 mm.*
A graceful lizard that is more closely-related to crag lizards than it is to other girdled lizards. Its nasals are in contact separating the rostral and the frontonasal. It lacks occipitals. The scales behind the head are small and granular. The dorsal scales are small, with no interspaced granules, in 40-43 transverse and 20-22 longitudinal rows. There is a pair of enlarged preanal plates, and 12-16 femoral pores on each thigh. The tail has regular whorls of keeled scales. The back is greyish olive, with numerous black streaks that fuse towards the rear. There is a reddish or orange-yellow band on the flanks, and often on the snout and the side of the head. The throat and chest are greenish-yellow to orange (especially in adult males). It characteristically has scattered enamel-blue spots, particularly on the sides of the head, hence its common and scientific names. **Biology and breeding:** It is common in suitable moist habitat, on coastal cliffs and small rock outcrops, where it forages for invertebrates. It may excavate a small tunnel in loose soil in a rock crack or beneath a boulder. It gives birth to 3-4 young in midsummer. **Habitat:** Rock outcrops in fynbos and forest fringes. **Range:** S. Cape, from Mossel Bay to Witelsbos.

### Cape Girdled Lizard

*Cordylus cordylus* (Pl. 66)
*(Endemic) SVL 65-85 mm; max. SVL 98 mm.*
This small girdled lizard has a flattened body and a triangular, flattened head that is rough only on the posterior head shields. Males develop wider heads than females. The nasals are usually in contact, separating the rostral and the frontonasal, which is in contact with the loreals. The sub-ocular does not reach the lip, and the prefrontals are usually in contact. The anterior parietals are smaller than the posterior ones. There are six small, non-spiny occipitals. The dorsal scales, which are large and faintly keeled (with the keels arranged in parallel rows) are in 22-30 transverse and 16-22 longitudinal rows. The ventrals are smooth (but faintly keeled along the flanks) and usually in 12 longitudinal rows. There is a pair of feebly enlarged preanal plates. There are 4-10 femoral pores and a patch of glandular scales on each thigh. These are present in females from coastal regions but not in inland, montane populations. The tail has whorls of large spines. Coloration is varied. It is usually dull brown to reddish-brown, with irregular darker markings, and sometimes with a pale cream, irregular vertebral stripe. The belly is dirty yellow to dull red-brown. **Biology and breeding:** These girdled lizards often live in dense colonies (up to 300 specimens per hectare) where there are suitable rock cracks in which to shelter. Adults are aggressive, and form social hierarchies with dominant males. In territorial disputes males circle one another, bobbing their heads and arching their backs. The weaker male usually

signals submission by moving its tail. Fights may ensue if dominance is not resolved by these rituals. They are active in the early morning and evening (and all day on overcast days), foraging for insects in the veld and dashing back to cover when danger threatens. Predators include snakes, small carnivores and small birds of prey (including owls). They mate in spring and give birth to 1-3 young in January-February. Hatchlings measure 69-80 mm TL. They have lived up to 15 years in captivity. **Habitat:** Diverse; coastal cliffs, rock plateaus in fynbos and montane grassland, and shale bands in mesic thicket. **Range:** Coastal regions of the Cape, from Saldanha Bay to East London, but absent from George to Witelsbos, where it is replaced by the blue-spotted girdled lizard, *C. coeruleopunctatus* (above). Inland, through Cape fold mountains and montane grassland of NE Cape and SE Free State, to inland Transkei (E. Cape). **Subspecies:** None are now recognized.

### Black Girdled Lizard *Cordylus niger* (Pl. 67)

*(Endemic) SVL 70-80 mm; max. SVL 92 mm.*
A medium-sized girdled lizard with a flattened body and a triangular, flattened head with smooth head shields. Males do not have larger heads than females. The nasals are usually in contact, separating the rostral and the frontonasal, which is in contact with the loreals. The prefrontals are not in contact. The subocular usually reaches the lip, and the prefrontals are usually in contact. The anterior parietals are smaller than the posterior ones. The occipitals are rectangular and smooth. The dorsal scales, which are large and faintly keeled (strongly keeled along backbone), are in 22-30 transverse and 16-22 longitudinal rows. The ventrals are smooth (but faintly keeled along the flanks) and in 10 longitudinal rows. There is a pair of feebly enlarged preanal plates. There are 5-10 femoral pores on each thigh. Females lack glandular scales in front of femoral pores. The tail has whorls of large spines. Coloration is uniform jet-black, but slightly paler below. **Biology and breeding:** A solitary species sheltering in small cracks. Its black colour enables it to absorb heat on overcast, misty days. **Habitat:** Rock outcrops in coastal fynbos. **Range:** Restricted to Table Mountain and the Cape Peninsula, with an isolated population on coastal rocks around Saldanha Bay.

### Oelofsen's Girdled Lizard *Cordylus oelofseni* (Pl. 104)

*(Endemic) SVL 55-65 mm; max. SVL 69 mm.*
A small lizard with a flattened body and a triangular, flattened head with rough head shields. The nasals are usually in contact, separating the rostral and the frontonasal, which is in contact with the loreals. The sub-ocular usually reaches the lip, and the prefrontals are usually in contact. The anterior parietals are smaller than the posterior ones. There are 4-8 (usually 5-6) small, irregular occipitals, that are sometimes spiny. The dorsal scales, which are large and faintly keeled (with the keels arranged in parallel rows), are in 22-26 transverse and 18-22 longitudinal rows. The ventrals are smooth and in 10 longitudinal rows. There is a pair of enlarged preanal plates. There are 6-9 femoral pores on each thigh. Females lack glandular scales in front of the femoral pores. The tail has whorls of elongate, large spines. The head, body, limbs and tail are black above with a faint, pale broken line along the backbone. There are two faint, light brown lines on the side of the neck. The belly and limbs are dark grey below. **Biology and breeding:** Solitary, sheltering in shallow

cracks in rock outcrops on mountain summits. Two to three young
are born in late summer to early autumn. **Habitat:** Rock outcrops in
mountain fynbos. **Range:** Western Cape fold mountains around
Piketberg and Tulbagh, with an isolated population at Landdroskop.

### Giant Girdled Lizard or Sungazer *Cordylus giganteus* (Pl. 65)
*(Endemic) SVL 150-180 mm; max. SVL 205 mm.*

A very large girdled lizard. The nasals are separated by the rostral and the
frontonasal. There are four very large, spiny occipitals. The dorsal scales
are spiny, in 22-25 transverse and 10-12 longitudinal rows. There is a pair
of enlarged preanal plates, and 10-12 femoral pores on each thigh. The
tail has whorls of very large spines. The back is yellow to dark brown, and
often extensively clouded with dark brown. The sides of the head, flanks
and belly are pale yellow, sometimes with grey-brown infusions on the
chest. Juveniles are more intensely marked, with irregular crossbars of red-
brown on the back, and black and yellow bands with many orange to red
scales on the tail. **Biology and breeding:** These terrestrial girdled lizards
live in colonies in burrows that they dig in silty, fine soil. The burrows are
usually about 17 m apart, and approximately 420 mm deep and 1 800 mm
long. They end abruptly, without an enlarged chamber, and may become
flooded during the rainy season. Most face north or northwest to catch
the sun. Each burrow is usually occupied by a single individual, although
adults will often share their burrow with juveniles; three species of small
frog also hibernate in winter in these burrows with the lizards. When a
predator enters the burrow, the sungazer retreats backwards towards the
mouth, lashing its spiny tail from side to side. If grasped, it will jam its
occipital spines into the tunnel roof. Sungazers are long-lived (longer than
20 years in captivity). They are often seen during the day, basking at the
entrance to their burrows or on a termite mound, staring at the sun –
hence the common name. They are sit-and-wait ambushers, and feed
mainly on invertebrates (beetles, grasshoppers, millipedes, termites and
spiders), although they will take small vertebrates if the opportunity arises.
They are dormant during winter and rarely seen above ground from May
to mid-August. Their numbers are declining (SA RDB, Vulnerable) due to
habitat destruction (maize and sunflower farming) and, to a limited extent,
because of collecting for the pet trade. One or two babies, measuring
115-150 mm TL, are born January-April, possibly only every 2-3 years.
**Habitat:** Flat or gently sloping *Themeda* grassland, or transitional
zones. **Range:** Small, scattered populations in NE Free State, extreme
W. KwaZulu- Natal and SE Mpumalanga.

### Lawrence's Girdled Lizard *Cordylus lawrenci* (Pl. 68)
*(Endemic) SVL 65-70 mm; max. SVL 75 mm.*

A small, thin girdled lizard with a flattened body and a triangular, flat
head with rough head shields. The nasals are slightly swollen and in
contact, separating the rostral and the frontonasal, and the subocular is
separated from the lip. The lower eyelids are opaque. There are six
occipitals, the middle pair being enlarged. The dorsal scales are keeled on
the back and moderately spiny on the flanks, in 24 transverse and 22
longitudinal rows. The ventrals are mostly smooth, and in 12 longitudinal
rows. There is a pair of enlarged preanal plates, and eight large femoral
pores on each thigh. The tail has whorls of large, spiny scales. The back,
head and tail are dark brown, with irregular black infusions and a few

yellow specks on the head and forebody. The belly is off-white to grey brown, with a black-flecked throat. **Biology:** A rare species known only from a few localities. Usually solitary or in diffuse colonies, living in rock cracks in small outcrops receiving frequent fog. (SA RDB, Restricted.) **Habitat:** Succulent karroid veld. **Range:** Richtersveld in N. Cape.

### Large-scaled Girdled Lizard     *Cordylus macropholis* (Pl. 66)

*(Endemic) SVL 60-65 mm; max. SVL 70 mm.*
A small, round-bodied girdled lizard. The nasals are in contact, separating the rostral and frontonasal. There are six strongly keeled occipitals. The nostril pierces the lower part of the nasal. The dorsal scales are very large, strongly-keeled and in 16-18 transverse and 14-18 longitudinal rows. The ventrals are keeled and in 10 rows. There is a pair of enlarged preanal plates, and 10-12 femoral pores on each thigh. The tail has whorls of very large spines. The back and flanks are grey to olive-grey, with irregular dark markings. The belly is pale grey. **Biology and breeding:** Terrestrial, this girdled lizard is found among dead wood or debris at the strand line, or sometimes in soft limestone cracks. Succulent *Euphorbia caput-medusae* plants in sand dunes are a favourite retreat, and may contain up to five lizards. Females grow bigger than males and are more common. The diet consists mainly of beetles. It is a very shy lizard, scuttling off when in danger. The olive-grey body is well camouflaged among twigs and dead leaves. One or two young are born in April-May. These measure 60-70 mm TL. **Habitat:** Coastal dunes and strand line. **Range:** Cape coast, from Yzerfontein to Kleinsee.

### McLachlan's Girdled Lizard     *Cordylus mclachlani* (Pl. 67)

*(Endemic) SVL 50-70 mm; max. SVL 73 mm.*
This small girdled lizard has a very flattened body and a triangular head with rough head shields. There are only 2-3 supraciliaries. The supranasals are in contact, separating the rostral and frontonasal. The nasals are small and slightly tubular. The anterior parietals are larger than the posterior ones. There are 5-8 spiny occipitals, and no enlarged chin shields. The dorsal scales are small, obliquely keeled and in 26-28 transverse and 21-25 longitudinal rows. The laterals are spiny and larger than the dorsals. The ventrals are smooth, in 12-14 longitudinal rows. There is a pair of feebly enlarged preanal plates, and 7-12 femoral pores are present on each thigh. The tail has whorls of very large spines. The back, tail and limbs are olive-brown, with numerous, irregular black markings and a few yellow speckles. The flanks are reddish-brown. The head is dark brown to blackish, with a faint, dark line from the snout through the eye. The belly is creamy white. **Biology:** (SA RDB, Restricted.) Shy and usually solitary, preferring to bask near cover. Seldom moves far from its retreat in narrow cracks on low sandstone outcrops. The tail is easily shed and many specimens have incomplete or regenerated tails. **Habitat:** Succulent karroid veld. **Range:** From Koue Bokkeveld north along eastern fringes of Cedarberg and Bokkeveld to Nieuwoudtville.

### Dwarf Girdled Lizard     *Cordylus minor* (Pl. 104)

*(Endemic) SVL 40-65 mm; max. SVL 68,5 mm.*
This small girdled lizard has a flattened body and a triangular head with rough head shields. There are three supraciliaries. The supranasals are in contact, separating the rostral and frontonasal. The nasals are small and

not tubular. There are 5-6, usually 6, upper labials. The anterior parietals are larger than the posterior ones. There are six occipitals, and no enlarged chin shields. The dorsal scales are small, obliquely keeled, and in 26-28 transverse and 24-26 longitudinal rows. The laterals are spiny and larger than the dorsals. The ventrals are smooth, in 14-16 longitudinal rows. There is a pair of feebly enlarged preanal plates, and both sexes have 3-6 femoral pores on each thigh. The tail has whorls of large spines. The back, tail and limbs are dirty brown in colour, with diffuse irregular black markings. The head is dark brown to blackish. The belly and upper labials are dirty white. **Biology:** Lives in scattered colonies. Shy; chooses small, vertical rock cracks in low, north-facing rock outcrops. **Habitat:** Succulent karroid veld. **Range:** Restricted to Matjiesfontein region in SW Karoo.

### Cloete's Girdled Lizard *Cordylus cloetei* (Pl. 104)

*(Endemic) SVL 40-65 mm; max. SVL 69,5 mm.*

This small girdled lizard has a flattened body and a triangular head with rough head shields. There are three supraciliaries. The supranasals are in contact, separating the rostral and frontonasal. The nasals are small and not tubular. There are 5, sometimes 6, upper labials. The anterior parietals are larger than the posterior ones. There are six occipitals, and no enlarged chin shields. The dorsal scales are small, obliquely keeled, and in 26-29 transverse and 24-26 longitudinal rows. The laterals are spiny and larger than the dorsals. The ventrals are smooth, in 14-16 longitudinal rows. There is a pair of feebly enlarged preanal plates, and both sexes have 4-6 femoral pores on each thigh. The tail has whorls of large spines. The back, tail and limbs are dirty brown in colour, with diffuse irregular black markings. The head is dark brown to blackish. The belly and upper labials are dirty white. **Biology:** This shy species lives in scattered colonies. **Habitat:** Found in sandstone outcrops in *Themeda* grassland. **Range:** Restricted to the Nuweveld Mountains near Fraserberg.

### Rooiberg Girdled Lizard *Cordylus imkeae* (Pl. 104)

*(Endemic) SVL 40-65 mm; max. SVL 67,8 mm.*

A small, colourful lizard with a flattened body and triangular head with rough shields. There are three supraciliaries. The supranasals are in contact, separating the rostral and frontonasal. The nasals are small and not tubular. There are 5-6, usually 5, upper labials. The anterior parietals are larger than the posterior ones. There are six occipitals, and no enlarged chin shields. The dorsal scales are small, obliquely keeled, and in 26-28 transverse and 24-26 longitudinal rows. The laterals are spiny and larger than the dorsals. The ventrals are smooth, in 14-16 longitudinal rows. There is a pair of feebly enlarged preanal plates, and both sexes have 4-6 femoral pores on each thigh. The tail has whorls of large spines. The back, tail and limbs are dirty brown, with diffuse irregular black markings. The head is dark brown to blackish; the belly and upper labials dirty white. **Biology:** Lives in granite rock crevices on upper mountain slopes. **Habitat:** Fynbos transitional veld. **Range:** Restricted to Rooiberg, Little Namaqualand.

### Dwarf Karoo Girdled Lizard *Cordylus aridus* (Pl. 67)

*(Endemic) SVL 40-60 mm; max. SVL 66,2 mm.*

The smallest girdled lizard, it has a flattened body and a triangular head with rough shields. There are three supraciliaries. The supranasals are in contact, separating the rostral and frontonasal. The nasals are small and

not tubular. There are 5-6, usually 5, upper labials. The anterior parietals are larger than the posterior ones. There are six occipitals, no enlarged chin shields. The dorsal scales are small, obliquely keeled, and in 26-28 transverse and 24-26 longitudinal rows. The laterals are spiny and larger than the dorsals. The ventrals are smooth, in 14-16 longitudinal rows. There is a pair of feebly enlarged preanal plates; both sexes have 4-6 femoral pores on each thigh. The tail has whorls of large spines. The back, tail and limbs are dirty brown, with diffuse irregular black markings. The head is dark brown to blackish; the belly and upper labials dirty white. **Biology:** Shy; lives in vertical rock cracks in low, north-facing Dwyka tillite outcrops. **Habitat:** Rocky karroid veld. **Range:** S. Karoo near Prince Alfred.

### Namaqua Girdled Lizard
*Cordylus namaquensis* (Pl. 68)

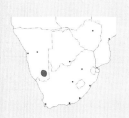

*(Endemic) SVL 75-80 mm; max. SVL 82 mm.*
A small girdled lizard with a flattened body and a triangular, flat head with rough shields (but with smooth second and third supraoculars). The nasals are slightly tubular and in contact, separating the rostral and frontonasal. The lower eyelids are opaque. There are eight occipitals, the middle ones often being small. The dorsal scales are smooth on the back and moderately spiny on the flanks, in 27-31 rows. The ventrals are mostly smooth, in 16-18 longitudinal rows. There is a pair of enlarged preanal plates, and both sexes have 9-10 femoral pores on each thigh. The tail has whorls of large, spiny scales. The back is chestnut to light brown in colour, usually with dark brown to black mottling. The side of the head has two blackish streaks. The lower labials are black-edged, and the belly is dirty white to pale brown. **Biology and breeding:** Rare; lives in rock cracks and crevices in mountains. Feeds on termites and beetles. Two to three young born in January-February after four- to five-month gestation. **Habitat:** Semi-desert. **Range:** Great Karasberg district in S. Namibia.

### Peers' Girdled Lizard
*Cordylus peersi* (Pl. 68)

*(Endemic) SVL 75-80 mm; max. SVL 85 mm.*
This small, thin lizard has a flattened body and a triangular, flat head with rough shields. The nasals are swollen and in contact, separating the rostral and frontonasal. The subocular borders the lip. The lower eyelids are opaque. There are six occipitals, the middle pair of which is often small. The dorsal scales are keeled on the back and moderately spiny on the flanks, in 22-24 transverse and 16 longitudinal rows. The ventrals are mostly smooth, and in 12 longitudinal rows. There is a pair of enlarged preanal plates, and both sexes have 9-12 large femoral pores on each thigh. The tail has whorls of large, spiny scales. The back and tail are jet-black. The belly is very dark purple-brown, with pale yellow femoral pores and glandular scales. **Biology:** Visible when basking on light-coloured rocks, but quickly retreats into a deep crack when approached. Prefers the upper surfaces of large shattered boulders on small, rocky outcrops. Some cracks may be home to several lizards. Captures large insects and caterpillars. **Habitat:** Succulent karroid veld. **Range:** Little Namaqualand.

### Karoo Girdled Lizard
*Cordylus polyzonus* (Pl. 69)

*(Endemic) SVL 90-105 mm; max. SVL 113 mm.*
A large, graceful girdled lizard with a flattened body. The supranasals are in contact, separating the rostral and frontonasal. The nasals are small and slightly tubular. The lower eyelids have transparent discs. There are two

occipitals. The dorsal scales are small, smooth on the back and keeled on the flanks, in 38-46 transverse rows. There is a pair of enlarged preanal plates, and 10-19 femoral pores on each thigh. There are two rows of large, spiny scales in each tail whorl. Coloration is regionally varied. In juveniles, the back is yellow-brown, chequered with dark brown and pale cream, and the tail is banded in dark brown. In adults, the body may retain the juvenile coloration (in specimens from S. Karoo), or become dark brown or black (central Cape, coastal Namaqualand and S. Namibia), uniform olive (S. Free State), olive-brown with vivid orange-red flanks (N. Cape), or even blue-green (Tygerberg, SW Cape). All populations have a characteristic black blotch on the side of the neck, and some individuals retain irregular black spots on the back. **Biology and breeding:** One of the most common lizards in the central karroid regions of the Cape. Found in diffuse colonies, living in sun-split rocks of small rock outcrops and lower mountain slopes. During the heat of the day it perches on a boulder, basking and making short forays to grab beetles or grasshoppers. During winter it may hibernate in a deep tunnel which it digs in soil beneath a large boulder. Very alert, at the first sign of danger it retreats into a rock crack and curls its tail over its head. Two (exceptionally 3-4) large babies (100-110 mm TL) are born in late summer (February-March). **Habitat:** Varied: Karroid regions, coastal renosterveld and succulent Karoo. **Range:** Central and W. Cape; into S. Free State and S. Namibia.

### Jordan's Girdled Lizard *Cordylus jordani* (Pl. 69)
*(Endemic) SVL 110-120 mm; max. SVL 127 mm.*
This species is similar to the Karoo girdled lizard, *C. polyzonus* (page 192), but grows larger and is more robust in build. It has only 5-8 femoral pores. There is a single row of scales in each tail whorl. The body is uniform olive-brown in adults, and there is no dark blotch on the side of the neck. Juveniles are buff-coloured, with a typical, dark, chequered pattern. **Biology and breeding:** Similar to that of Karoo girdled lizard. **Habitat:** Rocky hillsides. **Range:** Central Namibia, north of Aus.

### Herero Girdled Lizard *Cordylus pustulatus* (Pl. 67)
*(Endemic) SVL 70-75 mm; max. SVL 82 mm.*
This smallish, finely scaled lizard has a very flattened body and a triangular head with rough head shields. The nasals are in contact, separating the rostral and frontonasal, which is broader than it is long, and touches the loreals. There are six, non-spiny occipitals. The dorsal scales are small and smooth down the back, and in 30-32 transverse and 27-29 longitudinal rows. The laterals are keeled. The ventrals are smooth (except the outermost rows), in 14 longitudinal rows. There is a pair of feebly enlarged preanal plates. The tail has whorls of large spines. The back is either uniform olive-brown to dark brown, or, more usually, has numerous small, scattered, yellow spots that form a vague vertebral band. The belly is yellowish-brown. **Habitat:** Arid savannah. **Range:** Hereroland, Namibia.

### Zimbabwe Girdled Lizard *Cordylus rhodesianus* (Pl. 67)
*SVL 60-80 mm; max. SVL 91 mm.*
A small girdled lizard with a very flattened body and a triangular head that has smooth or slightly rough head shields. The nasals are usually in contact, separating the rostral and the frontonasal, which is four-sided and separate from the loreals. There are six, non-spiny occipitals.

GIRDLED LIZARDS & RELATIVES **193**

The dorsal scales are small and slightly keeled down the back, in 25-29 transverse and 20-26 longitudinal rows. The laterals are keeled. The ventrals are smooth (except the outermost preanal plates) and in 12-14 rows. Both sexes have 5-8 femoral pores on each thigh. The tail has whorls of large spines. The back is olive-brown, with irregular darker markings and sometimes with paler blotches on the upper flanks. The belly is yellowish or greyish-white. **Biology:** This girdled lizard is long-lived and slow-growing. It lives under stones and in rock cracks on rocky outcrops, and feeds on beetles and grasshoppers. Predators include the berg adder. **Habitat:** Montane grassland. **Range:** Eastern Highlands of Zimbabwe and adjacent Mozambique, with an isolated population on Nyika Plateau, Malawi.

### Tasman's Girdled Lizard

*Cordylus tasmani* **(Pl. 66)**

*(Endemic) SVL 65-75 mm; max. SVL 81 mm.*
A small girdled lizard with a rounded body and a triangular head, that is not obviously flattened and has slightly rough head shields. The nasals are usually in contact, separating the rostral and the frontonasal, which is in contact with the loreals. There are six small, non-spiny occipitals. The dorsal scales are large, slightly keeled and in 22-30 transverse and 16-20 longitudinal rows. The ventrals are smooth, and in 10-12 longitudinal rows. There is a pair of feebly enlarged preanal plates and both sexes have 4-6 femoral pores on each thigh. The tail has whorls of large spines. The back is reddish-brown to mahogany, with irregular darker markings, sometimes with a pale cream, irregular vertebral stripe. The belly is dirty yellow to dark red-brown. **Biology and breeding:** Lives under the 'apron' of dead leaves on tall aloes, or on dead aloe stems lying on stony slopes; it can also be found under the bark of trees or in piles of rotting spekboom trunks, and will occupy cracks in limestone or sandstone outcrops. It feeds on small invertebrates. It is usually shy and difficult to approach. One to three young (70-75 mm TL) are born in late summer (February-March). **Habitat:** Mesic thicket. **Range:** Algoa Basin in E. Cape, including St Croix Island.

### Tropical Girdled Lizard

*Cordylus tropidosternum* **(Pl. 66)**

*SVL 60-75; max. SVL 88 mm.*
This small, round-bodied girdled lizard does not have a flattened head, and its head scales are rough and keeled. The nasals are in contact, or are separated by the rostral and frontonasal. There are six occipitals. The dorsal scales are very large, strongly keeled and in 22-27 transverse rows. The lateral scales are separated by granular interspaces. The ventrals are smooth (with the outer rows keeled in the typical race), and in 12-14 rows. There is a pair of enlarged preanal plates, and both sexes have 6-9 femoral pores on each thigh. The tail has whorls of large spines. The back and flanks are a dirty straw colour, grey-brown or dark brown, and sometimes uniform but more often irregularly blotched in dark brown, with off-white flecks along the backbone. There is a dark brown to black lateral band from the neck to the groin. The belly is off-white to straw-yellow. The femoral pores are yellow. **Biology and breeding:** This lizard lives under loose bark, in hollow logs of trees, and in tree stumps. It is usually very shy and secretive. It feeds on moths and spiders, and is very fond of winged termites. It lays down fat reserves to tide it over the dry winter season. Usually two (but sometimes up to four) young (60-70 mm TL) are

*C.t. jonesi*

*C.t. tropidosternum*

194

born in midsummer. **Habitat:** Dry lowveld, particularly mopane savannah. **Range:** E. African lowlands, south to the N. Province, Mpumalanga lowveld and adjacent regions. **Subspecies:** There are two races, and both occur in the region. *C.t. tropidosternum* is larger (up to 88 mm SVL), and the 3-4 outer rows of ventrals are keeled; it is found in E. Africa, reaching its southernmost limit in E. Zimbabwe. *C.t. jonesi* is a small race (up to 75 mm SVL), and all its ventrals are smooth; this southern race occurs in N. Province, E. Botswana, Mpumalanga, N. Zululand and S. Mozambique.

### Transvaal Girdled Lizard    *Cordylus vittifer* (Pl. 67)

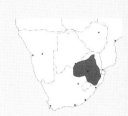

*SVL 70-85 mm; max. SVL 95 mm.*
A small girdled lizard with a very flattened body and a triangular head with rough head shields. The first row of dorsals is elongated. The nasals are in contact, separating the rostral and frontonasal. There are six occipitals. The dorsal scales are small and strongly keeled, in 24-26 transverse and 18-25 longitudinal rows. The laterals are spiny. The ventrals are smooth, in 16-18 rows (but 14-16 in some populations). There is a pair of enlarged preanal plates. Usually, both sexes have 6-8 femoral pores on each thigh, but these are fewer, and are sometimes absent, in females of some populations. The tail has whorls of very large spines. The back is either uniform straw-coloured, yellow-brown to dark brown, or has irregular, darker spots that are sometimes arranged to form dorsolateral bands. A pale cream-white vertebral stripe is often present. The flanks are orange-brown. The head has a few scattered, yellow spots. The belly is dirty white to light brown. An isolated population in extreme NE Free State, with a prominent dark lateral band and glandural scales on the thighs in females (max. SVL 77 mm), may represent a distinct species. **Biology and breeding:** Lives in cracks in small rock outcrops, feeding on beetles, grasshoppers, etc. One to four young, 65-75 mm TL, born in early summer. **Habitat:** Rock outcrops in grassland. **Range:** Gauteng and adjacent Mpumalanga, N. Free State, SE Botswana, Swaziland, and Kwa-Zulu-Natal; one record from Mozambique. **Subspecies:** None recognized.

### Machodoe's Girdled Lizard    *Cordylus machadoi* (Pl. 104)

*SVL 60-70 mm; max. SVL 78 mm.*
This species is similar to, and was once treated as an isolated race of, the Transvaal girdled lizard, *C. vittifer* (page 195). It is a small girdled lizard in which the first row of dorsals is also elongated. The body is very flattened and the triangular head has rough head shields. The nasals are in contact, separating the small rostral from the frontonasal. The dorsal scales are small and strongly keeled, in 26-28 transverse and 22-23 longitudinal rows. The smooth ventrals are in 16 rows. Males have 6-7 femoral pores on each thigh. It is uniform dirty yellow-brown above, and paler on the sides of the body, tail and belly. The head is dark brown above but the lips are paler. **Biology and breeding:** Solitary or in pairs, living in cracks in small rock and calcrete outcrops. **Habitat:** Arid savannah. **Range:** Huila Province, S. Angola to extreme N. Kaokoveld, Namibia.

### Warren's Girdled Lizard    *Cordylus warreni* (Pl. 70)

*(Endemic) SVL 105-130 mm; max. SVL 142 mm (C.w. barbetonensis).*
This large girdled lizard has a flattened body. The nasals are separated by the rostral and frontonasal. There are 5-8 occipitals (see Subspecies). The dorsal scales are spiny, in 24-37 transverse rows (see Subspecies). There is a

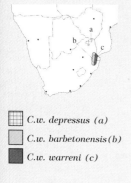

C.w. depressus (a)

C.w. barbetonensis (b)

C.w. warreni (c)

pair of enlarged preanal plates, and only males have 7-13 femoral pores on each thigh. The tail has whorls of large, spiny scales. The back is dark brown to black, with varying degrees of yellow spotting and/or barring (see Subspecies). **Biology and breeding:** This species is found on rocky mountain slopes, favouring deep cracks in large boulders that are sheltered by trees. It is very shy and difficult to approach. The diet includes large invertebrates (beetles, grasshoppers, etc.), small land snails, small lizards and even frogs. Two to six young (90-130 mm TL) are born in late summer. **Habitat:** Montane, well-wooded rocky outcrops. **Range:** Eastern escarpment from Ubombo Mountains in Zululand, through Mpumalanga Drakensberg, to the Soutpansberg in N. Province.

**Subspecies:** The taxonomy of this species has been revised recently, with some races being elevated to full species status. Only three disjunct races are now recognized and all occur in the region. C.w. depressus (a) has a dark brown back with irregular, scattered, large yellow spots or bars. It occurs widely in the N. Province. C.w. barbertonensis (b) also has a very dark brown back with bright yellow bars or large spots on the back. It is found from Barberton in Mpumalanga to S. Swaziland. C.w. warreni (c) has a dark brown back with small yellow, black-edged spots forming vague bands; it occurs along the Lebombo Range from extreme SE Mpumalanga, through E. Swaziland to Maputaland.

### Gorongosa Girdled Lizard     *Cordylus mossambicus* (Pl. 105)
*(Endemic) SVL 75-100 mm; max. SVL 112 mm female.*

A large lizard with a flattened body. Its small collar renders it unique among girdled lizards. The nasals are separated by the rostral and fronto-nasal. There are 6 (rarely 7-8) occipitals. The dorsal scales are in 35-46 transverse rows and imbedded in granular skin. There is a pair of enlarged preanal plates, and only males have 8-11 femoral pores on each thigh. The tail has whorls of spiny scales, that are largest on the sides. Males develop bright breeding colours. Females and juveniles are dark brown above, with transverse rows of small yellow spots, and grey brown below. Females have dark brown mottling on the throat. Breeding males have a uniform blackish back with bright orange to yellow flanks. The chin and throat are blackish, whilst the belly is orange or yellow with a brown patch in front of the cloaca. **Biology:** This girdled lizard lives in cracked boulders in montane grassland or well-wooded lower slopes. **Habitat:** Prefers large rock outcrops in mesic savanna. **Range:** Found in the Gorongosa Mountains in Mozambique to the lower slopes of the Chimanimani Mountains in Zimbabwe.

### Regal Girdled Lizard     *Cordylus regius* (Pl. 71)
*(Endemic) SVL 125-135 mm; max. SVL 143 mm.*

This species is closely related to Gorongosa girdled lizard (above). It is large with a flattened body. The nasals are separated by the rostral and frontonasal. There are 4-8 (usually 6-7) occipitals. The dorsal scales are spinose and in 34-40 transverse rows. There is a pair of enlarged preanal plates, and only males have 7-11 femoral pores on each thigh. The tail has whorls of spiny scales, that are largest on the sides. Males develop bright breeding colours. Females and juveniles have pale brown heads and dark brown backs, with transverse rows of small cream spots that are more numerous on the neck. The flanks are yellowish brown with vague yellow vertical bars. The body is grey-brown below with dark brown mottling on

the throat; the lower lips are dull red. Breeding males have blackish backs that lack cream spots; their flanks are bright orange to yellow in colour. The chin and belly are also yellowish, and the throat dark and mottled. **Biology and breeding:** A shy species that prefers to shelter in large cracks in shaded boulders, and rarely moves from cover. The diet consists mainly of millipedes and beetles, but can be supplemented with spiders, caterpillars, grasshoppers and other large insects. Four to six young (90-115 mm TL) are normally born in midsummer. **Habitat:** Prefers granite outcrops in miombo savannah. **Range:** Found in SE Mutare District of Zimbabwe.

### Waterberg Girdled Lizard *Cordylus breyeri* (Pl. 105)

*(Endemic) SVL 110-120 mm; max. SVL 145 mm.*
A large lizard distinguished from the similar Van Dam's girdled lizard (below) by its brown colour and spiny appearance. It has a flattened body and triangular head. The nasals are separated by the rostral and fronto-nasal. There are 3-4 spiny occipitals separated in the middle by 0-3 smaller scales. The dorsal scales are keeled, becoming very spiny on the flanks, and are arranged mostly in 26-28 transverse rows. The smooth ventral scales are in 12-14 longitudinal rows. There is a pair of enlarged preanal plates. Males have 10-14 (usually 11-13) femoral pores on each thigh. The tail has whorls of large, spiny scales that are almost hooked on the sides. The back is brown to yellow- or greyish-brown, with irregular pale yellow-ish bars and darker blotches. The head is dark brown and the lips white. The flanks are brown to pale greyish-brown, and the belly brown to dark brown; males have white glandular scales on their thighs. The tail is brown with scattered dark and light spines. **Biology and breeding:** A shy species; usually found sheltering in deep, shaded cracks on the cool side of rock outcrops. Mostly solitary or in pairs. Two to four large babies, measuring 110-120 mm TL, are born in summer. **Habitat:** Prefers rock outcrops in open savannah. **Range:** Found in Waterberg and surrounding areas, N. Province.

### Van Dam's Girdled Lizard *Cordylus vandami* (Pl. 70)

*(Endemic) SVL 110-120 mm; max. SVL 145 mm.*
A large lizard with a flattened body and triangular head. The nasals are separated by the rostral and frontonasal. There are four occipitals (not very spinose) that may be separated in the middle by 1-4 smaller scales. The dorsal scales are spiny, in mostly 27-29 transverse rows. The smooth ventral scales are in 12-14 longitudinal rows. There is a pair of enlarged preanal plates. Males have 10-17 (usually 12-14) femoral pores on each thigh. The tail has whorls of large, spiny scales. The back is dark reddish-brown with up to six fragmented yellow crossbars, extending from behind the head onto the tail. The head is uniform dark brown, sometimes with pale edges to the head shields. The flanks are grey-brown to yellowish with irregular bars, and the belly dirty yellow-brown with scattered blotches. The throat is yellowish with brown chevrons. The tail is banded yellow and dark brown. **Biology and breeding:** A shy and solitary species (occasionally found in pairs), inhabiting large rock cracks in shaded rock outcrops. From 2-6 babies (usually 3-4) are born in summer. **Habitat:** Prefers rocky outcrops in mesic savannah. **Range:** Found in N. Province and eastern escarpment of Mpumalanga, possibly extending into Mozambique.

# Flat Lizards    *Platysaurus*

These unmistakable and bizarre creatures are some of our most beautiful lizards. The body is very flattened and covered with granular scales. The legs and tail are well developed and often have scattered spiny scales. The eyes and eyelids are well developed, and the eardrums are visible. Femoral pores occur in both sexes; large in males and as small pits in females.

The flattened shape of these 'platys' (or 'flatties') permits them to squeeze under thin rock flakes where they are safe from predators. Up to 12 individuals may squeeze into the same crack, although it is unusual to find adult males together during the breeding season. They are restricted to certain types of rock (for example granite, gneiss and some sandstones), and are therefore found in isolated populations. Sociable, they form dense colonies. Prime territories on the rock faces are defended by dominant males during the breeding season. These depressed dandies are clothed in Jacobean splendour, the colours varying from species to species. They are most vivid on the belly, where their intensity of colour is hidden from predators. Females and juveniles have black backs, usually attractively marked with three pale, longitudinal, dorsal stripes. Males grow slightly larger than females. In confrontations, males circle each other and expose their brightly coloured bellies by tilting sideways. In courtship, males present head-on to females, raising the head and forebody on straightened forelimbs, revealing the bright coloration of the throat and chest. They mature at the end of their second or third year. Unlike other cordylids, they are oviparous and lay only two eggs, usually in November-December. The eggs are large, elongate (7-10 x 17-22 mm) and soft-shelled, and are laid in deep cracks, usually in damp leaf mould. Numerous females may nest in the same crack, where as many as 30 eggs may be laid. Most platys feed on small invertebrates (flies, beetles and larvae), although some (for example *P. broadleyi*, *P. guttatus*, *P. ocellatus* and *P.i. wilhelmi*) also eat plant material (flower petals, young leaves, fruits and seeds). They are relatively long-lived, and have lived for longer than 14 years in captivity. When attacked by a snake, they may form a ring by holding their tail in the mouth to prevent being swallowed.

This genus has speciated explosively in Zimbabwe and adjacent areas, where 14 species (some with local races) have evolved. Two closely-related and isolated species occur in NW Cape and S. Namibia. Thirteen species, 12 of which are endemic, occur in the region. Species and subspecies are often identified by the male's breeding colours, which makes the identification of females and juveniles difficult. However, few species are sympatric (except in the Waterberg-Soutpansberg region) and if the locality is known, there is little difficulty identifying the species.

## Cape Flat Lizard    *Platysaurus capensis* (Pl. 74)

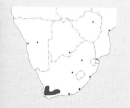

*(Endemic) SVL 70-75 mm; max. SVL 86 mm male, 80 mm female.*
The lower eyelids of this platy are opaque, and each is divided with a series of vertical septa. The enlarged supranasals are in contact behind the rostral. The middle row of gulars is not very enlarged. The scales on the sides of the neck are flattened and not enlarged. There are fewer than 98 transverse granules across the back. The ventrals are in 18-22 longitudinal rows. Males have 13-20 femoral pores. Females and juveniles have a dark brown back, with three broad, cream stripes that may be broken up into spots, or there may be spots between the stripes; the tail is straw-coloured, and the belly is white with a blackish patch in the middle that may be

surrounded by diffuse orange-yellow. In adult males, the head and most of the body are Prussian blue to blue-green (northern specimens have numerous pale spots), and faint dorsal stripes may persist. The rear of the body is red-brown to pale brown, and the tail is red-brown. The throat is light blue and lacks a collar. The chest is dark blue, and the belly is black in the centre. The forelimbs are blue, the hind limbs, tail and rear of the body are red below. **Biology:** These beautiful lizards are common on granite outcrops in the Richtersveld, but rarely form dense colonies. The beautiful males are shy and difficult to approach. A pair of eggs are laid beneath a sunny rock crack in November-December, and a second clutch may be laid later in the summer. **Habitat:** Succulent veld. **Range:** Lower Orange River from Goodhouse to the Richtersveld, extending south to Garies in Namaqualand and along Fish River into S. Namibia.

### Broadley's Flat Lizard

*Platysaurus broadleyi* **(Pl. 105)**
*(Endemic) SVL 70-75 mm; max. SVL 86 mm male, 76 mm female.*
Very similar in scalation to the Cape flat lizard, *P. capensis* (above), but differs in having finer scalation on the top of the forelimbs, and 92-117 transverse granules across the back. The ventrals are in 19-23 longitudinal rows. Males have 15-18 femoral pores. Females and juveniles have a dark brown back, with three broad, cream stripes that may be broken up into spots, or may have spots between them. The belly is white, sometimes with a blackish patch in the middle, and is suffused with pale orange to the rear; the tail is straw-coloured. In adult males, the top of the head is bluish, and the back greenish, with a darker area in the middle and with vestiges of the juvenile stripes and spots. The forelimbs are yellow to orange, the throat is dark blue, and the belly is black in front merging into orange towards the tail. The tail is tan above, and orange below and on the sides. **Biology and breeding:** These beautiful lizards are common on the smooth granite walls of the Augrabies Falls National Park, where they tolerate thousands of tourists. In summer they gorge on swarms of black flies that congregate near rivers, but can also be seen feeding on the ripe berries of Namaqua fig trees. A major predator is the rock kestrel. Sexual maturity is reached at around 64 mm SVL in both sexes. Females lay two egg clutches in early summer. **Habitat:** Rocky, arid savannah. **Range:** Lower Orange River between Augrabies Falls and Pella.

### Sekukhune Flat Lizard

*Platysaurus orientalis* **(Pl. 74)**
*(Endemic) SVL 70-75 mm; max. SVL 90 mm.*
A large platy with a transparent 'window' in each lower eyelid. The supranasals are fused with the nasals. The middle row of gulars is enlarged. The scales on the sides of the neck are conical and enlarged, and the ones on the heels and at the base of the tail are spiny. The ventrals are in 20-22 longitudinal rows. There are 20 femoral pores in males. Females and juveniles have a black back that is marked with three broad, cream-coloured stripes with 1-2 faint spots between them. The throat is white with three dark stripes, and the belly is white with black spots. Adult males have a dark green head with three pale stripes. The body is green with a few faint, light spots, and the tail is orange or red above and yellow below. Ventral coloration varies (see Subspecies). **Biology and breeding:** Two eggs (17 x 7,5-8,5 mm) are laid in a rock crack in early summer. The diet consists mainly of insects and caterpillars. **Habitat:** Mesic savannah. **Range:** Mpumalanga Escarpment. **Subspecies:** Two races are recognized.

*P.o. orientalis (a)*
*P.o. fitzsimonsi (b)*

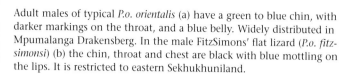

Adult males of typical *P.o. orientalis* (a) have a green to blue chin, with darker markings on the throat, and a blue belly. Widely distributed in Mpumalanga Drakensberg. In the male FitzSimons' flat lizard (*P.o. fitzsimonsi*) (b) the chin, throat and chest are black with blue mottling on the lips. It is restricted to eastern Sekhukhuniland.

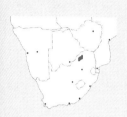

## Dwarf Flat Lizard  *Platysaurus guttatus* (Pl. 74)
*(Endemic) SVL 65-70 mm; max. SVL 80 mm.*

A small platy in which the transparent 'window' in the lower eyelid is entire in the north, and split in the south of its range (below lat. 20°S). The supranasals are fused with the nasals. The middle row of gulars is enlarged. The scales on the sides of body are flattened and only just larger than those on the back. The ventrals are mostly in 18-20 longitudinal rows. Scales on the heels and at the base of the tail are not spiny (some specimens from SW foothills of Waterberg have spiny tails). Males have 13-20 femoral pores. Females and juveniles have a dark brown back, with three narrow, broken, pale stripes and numerous pale spots between the stripes. The throat is blue-white, and the chest and belly are white. Adult males have a green to blue-green back, with numerous pale spots, three pale stripes on the head, a bright orange tail that is paler below, a pale green throat with black specks, no collar, a light blue chest and a dark blue belly. Their sides are blue, but green to orange when immature. **Biology and breeding:** Very agile; found in small family groups on isolated rocky outcrops. Two white eggs are laid during November-December. **Habitat:** Arid and mesic savannah. **Range:** Isolated populations in N. Province, probably extending into E. Botswana. **Subspecies:** None recognized. Occurs with the Waterberg flat lizard (below) on Blouberg.

## Waterberg Flat Lizard  *Platysaurus minor* (Pls. 74 and 105)
*(Endemic) SVL 60-65 mm; max. SVL 73 mm.*

A small platy in which the transparent 'window' in the lower eyelid is divided (entire in south). The supranasals are fused with the nasals. The middle row of the gulars is enlarged. The scales on the sides of the body are rounded, raised and larger than those on the back. The ventrals are in 17-20 longitudinal rows. The scales on the heels and at the base of the tail are not spiny. Males have 16-20 femoral pores. The three longitudinal stripes which mark the body are always entire in females, and sometimes divided in males. Adult males' lips are blue, the colour extending onto the side of the head, the neck and the shoulders. A lateral orange-red streak runs between the limbs and extends onto the sides of the belly. The back and the upper parts of the limbs are brownish-black and marked with numerous small off-white spots. The tail is red-brown above, bright brick-red below. The chin and throat may be yellow to blue, becoming dark blue-black on the mid-belly. **Biology and breeding:** Usually occurs in small family groups. Feeds mainly on insects, although plants are taken occasionally. Two eggs are laid in summer. **Habitat:** Rocky sandstone outcrops in savannah at altitudes of 900-2 000 m. **Range:** Waterberg in N. Province, north to the foothills of Blouberg.

## Emperor Flat Lizard  *Platysaurus imperator* (Pl. 105)
*(Endemic) SVL 100-120 mm; max. SVL 146 mm male, 120 mm female.*

A magnificent giant platy that is closely related to the common flat lizard, *P. intermedius* (below), but is immediately distinguishable by its great size and striking coloration. The lower eyelids are opaque, and each is divided into a series of vertical septa. The supranasals are fused with the nasals. The middle row of gulars is not very enlarged. The scales on the sides of the neck are conical and enlarged, and those on the flanks are no larger than those on the back. The ventrals are in 22-28 longitudinal rows. There are 17-24 femoral pores in males. Females and juveniles are black, with three light cream stripes (yellow on the head), the middle stripe being narrow and broken towards the rear. The tail is straw-coloured. The throat is white, and the belly largely black. Adult males have an ochre-yellow head, a crimson body with numerous large, pale spots anteriorly, that are ochre-yellow towards the rear and on the tail. The limbs are black. The throat is brick-red, with a broad black collar. The chest is reddish or yellowish, the belly is black, and the tail is orange to light yellow below. **Biology and breeding:** This platy is the largest in the genus. A large male and several attendant females usually command the tops of massive boulders on gneiss hills, and feed mainly on beetles, caterpillars and ants. Clutches of two large eggs (27 x 12 mm) are laid in summer. It has lived for up to 14 years. Threatened by over-collecting for the pet trade. **Habitat:** Mesic savannah. **Range:** NE Zimbabwe and adjacent Mozambique.

## Common Flat Lizard    *Platysaurus intermedius* (Pls. 75 and 106)

*SVL varied, from 65-80 mm to 90-120 mm (see Subspecies); max. SVL 129 mm.*
A medium to large platy with opaque lower eyelids, each divided into a series of vertical septa. The supranasals are fused with the nasals. The middle row of gulars is not very enlarged. The scales on the sides of the neck are conical and enlarged, and may be spinose or rounded. The scales on the flanks are no larger than those on the back. The ventrals are in 14-26 longitudinal rows (see Subspecies). There are 12-28 femoral pores in males. Females and juveniles are black, with three buff stripes that sometimes have light spots between them. The belly is brownish in the centre and white at the edges. Adult males have varied coloration (see Subspecies). **Biology and breeding:** This is the most widely distributed and common platy. It lives under exfoliating rock flakes and may form dense colonies (for example at Rhodes Grave in the Matopos, Zimbabwe). Two elongate eggs (14-22 x 8-11 mm) are laid in November-December in communal egg sites in a sun-warmed, soil-filled rock crack. The hatchlings (SVL 30-35 mm) emerge in late December-January. **Habitat:** Varied rock types (granite, sandstone, quartzite) in mesic and arid savannah. **Range:** Throughout most of Zimbabwe, N. Province, and Mpumalanga, with peripheral races in S. Malawi, E. Botswana, Swaziland and adjacent Mozambique and N. KwaZulu-Natal. **Subspecies:** Nine races recognized, eight of which occur in the region (the other, *P.i. nyasae*, occurs in Malawi and adjacent central Mozambique). *P.i. wilhelmi* (g) has different-sized back scales, those covering the pale dorsal stripes being the largest. The ventral scales are in 16-18 rows. It has a dull olive-green to brown back with a few scattered, pale spots. The tail is red, becoming straw-coloured towards the tip, and the belly is blue, becoming black in the centre. This race occurs in S. Mpumalanga. It may be more closely-related to the Lebombo flat lizard, *P. lebomboensis* (page 203). All other races have dorsal scales that are uniform in size.

A group of three subspecies with 20-22 ventral scale rows occurs north of the Soutpansberg and south of Zambezi River; the first two have the nasals in contact and four upper labials in front of the subocular.

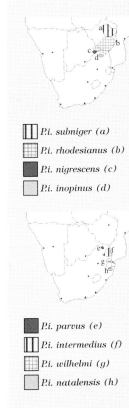

*P.i. subniger (a)*

*P.i. rhodesianus (b)*

*P.i. nigrescens (c)*

*P.i. inopinus (d)*

*P.i. parvus (e)*

*P.i. intermedius (f)*

*P.i. wilhelmi (g)*

*P.i. natalensis (h)*

*P.i. rhodesianus* (b) is a large race (SVL 100-120 mm); it has a blue-green to yellow-green head, with three faint stripes. Its back is blue-green anteriorly (but red in specimens from Mozambique), and red (in the west) or green (in the east) posteriorly. The tail is greenish or yellowish. Two ventral colour phases occur: the 'red' phase has a blue throat with a black collar and a terracotta chest; the 'green' phase has a yellow throat with a black collar, and a blue or green chest. This subspecies occurs in Zimbabwe (except in the north-east), E. Botswana and N. Province. *P.i. nigrescens* (c) is smaller (SVL 75-90 mm), and has a black head and body with faint yellow spotting on the rear. The tail is bright orange. The chin and throat are black, with an irregular yellow patch. The chest and belly are black, with scattered yellow scales. It occurs in the vicinity of Shoshong Hills in NE Botswana. *P.i. subniger* (a) is similar in size to *P.i. rhodesianus*; it has five upper labials in front of the subocular and the nasals are separated. It has a dark green back, becoming brown or black posteriorly (but uniform red in males from Trelawney, Zimbabwe), with pale spots. The tail is orange. The throat is orange, yellow or white, and the chest and belly are black.

A group of three subspecies with 16-18 ventral scale rows occurs south of the Soutpansberg; two have the occipital touching the parietal, and a bright green head and body. *P.i. parvus* (e) is a small race (SVL 65-75 mm) and has a dark green back anteriorly (and red-brown posteriorly), with numerous pale spots. The tail is dull orange. The throat is pale blue with the collar reduced to a black blotch on either side of the neck. The chest and belly are blue. This race is found on Blouberg in N. Province.
*P.i. natalensis* (h) has a grass-green back, with numerous pale spots and three faint pale stripes. The tail is bright orange. The throat is yellow or pale blue, usually with black blotches and a black collar. The chest is light blue, and the belly Prussian blue. It occurs in Swaziland and KwaZulu-Natal. *P.i. intermedius* (f) (SVL 85-100 mm) has the occipital separated from the parietal. The head and body are dull green to brownish above, with faint stripes and numerous pale spots. The tail is reddish to yellowish. The throat is blue and lacks a collar. The chest is blue, and the belly blue-black in the centre. This subspecies is found in and around Pietersburg, N. Province. A final race, *P.i. inopinus* (d), is also found in the foothills of the Blouberg, N. Province. Is similar to *P.i. parvus* in size and appearance, but differs in having more ventral scale rows (22-26), pale thighs with black spotting, and lacking the paired black collar blotches.

### Orange-throated Flat Lizard     *Platysaurus monotropis* (Pl. 106)
*(Endemic) SVL 65-73 mm; max. SVL 77 mm.*
This medium-sized platy has an opaque lower eyelid which is divided by a series of vertical septa. The nasals are separated. The middle row of gulars is enlarged. The scales on the sides of the neck are spiny but not enlarged, and those on the back are all of similar size. The ventrals are in 17-21 longitudinal rows. Males have 17-19 femoral pores. Females and juveniles are blackish-brown above, with three white longitudinal stripes. The tail is buffy brown, tinged with grey on sides. The chin and throat are yellow with dark markings. The chest and belly is pinkish-brown, heavily marked with dark markings at the scale margins. Adult males have a mottled orange and blackish head, with orange lips that extend onto the temporals. Orange speckles on the neck merge with a blue-green colour that separates the neck from the blue back. The neck and sides of the body are ultramarine. The tail is bright brick red, the limbs blue to blue-

green above. The chin and throat are orange, with a broken black collar. The belly is pale green to blue. Underside of limbs are blue to ultramarine, with pinkish to reddish femoral pores. **Habitat:** Large sandstone outcrops in mesic savanna. **Range:** N. Province on the foothills of Blouberg.

### Ocellated Flat Lizard
*Platysaurus ocellatus* **(Pl. 106)**
*(Endemic) SVL 75-85 mm; max. SVL 94 mm.*
This large platy has similar scalation to the Cape flat lizard, *P. capensis* (page 198), but has different coloration, lacking the three dorsal stripes. It has opaque lower eyelids, each divided by a series of vertical septa. The supranasals are fused with the nasals. The middle row of gulars is very enlarged. The scales on the sides of the neck are spiny but not enlarged, and the collar is straight and composed of large plates. The ventrals are in 14 (rarely 12) longitudinal rows. Males have 13-18 femoral pores. Females and juveniles have a bronze back, with numerous pale, ill-defined spots. The tail is blackish. The throat is white speckled with grey. The belly is cream, and yellow under the base of the tail. Adult males have a uniform black-brown head, and an olive-brown back with sulphur-yellow, dark-edged spots. The tail is brown above and orange to yellow below (but orange to yellow above and below in very large specimens). The belly is pale green to blue. **Biology and breeding:** Very common on quartzite rock outcrops, feeding mainly on beetles but also eating flowers, leaves and seeds. Two eggs (measuring 21 x 9 mm) are laid in October-November. **Habitat:** Low miombo woodland. **Range:** Lower western slopes of Chimanimani Mountains in Zimbabwe and adjacent Mozambique.

### Pungwe Flat Lizard
*Platysaurus pungweensis* **(Pl. 106)**
*(Endemic) SVL 75-82 mm; max. SVL 91 mm male, 80 mm female.*
A medium-sized platy that resembles the common flat lizard, *P. intermedius* (page 201), but is smaller and has only 14-16 longitudinal rows of ventrals. It has opaque lower eyelids, each divided by a series of vertical septa. The supranasals are fused with the nasals. The middle row of gulars is not very enlarged. The scales on the sides of the neck are spiny and enlarged, and those on the flanks are no larger than those on the back. Males have 13-20 femoral pores. Females and juveniles have a black back with three buff stripes, the middle one often being broken into spots or ending on the neck; there are no spots between the stripes. Adult males have varied coloration (see Subspecies). **Biology:** Common on low rock outcrops and large koppies. Feeds on beetles and ants. **Habitat:** Mesic savanna. **Range:** E. Zimbabwe and Mozambique. **Subspecies:** Two races and both occur in the region. *P.p. pungweensis* has an occipital. Adult males have a brown back with yellow spots, a tail that is brown above and red on the sides, a blue throat blotched with black, a black collar and a blue chest and belly; females have a bluish-white belly. It occurs in the eastern Highlands of Zimbabwe and Mozambique. *P.p. blakei* has a small occipital, or lacks one. Adult males have a dark green back, a red tail, a grey throat that lacks a collar, and a purple to black chest and belly; females have a blackish belly. It is found on S. Manica Platform in central Mozambique.

### Lebombo Flat Lizard
*Platysaurus lebomboensis* **(Pl. 106)**
*(Endemic) SVL 60-70 mm; max. SVL 75 mm.*
This small to medium-sized platy is similar to Wilhelm's flat lizard, *P.i. wilhemi* (page 201), but has a blackish back. It has opaque lower eye-

☐ *P.p. baklei*

■ *P.p. pungweensis*

lids, each divided by a series of vertical septa. The nasals are usually in contact. The granules on the back vary in size, becoming large and conical on the flanks. The heels and sides of the tail are spiny. The ventrals are in 15-20 longitudinal rows. Males have 14-19 femoral pores. Females and juveniles have a brownish-black back, with three pale stripes and spots between them. The tail is blackish, fading to a straw colour on the sides and pale orange-brown below. The belly is bluish-white, sometimes with black in the middle, and with dark spots on the throat and chin. The back of adult males is blackish-grey to all black, sometimes retaining brown stripes. The lips are green with black blotches. A broad orange-red streak extends from the neck to the armpits. The limbs are brownish to grey-black above, pale-orange to reddish on the thighs. The tail is brownish above, the belly black with a blue patch in the middle. The chin and throat are mottled greenish-blue. **Habitat:** Large rocky faces in thicket and grassland. **Range:** Middle Lebombo Range between Swaziland, Mozambique and KwaZulu-Natal.

### Soutpansberg Flat Lizard    *Platysaurus relictus* (Pl. 74)
*(Endemic) SVL 580-650 mm; max. SVL 73 mm.*
This small platy has opaque lower eyelids, each divided by a series of vertical septa. The supranasals are fused with the nasals. The middle row of gulars is not very enlarged. The scales on the sides of the neck are flattened and enlarged, and those on the flanks are no larger than those on the back. The ventrals are in 18-20 longitudinal rows. There are 18-20 femoral pores in males. Females and juveniles have a dark brown back, with three cream stripes and a few spots between the stripes. The tail is straw-coloured. Adult males have a dark green back and limbs, with pale yellow-green marks on the head, a faint yellow-green stripe along the backbone and numerous yellow-green spots. The tail is bright orange. The throat is blue-white, with a black collar. The chest and belly are dark blue. **Biology:** A quick and alert platy that lives on sandstone outcrops (SA RDB, Restricted). **Habitat:** Arid savannah. **Range:** Waterberg and northern side of Soutpansberg in N. Province.

### Striped Flat Lizard    *Platysaurus torquatus* (Pl. 106)
*SVL 65-70 mm; max. SVL 76 mm male, 72 mm female.*
This small platy is the only species in the genus in which males retain the pale longitudinal stripes, and females and juveniles have uniform Cambridge blue tails. It has opaque lower eyelids, each divided by a series of vertical septa. The supranasals are fused with the nasals. The middle row of gulars is not very enlarged. The scales on the sides of the neck are flattened and enlarged, and those on the flanks are larger than those on the back. The ventrals are in 16-20 longitudinal rows. Males have 15-22 femoral pores. Females and juveniles have a blackish-brown back, with three buff stripes with a few or no spots between them. The tail is blue, with a dark median stripe. The throat and chest are white, and the belly and base of the tail are orange. Adult males have a dark brown back with three buff stripes. The flanks and tail are bright orange. The limbs are grey-brown. The throat is white, with a black collar. The chest is orange or yellow, suffused with bright green, and becoming Prussian blue on the belly. **Biology:** Gregarious on flat outcrops, particularly along river courses. Feeds on ants, beetles and some caterpillars. Two eggs (19 x 7 mm) are laid in December. **Habitat:** Mesic savannah. **Range:** NE Zimbabwe, extending into west-central Mozambique and S. Malawi.

# Crag Lizards    *Pseudocordylus*

These beautiful tyrants are some of the largest cordylids, surpassed in size only by the sungazer, *Cordylus giganteus* (page 189). They are very similar in appearance to the girdled lizards, *Cordylus* (page 185), differing only in that the neck and back are usually covered with granular scales, the body scales lack osteoderms, and the tail is less heavily spined.

Rock-living, crag lizards usually inhabit a large fissure in a shattered boulder that commands a good vantage point from which to spot potential danger and forage for food. Unlike the flat lizards, *Platysaurus* (page 198), they are not sociable, and a crack is usually occupied by a single individual. They may, however, aggregate in diffuse colonies in good habitat and hibernate communally in deep cracks. They eat a wide range of large invertebrates, including beetles, crickets and grasshoppers, and also take small vertebrates, particularly other lizards. They have tremendously strong jaws and an unusual, hinged skull structure that allows the shape of the head to thicken if the jaws are clammed shut.

This is effectively used as a defence: the lizard wedges its head into a narrow part of a crack, and as long as it clenches its jaws, the top of the head and lower jaw will be tightly jammed against the rock walls. To prevent damage to the lizard, the scales on the top of the head are thickened with bony osteoderms. Their bulldog-like tenacity makes it almost impossible to pull them from their retreats. Although large and aggressive, they are very wary, and quickly retreat into their cracks at the first sign of danger. Viviparous, the females give birth to 7 young in late summer. These disperse and are usually found in marginal habitats on the lower mountain slopes. Later, as they grow and mature they seek more permanent homes in more prominent positions.

There are seven species, and all are endemic. The blue-spotted girdled lizard, *C. coeruleopunctatus* (page 187) is closely-related to the graceful crag lizard, *P. capensis*, and dwarf crag lizard, *P. nebulosus* (below), and should perhaps be transferred to this genus. This illustrates the close relationship between the two genera. Crag lizards are distributed in a wide arc in the old mountain escarpment of South Africa, from the Cedarberg in the west, through the Cape fold mountains and the inland mountains of E. Cape, KwaZulu-Natal and Mpumalanga, to the Soutpansberg in N. Province.

### Graceful Crag Lizard    *Pseudocordylus capensis* (Pl. 71)

*(Endemic) SVL 65-70 mm; max. SVL 78 mm male, 75 mm female.*

This gracile species has long toes and a thin tail. The flanks are entirely covered with granular scales. The nasals are in contact, separating the rostral and frontonasal. Each nostril pierces the lower part of the nasal. The temporal scales are small and in three rows. Rows of enlarged scales along the middle of the back are separated by granular scales. There are 15-18 femoral pores on each thigh. The tail is spinose and considerably longer than the body. The body, head and tail are blue-black in colour, with yellow blotches and vermiculations, particularly on the top of the head; these are fainter on the back. The belly is uniform slate grey, and sometimes paler in the centre. The throat has a rust-red suffusion in some populations. **Biology and breeding:** This species may be found together with the Cape crag lizard, *P. microlepidotus* (page 208), but prefers more vertical cliff faces. It is agile and runs at speed over the smooth rocks. Very alert, it retreats at the first sign of danger. They form small, diffuse colonies and several specimens (usually a male and a female) may be found in the same crack. They feed on insects, particularly bees and wasps. One to three babies are born in December-January. **Habitat:** Prefers mountain fynbos. **Range:** Isolated populations from Cedarberg in the north through Cape fold mountains to Kammanassieberg. **Subspecies:** None are now recognized.

### Dwarf Crag Lizard    *Pseudocordylus nebulosus* (Pl. 104)
*(Endemic) SVL 70-75 mm; max. SVL 76 mm.*
This small species is easily confused with juvenile graceful crag lizards, *P. capensis* (page 205). It is lightly built with long toes and a thin tail. The flanks are covered with keeled scales surrounded by granules. The nasals are in contact, separating the rostral and frontonasal. The nostril pierces the lower part of the nasal. There are four supraciliaries and the temporal scales are small and in three rows. There is no occipital. Two rows of enlarged scales along middle of the back are not separated by granular scales. The ventrals are in eight longitudinal rows. There are 9-11 femoral pores on each thigh. The tail is spinose, longer than the body, and has two scale rows per whorl. The body, head and tail are jet black. Two rows of yellow blotches occur along the backbone (sometimes absent), with a few other yellow markings in the neck region and back. The belly and throat are uniform slate grey. **Biology and breeding:** A very rare and restricted species that inhabits moist habitats in the mist-belt of mountain summits. Agile and alert, retreating into narrow rock cracks in sandstone outcrops when disturbed. **Habitat:** Mountain fynbos. **Range:** A single, isolated population in the Hottentots-Holland Mountains of the SW Cape.

### Lang's Crag Lizard    *Pseudocordylus langi*
*(Endemic) SVL 70-90 mm; max. SVL 106 mm male, 83 mm female.*
This medium-sized crag lizard is similar in appearance to the Drakensberg crag lizard, *P. melanotus* (below), but breeding males lack the yellow flanks. It has small, granular scales on its flanks. There is a single row of 4-6 elongate temporal scales. The nasals are in contact, separating the rostral and the frontonasal, which is undivided. There are usually four upper labials anterior to the subocular, and five lower labials. This species lacks occipitals. Both sexes have 11-17 very small femoral pores. The back and head are olive-grey, and heavily blotched and streaked in black. The back has numerous pale grey-green blotches that form irregular crossbars. There are two large black blotches on the side of the neck, followed by a series of 1-6 bright sky-blue blotches. The belly is slate-grey, with dark blotches. The throat has a large, dark brown patch, flanked by three narrow, brown stripes. **Biology:** Found in small colonies and may live in the same crack as the Drakensberg crag lizard. It eats beetles and flying insects, as well as large amounts of the leaves and flowers of everlasting daisies and other plants (SA RDB, Restricted). **Habitat:** Rock outcrops in montane grassland. **Range:** Summit of KwaZulu-Natal Drakensberg (2 600-3 000 m).

■ *P.m. melanotus*

☐ *P.m. subviridis*

### Drakensberg Crag Lizard    *Pseudocordylus melanotus* (Pl. 73)
*(Endemic) SVL 80-120 mm; max. SVL 143 mm male .*
A medium-sized crag lizard that has the scales on its flanks separated by granular interspaces. There is usually a single row of 4-6 elongate temporal scales. The nasals are in contact, separating the rostral and the frontonasal, which is undivided and touches the anterior loreals. There are usually three upper labials anterior to the subocular, and six lower labials.

Occipitals number up to 13, but may be absent. There are 5-13 femoral pores (but these are undeveloped in *P.m. melanotus* females). Coloration is complicated; regional differences occur and breeding males are more colourful (see Subspecies) and also develop bigger heads. In females, the back is greyish to olive-brown, with extensive, irregular pale spots. The sides of the head, neck and body are yellowish-green, yellow or orange, often with dark dorsal coloration extending as bars onto the flanks. There are 1-2 black spots on the side of the neck. The belly is off-white, suffused with pale orange at the edges. **Biology and breeding:** Found in large, diffuse colonies in suitable habitat, but rarely with more than a single dominant male in a rock crack. Out of the breeding season individuals may share cracks. They are ambush predators, sitting on a vantage point looking for prey. They feed on small beetles and flying insects, and berries in season. One to six babies (46-48 mm SVL, 2-3 g) are born in December-January, after a three- to four-month gestation period. **Habitat:** Rock outcrops on mountain plateaus and in rolling grassland. **Range:** Escarpment mountains from Amatola Mountains to Gauteng and Mpumalanga escarpment, extending on to NE Free State highveld and N. KwaZulu-Natal. **Subspecies:** Two races, both occur in the region. *P.m. melanotus* has a divided frontonasal; femoral pores in females are only shallow pits. Breeding males have 1-17 glandular femoral scales; a broad dark brown to black band on the back (sometimes with small, pale flecks); bright orange on the flanks and sides of the neck; a red-brown temporal region; and a diffuse blue-grey patch on the throat. This larger northern race extends from Gauteng and Mpumalanga escarpment east to N. KwaZulu-Natal and north to NE Free State. *P.m. subviridis* does not exceed SVL 118 mm, has an undivided frontonasal, and the lateral scales are larger than the spaces between them. Females have well-developed femoral pores. Breeding males have a black back, with numerous large pale olive-grey blotches; an olive-grey head and temporal region; and their flanks and sides of their tails are heavily suffused with black and orange. This race is found from Mont-aux-Sources, through Lesotho and Transkei (E. Cape) underberg, with an isolated population on Amatola Mountains in E. Cape.

### Northern Crag Lizard   *Pseudocordylus transvaalensis* (Pl. 73)

*(Endemic) SVL 130-140 mm; max. SVL 151 mm male, 134 mm female.*
The largest crag lizard in which the frontonasal is usually undivided and the nasals separated. There are usually four suboculars, and two rows of temporals (which may be irregular). The lateral scales are smaller than the spaces between them. Females have well-developed femoral pores. Breeding males are dark olive (sometimes yellowish) with 8-9 dark cross-bars that fade with age. The flanks are yellow to olive-yellow, as are the limbs which are also blotched with black. The tail is yellow to orange above, paler below, with regular dark bars on the sides. The head is dark grey-black above, and paler on the sides and below. The belly is olive to yellowish with scattered dark infusions. Females are olive-coloured with dark crossbars. The brown head has dark markings and becomes paler on the sides. The throat is blackish, the belly pale olive and the tail heavily barred with black. **Biology and breeding:** Found singly or in small groups, usually consisting of a single dominant male and a number of females and juveniles. Two to seven young (up to 82 mm TL) are born in midsummer. **Habitat:** Rock outcrops in grassland on mountain summits. **Range:** Found in three isolated populations in S. Northern Province.

**Spiny Crag Lizard**  *Pseudocordylus spinosus* (Pl. 71)
*(Endemic) SVL 80-85 mm; max. SVL 89 mm male and female.*
This small crag lizard has rough scales. The lateral scales are spiny and are not separated by granules, and there is a single row of elongate temporal scales. The nasals are in contact, separating the rostral and the fronto-nasal, which is undivided and small and does not touch the anterior loreals. There are usually 3-4 upper labials anterior to the subocular, and six lower labials. This species lacks occipitals. There are 3-5 femoral pores in both sexes. The back is dull brown, with pale, elongate spots forming irregular rows. The head is dark brown to black, with pale labials. The belly is pale brown. There is a pair of parallel grey stripes on the throat. Breeding males develop bright orange flanks and spots. **Biology and breeding:** Wary and difficult to approach (SA RDB, Restricted). Prefers scattered boulders in open grassland, where it feeds on small beetles, cockroaches, etc. One to four babies are born in late summer. **Habitat:** Mountain slopes. **Range:** Lower slopes (1 500-2 500 m) of Drakensberg, from Giant's Castle in KwaZulu-Natal to Golden Gate in Free State.

**Cape Crag Lizard**  *Pseudocordylus microlepidotus* (Pl. 72)
*(Endemic) SVL 110-130 mm; max. SVL 145 mm male, 140 mm female.*
This very large crag lizard has the scales on its flanks surrounded by granules. The temporal scales are in 1-3 rows, sometimes with the upper row elongated (in *P.m. namaquensis*). The nasals are in contact, or are separated by the rostral and frontonasal (in *P.m. microlepidotus*). The frontonasal is undivided. There are usually five upper labials anterior to the subocular. Males have 5-6 femoral pores on each thigh. Males are beautifully coloured; the back is dull reddish-brown to dark brown,

▊ *P.m. microlepidotus*

▨ *P.m. namaquensis*

▦ *P.m. fasciatus*

▩ *P.m. subsp.*

usually with 7-8 large, irregular, yellowish (bright lemon-yellow in *P.m. namaquensis* and orange in *P.m. fasciatus*) crossbars. (S. Transkei populations are uniform dark brown, with numerous thin, irregular, pale yellow bars). The heavy jaw muscles are deep red-brown, and the throat is suffused with grey-blue (the pattern and extent of which vary in different populations). Males do not get bigger heads than females, but do have glandular scales along the backbone. The underside of the limbs and tail, sides of the belly and the lips are yellow (again, orange in *P.m. fasciatus*). The upper surface of the tail has 10-13 irregular, yellow and dark brown bars. **Biology and breeding:** This lizard selects large rock cracks often partly filled with soil, within which it excavates a chamber. It forages for food on adjacent flat rocks, eating large grasshoppers, beetles, etc., and will readily kill small lizards (agamas and geckos). It bites readily and painfully, and holds on with a bulldog-like tenacity. It hibernates in winter in a deep retreat. Very pugnacious, males and females maintain exclusive territories. Three to seven (usually four) young are born in January-March (97-110 mm TL). **Habitat:** Mountain plateaus and upper slopes in fynbos or montane grassland. **Range:** Throughout Cape fold mountains, inland mountain ranges of old Cape escarpment, and S. Transkei (E. Cape). **Subspecies:** Three subspecies are recognized and all occur in the region. In the typical race, *P.m. microlepidotus*, the fronto-nasal and rostral are in contact, and the dark crossbars on the back extend onto the flanks; it occurs in Cape fold mountains, from Cedarberg to Port Elizabeth. *P.m. namaquensis* has the frontonasal and rostral separated, the dark crossbars not extending onto the flanks, the last lower labial having a ridge, and the throat with a figure-of-eight-shaped dark, bluish mark;

it is found on Nuweveldberg from Sutherland to Beaufort West. *P.m. fasciatus* also has the frontonasal and rostral separated, the dark cross-bars on the back extending onto the flanks, the last lower labial lacking a ridge, and the throat a uniform bluish colour; occurs on inland mountains of E. Cape. Taxonomy of Transkei populations under investigation.

# Monitors
## FAMILY VARANIDAE

This small family of about 46 living species contains the world's largest lizards. They are closely related to the unusual earless monitor from Borneo (subfamily Lanthanotinae), and the North American Gila monster and Mexican beaded lizard (family Helodermatidae); the latter are the world's only poisonous lizards. Monitors are not poisonous. Very large fossils (approaching 6 m) are known from the Pleistocene epoch of S. Asia and Australia. All living monitors are placed in the genus *Varanus*.

All monitors are similar in appearance, having well-developed limbs and strong claws; a long tail that is usually laterally compressed and cannot be shed or regenerated; a long and flexible neck; small, polygonal, non-overlapping, bead-like scales that lack osteoderms; a single pair of preanal pores; and a long, smooth, retractile tongue, similar to a snake's. Size ranges from 200 mm to more than 2 m, with the Komodo dragon (*V. komodoensis*) of Java attaining over 3 m.

Most varanids are semi-aquatic, which has allowed them to colonize much of the East Indies; they are, however, absent from Madagascar and other Indian Ocean islands. All, except one Asian species, are predatory. Small species eat insects, while larger species take anything they can overcome. The Komodo dragon is capable of killing deer and small water buffalo, and very rarely may also kill humans. The food is swallowed whole or is torn to bits with the strong claws. Monitors are shy lovers, and mating and egg-laying are rarely observed. They are oviparous laying large, soft-shelled eggs in holes or termite nests. Males of some species engage in ritualized wrestling contests to determine the dominant males and their territories. The skins are attractive, and hundreds of thousands of varanids are slaughtered each year for fashion. All varanids are protected in southern Africa.

Their distribution is restricted to the Old World with the greatest diversity occurring in Australia. Only five of the 46 species occur in Africa, with two reaching the subcontinent.

### Rock or White-throated Monitor     *Varanus albigularis* (Pl. 63)
*SVL 400-500 mm; max. SVL 850 mm, TL 1 750 mm.*

This very large, stout lizard has strong, stocky limbs and sharp claws. The skin is tough and covered with small, bead-like scales, in 110-167 rows at midbody. The head has a bulbous snout, with the nostrils slit-like and nearer to the eyes than to the end of the snout. The tail is longer than the body, and cylindrical at the base but compressed towards the tip. The back is dark grey-brown above, with 5-6 pale yellow dark-edged blotches. The top of the head and neck are dark brown. The limbs are spotted with pale yellow, and the tail is banded in dark brown and off-white. The belly is dirty yellow with scattered spots. Juveniles are more intensely marked, and despite the common name, which refers to the white throat of adults, have blackish throats. **Biology and breeding:** This monitor lives in a

*V.a. albigularis*

tunnel that it digs under rock overhangs, or in a disused animal burrow, a hole in a tree or a rock crack. It is usually solitary and hibernates, semi-dormant in its retreat in winter. Its skin is usually dulled with dirt and grime, and sullied with patches of unshed skin. It is also well-adorned with ticks in the soft skin around the eyes, nostrils and limb joints. The diet consists mainly of invertebrates (millipedes, beetles, grasshoppers and land snails) although it will kill and eat any animal small enough to swallow, and also scavenges on carrion; baby tortoises are frequently eaten. In defence it adopts a side-on posture and lashes its tail. It will bite and hold on like a bulldog; if held behind the head it usually ejects its cloacal contents, and finally it may sham death, hanging limp (but still keeping its eyes open). If this ruse works and it is released, it scampers to safety at the first opportunity. The martial eagle and the ratel are main predators on adults. It rarely tames in captivity and, because of its size, needs a large enclosure. The flesh is reported to taste like chicken, but this monitor is protected by Provincial legislation (CITES, Appendix 11). They are great wanderers, and may have home ranges up to 28 sq. km. Mating occurs in August-September. The female may occasionally lay her eggs in a live termite nest, as does the Nile monitor, *V. niloticus* (below), or even in a hollow tree, but normally uses a hole dug in soft moist soil. She may dig several 'test holes' before selecting a suitable spot. In early summer (October-November) from eight to 51 eggs (53-61 x 35-39 mm, 32-46 g) are laid, depending on the size of the female. The eggs hatch in 110-120 days in captivity (27°C), but take much longer in the wild. Hatchlings measure 220-282 mm TL and weigh 18-21 g. Many clutches are eaten by the banded mongoose. It has lived up to 11 years in captivity. **Habitat:** Savannah and moister karroid areas. **Range:** Throughout the savannah and semi-desert regions of the subcontinent, but absent from W. Cape. Elsewhere, to the savannahs of East Africa. **Subspecies:** Only the typical race occurs on the subcontinent. It has 137-167 midbody scale rows and a white throat in adults. A poorly-defined race, *V.a. angolensis*, from Angola and adjacent NW Zambia, has large scales on the head and along the backbone, and retains the black throat in adults. It has only 110-138 mid-body scale rows. A small species (*V. exanthematicus*) from the West African savannahs has a more uniform colour pattern, lacks the white throat, and has enlarged scales on the back of the neck and only 75-100 midbody scale rows; it is now treated as a separate species.

### Nile or Water Monitor

*Varanus niloticus* (Pl. 63)
*SVL 600-800 mm; max SVL 980 mm, TL 2 420 mm.*
This is the second largest African lizard (probably surpassed by its close relative, *V. ornatus*). It has a stout body with powerful limbs and strong claws. The skin is tough and covered with small, bead-like scales. The head has an elongate snout, and the nostrils are round and situated mid-way between the eyes and the end of the snout. The tongue is dark. The tail is much longer than the body, and is laterally compressed, with a low dorsal crest. Adults are greyish-brown to dirty olive-brown on top of the head and back, with scattered darker blotches and from 6-11 light yellow bands or spots on the body, and 10-18 light crossbands on the tail. The limbs are spotted. The belly and throat are paler, with black bars. Juveniles are beautifully patterned in black and yellow. **Biology and breeding:** The Nile monitor is common in major river valleys foraging for food in the marginal vegetation. It is an excellent swimmer, using its long,

oar-like tail. It often basks on rock outcrops or tree stumps. In temperate regions, it may hibernate communally in a large rock crack on a rocky cliff or koppie bordering a river. The diet is varied. Adults forage in freshwater pools for crabs and mussels, but will also take frogs, fish, and birds and their eggs; they also excavate and eat the eggs from terrapin, sea turtle, and unattended crocodile nests. Juveniles rarely enter deep water, but shelter in marginal reed beds where they hunt for frogs and insects. Adults' teeth are rounded and peg-like (ideal for crunching crabs), unlike the sharp, recurved teeth of juveniles. When disturbed, they dive into the water and swim underwater to the safety of the reed beds. If cornered, they bite and lash the tail in defence, like the rock monitor, *V. albigularis* (page 209). Crocodiles and pythons are major predators on adults. Their flesh is edible and the fat is used for tribal medicine. They are, however, protected by Provincial legislation (CITES, Appendix II). After spring rains (August-September), the female excavates a hole in a living termite nest and lays 20-60 eggs (54-64 x 30-40 mm). This may take 2-3 days to complete. The termites then repair their nest, and the monitor eggs develop inside it, incubated at a constant temperature and humidity. It may take up to a year before the young emerge, although in captivity (at 30°C), they hatch in 129-175 days. The young (200-320 mm TL, 23-32 g) emerge together, digging themselves out of the rain-softened nest the following summer. **Habitat:** Rivers, pans and major lakes. **Range:** Sub-Saharan Africa, extending along the Nile River to Egypt. On the subcontinent, it occurs through the eastern part of the region, extending along the Orange River to the Atlantic Ocean, Fish River Canyon into central Namibia, and along the south coast to the Kromme River valley; absent from W. Cape. **Subspecies:** At present no races are recognized. A closely-related species (*V. ornatus*), with few bands on the body (4-6) and tail (9-12) and a pale tongue, occurs in the rain forests of W. Africa, and the Democratic Republic of Congo (former Zaïre).

# Agamas
## FAMILY AGAMIDAE

These small to large lizards have either a cylindrical or a flattened body, well-developed limbs and a tapering tail. The head is large, with a distinct neck. The prominent eyes have movable eyelids. The pineal eye, which is visible as a small depression on the crown of the head, is often well developed. The ear openings are rarely covered with scales. The head scales are small and irregular, while those on the body are overlapping, keeled and often drawn into spines. The tail is usually long, and cannot be shed or regenerated.

They are diurnal and mainly terrestrial, although there are some specialized rock-living and arboreal forms. Many feed mainly or exclusively on ants, while others are primarily herbivores. They often form social groups, and display well-developed territorial behaviour; males are often brightly coloured and/or adorned with frills, crests or throat fans to enhance their displays. Most are oviparous, although a few Asian species are viviparous.

It is a large family comprising about 320 species in over 50 genera, which are distributed throughout most of the Old World. The greatest diversity occurs in Asia and Australia, where they are believed to have originated, with subsequent dispersal into Africa. Closely related to chameleons, agamas are replaced in the New World and Madagascar by a number of families, previously grouped under the Iguanidae. Only two genera occur on the subcontinent.

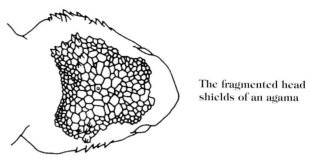

The fragmented head
shields of an agama

## Agamas   *Agama*

Agamas are plump, short-bodied lizards with thin tails and triangular heads. The head is covered with small scales, and has an enlarged occipital scale under which lies the pineal eye. Two fang-like teeth are found in the upper jaw. The large eyes have scaly eyelids and round pupils. The legs are long and muscular, with thin toes. Preanal pores are present in males.

These active, diurnal and territorial lizards occupy a variety of habitats. Some species are rock-living, others are mainly terrestrial but may climb into trees. They feed almost exclusively on ants and termites, although a few supplement their diet with beetles and other insects. Males grow larger than females and develop vivid breeding colours. They engage in territorial displays, maintaining exclusive home ranges and chasing off vanquished opponents. Females and juveniles are more cryptically coloured to match the soil or lichen-covered rocks. All lay relatively large clutches of soft-shelled eggs in a hole that is dug in the ground. In some species, as in tortoises and crocodilians, the sex of the young may be determined by the egg incubation temperature.

This wide-spread genus is distributed throughout Africa and the near East. At present, it contains approximately 30 species, although species boundaries for many still have to be finalized.

Ten species occur on the subcontinent, four of which are endemic.

### Ground Agama                          *Agama aculeata* (Pl. 78)
*SVL 75-100 mm; max. SVL 117 mm male, 106 mm female.*
A medium-sized agama with a triangular head and a relatively rounded snout. The earholes are large and the tympanums are visible. The scales on the top of the head overlap towards the snout. The body is fat with sturdy limbs. The scales are strongly keeled and directed obliquely inwards towards the backbone. The enlarged spines are arranged more or less in regular rows along the back. There are 75-115 scale rows at midbody. The ventrals are smooth. The fifth toe is long, reaching to the end of the first toe. A dorsal crest is present but is weakly developed, and sometimes extends onto the tail. The tail is usually longer than the head and body in both sexes (but shorter in the female *A.a. distanti*). Males have a single row of 9-14 preanal pores, and grow slightly larger than females. The body is olive to reddish-brown (and sometimes grey to yellowish), usually with a distinct grey-yellow dorsal streak which sometimes has a thin central

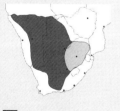

A.a. *aculeata*

A.a. *distanti*

black line. There are 4-5 paired, darker blotches on the back that continue as 10-13 irregular bars on the tail. There are often two bars or chevrons between the eyes. The belly is creamy white to pale dirty pink. Males have three parallel, blue-black lines that border a central network, on each side of the throat; females have only the central network, which may be faint or even absent. Breeding males develop deep blue sides to the head.

**Biology and breeding:** Although terrestrial, these agamas will often climb into low scrub to bask. A short hole dug in loose soil at the base of a bush serves as a retreat. Usually solitary, but comes together to form monogamous pairs in the breeding season. The diet consists almost exclusively of termites or ants, and they can often be seen browsing on a stream of ants passing to and from a nest. When disturbed, they run at top speed with the tail curved upwards, and then stop abruptly, hugging the ground and relying on their superb camouflage to escape detection. Predators include the greater kestrel, and other small raptors. About 17% of individuals have broken tails. The female lays 8-18 eggs, usually 11-12, (13-16 x 9-11 mm) in a hole in sandy soil; the hole is often dug under a stone or at the base of a bush. Incubation is rapid at 30°C, taking 45-50 days. Hatchlings measure 56-65 mm TL. Breeding starts in early summer, and a second clutch of eggs may be laid in February. **Habitat:** Semi-desert and sandveld savannah. **Range:** Throughout most of the subcontinent, absent only from moister coastal regions and true desert. Elsewhere, to S. Angola and Tanzania. **Subspecies:** Only two races are recognized (*A. armata* is a full species); both occur in the region. *A.a. aculeata* has smooth dorsal head shields, and the fourth toe is longer than the third; it is found in the western regions, through the Cape, Namibia and W. Botswana to S. Angola. *A.a. distanti* has rough dorsal head shields and the third toe is longer than the fourth; it is found in the Free State and the N. provinces.

### Peter's Ground Agama     *Agama armata* (Pl. 78)

*SVL 70-80 mm; max. SVL 94 mm.*

This smallish agama has a broad head, with rough shields and a short, rounded snout. The scales on the top of the head overlap towards the snout; those on the back are strongly keeled and directed obliquely inwards towards the backbone, with six rows of enlarged, keeled spines running along the body. There are 88-105 scale rows at midbody. The ventrals are smooth or bluntly keeled. The fifth toe is long, reaching to the end of the first toe. The tail is just longer than the head and body, and is spiny. There is a single row of 9-18 preanal pores in males. The back varies in colour from yellowish-grey to reddish-brown, usually with 4-5 paired pale to dark blotches bordering a broken series of pale blotches along the backbone, that may fuse in males. The head in females and juveniles has 2-3 pale bars between the eyes. In breeding males it becomes infused with blue, particularly on the sides. The belly is white with a grey-blue reticulate pattern on the throat that may extend onto the chest.

**Biology and breeding:** Terrestrial, living in short burrows in deep sandy areas and calcrete flats. Feeds mainly on ants and beetles, but termites and wasps are also taken. From 9-16 eggs (14-15 x 8-9,5 mm) are laid in midsummer. Hatchlings emerge in March. Predators include sand snakes and mongooses. **Habitat:** Mesic and sandveld savannah. **Range:** From the Caprivi-Botswana border, into N. Province and through Zimbabwe to Zambia and Mozambique.

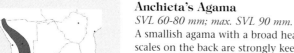

## Anchieta's Agama    *Agama anchietae* (Pl. 78)

*SVL 60-80 mm; max. SVL 90 mm.*

A smallish agama with a broad head and a short, rounded snout. The scales on the back are strongly keeled and directed obliquely inwards towards the backbone, with a few scattered spines. There are 90-105 scale rows at midbody. The ventrals are keeled. A dorsal crest is present, but is weakly developed on the nape. The tail is about half as long as the head and body, and has a serrated crest in males. There is a single row of 10-12 preanal pores in males. The toes are short, and spiny scales on the soles of the feet are black-tipped. Breeding adult males are pinkish-brown above, with fine grey and yellow flecks, and 4-5 dark brown to black crossbands that are sometimes separated by a pale dorsal streak. The flanks are reddish-brown. The tail is banded. The head is bright blue-green, with a large, dark blue spot on the throat. Females and non-breeding males have mottled brown and grey heads. The belly is white to pale yellow, and there are dark bluish to grey-black wavy stripes on the throat. **Biology and breeding:** This species is similar in habits and behaviour to the southern rock agama, *A. atra* (below), but does not form dense colonies, and prefers bedrock and small rock piles. The female lays l0-12 soft-shelled eggs (15-16 x l0-11 mm). **Habitat:** Semi-desert and arid savannah. **Range:** NW Cape through Namibia and Angola to S. Democratic Republic of Congo (former Zaïre).

## Southern Rock and Knobel's Agama    *Agama atra* (Pl. 76)

*(Endemic) SVL 70-120 mm; max. SVL 135 mm.*

A large agama with a flattened body and large limbs. The scales on the back are very small, with scattered, enlarged spines (females lack enlarged spines and their scales are distinctly keeled). There are 90-180 scale rows at midbody. The ventrals are smooth. A dorsal crest is present and extends well onto the tail. The tail is half as long as the head and body and is compressed in males and cylindrical in females. There is a single row (and occasionally two) of 9-16 preanal pores in males. Breeding adult males are olive-green to red-brown above, marbled with dark maroon to black, and with scattered, pale-centred spots. An orange-yellow to whitish vertebral streak extends from the neck to the tip of the tail. Gravid females have red-blotched flanks. The head and forelimbs are blue to greenish-blue. The throat is intense ultramarine to purple-blue in colour, with irregular dark stripes that may extend onto the belly. The tail is greyish-white to yellow, usually with dark crossbands. Females and non-breeding males are mottled in tan, cream and dark brown above, sometimes with red blotches on the flanks. The belly is off-white, and there is a bluish network on the throat. **Biology and breeding:** This species usually lives on rock outcrops and mountain plateaus, but is also found on rocky plains, and may even shelter under the bark of dead trees. Along the Cape coast they forage among driftwood on the beach. They feed mainly on ants and termites, although beetles and grasshoppers are also taken, and coastal populations may eat various intertidal arthropods. Plant material may also be eaten. They may form dense colonies (up to 165 specimens per hectare). Both males and females form hierarchies and maintain territories. Male territories are larger (approximately 90 sq. m), and contain those of several females. There is always a dominant male and female; the female may mate with any male that gains access. A dominant male perches on the highest point of his territory, nodding his brightly

■ *A.a. atra*

□ *A.a. knobelli*

214

coloured head as a signal for lesser males to pay due respect and stay clear. When danger threatens, they hug the rock; the bright head fades and becomes camouflaged against the lichen-covered rock. If this fails, they scamper off at top speed, leaping from boulder to boulder, to shelter in a deep crack. Nonetheless, many fall prey to rock kestrels and other predators. Juveniles are frequently eaten by snakes (particularly cross-barred sandsnakes and spotted house snakes). Egg development starts in August-September. Gravid females, bulging with eggs, bask to speed the formation of yolk from the fat stores laid down in the previous autumn. A first clutch of 7-18 oval, soft-shelled eggs (15-18 x 10-12 mm) is laid in October-November in a shallow hole dug in damp soil; a second clutch is usually laid in January-February. It may take over 3 hours for the female to dig the nest hole, lay her eggs and then refill and camouflage the site. Incubation takes 2-3 months. Hatchlings measure 51-59 mm TL. The race *A.a. knobeli* breeds throughout the year. **Habitat:** Semi-desert to fynbos, from sea level to mountain tops. **Range:** Throughout the Cape (absent only from northern sandy areas), north to S. Namibia, and east to KwaZulu-Natal and Mpumalanga escarpment. **Subspecies:** Two races are recognized although these may prove to be separate species. *A.a. atra* is smaller (female max. SVL 90 mm; male, 110 mm), the vertebral crest weakly developed on the back and tail, and the keels on the flank scales pointing outwards; it occurs over most of the range. *A.a. knobeli* grows larger in both sexes (female max. SVL 105 mm; male, 135 mm), has a well-developed vertebral crest over the tail, and the keels on the flank scales point towards the backbone; it is found in S. Namibia and Namaqualand as far south as the Knersvlakte.

### Etosha Agama                    *Agama etoshae* (Pl. 78)

*(Endemic) SVL 60-70 mm; max. SVL 75 mm.*

A small agama with a broad head and a rounded snout. The earholes are small and the tympanums are not visible. The scales on the top of the head overlap feebly towards the tail. The back scales are strongly keeled and directed obliquely inwards towards the backbone. Enlarged spines are scattered on the flanks, sometimes in irregular rows. The ventrals are feebly keeled. The fifth toe is short, reaching only the base of the first. A weak dorsal crest extends onto the tail base. The tail is longer than the head and body in males, and shorter in females. Males have a single row of 10 preanal pores. The back is pale yellowish-white to rust-red, usually with four dark, pale-ringed blotches. There are two dark bars between the eyes. The tail has 10-12 dark, paired, semi-circular marks. The belly is cream. In breeding males the gular is bright yellow with a central black pentagonal spot surrounded by short black streaks; in females it is uniform bright orange. **Biology:** Terrestrial; forages for beetles and termites in sandy, flat country. In summer, active in the morning and evening, retreating beneath ground during the mid-day heat. At night, shelter in a hole dug at the base of a bush. May be solitary but also found in pairs, or in loose colonies supported by extensive burrow systems. The latter usually have only a few dominant males. Shuffle into loose sand both to conceal themselves and to avoid the heat. Occasionally protrude their eyes to clear sand grains from around the eyelids, and to aid the shedding of old skin. Can be seen displaying their gular pattern from the top of rock piles, but are shy and difficult to approach. **Habitat:** Sandveld. **Range:** Etosha Pan, N. Namibia, north to Ovamboland and west to Kaokoland.

## Southern Spiny Agama
*Agama hispida* (Pl. 77)

*(Endemic) SVL 80-95 mm; max. SVL 110 mm.*

A medium-sized agama with a broad head and a rounded snout. The earholes are small, and the tympanums are not easily seen. The scales on the top of the head overlap towards the tail. The back scales are strongly keeled and directed obliquely inwards towards the backbone. Enlarged spines are arranged in regular rows along the back. There are 70-90 scale rows at midbody. A dorsal crest is present but is weakly developed and does not extend onto the tail. The tail is longer than the head and body in males, and slightly shorter in females. The ventrals are keeled. Males have a single row of 10-12 preanal pores. Coloration is varied; breeding males have a vivid, almost metallic, yellow-green head and body, with indistinct darker and paler blotches. The belly is bluish-grey to blue-green, darker on the chin and throat, and with irregular blue blotches on the gular region. Females and juveniles are olive to brown above, with 4-5 darker crossbars that extend more faintly onto the limbs and tail. The belly is yellow-white to pale green in colour, with a dark network on the throat that sometimes extends backwards. **Biology and breeding:** Terrestrial, these agamas live in a short tunnel dug at the base of a bush in open, sandy veld, and frequently use burrows in ground squirrel colonies. Ants and beetles form the main diet. Large males can often be seen displaying from boulders. They do not form colonies. From 7-11 eggs (17-19 x 11-12 mm) are laid in October-November. **Habitat:** Prefers arid semi-desert and coastal dunes. **Range:** It is found in the W. and N. Cape, extending into S. Namibia, and there is an isolated population in the NW Free State. **Subspecies:** No races are recognized; the Makgadikgadi spiny agama is now considered a full species.

## Makgadikgadi Spiny Agama
*Agama makarikarica* (Pl. 78)

*(Endemic) SVL 55-70 mm; max. SVL 75 mm.*

A very small agama with a broad head and a rounded snout. The earholes are small and the tympanums are not visible. The back scales are strongly keeled and directed obliquely inwards towards the backbone. Enlarged spines are arranged in 3-4 regular rows on the flanks. The ventrals are feebly keeled. The fifth toe is short, reaching only the base of the first. A weak dorsal crest extends along the back but not onto the tail, which is slightly longer than the head and body in males, and shorter in females. Males have a single row of 10-12 preanal pores. The back is grey to grey-brown above, usually with four large paired dark blotches. A pale yellowish vertebral streak may be present in some individuals. A distinct X-shaped mark occurs on the snout. Two dark bars run from the eye above and below the ear, and one or two dark brown chevrons may run between the eyes across the crown. Bright yellow blotches occur on either side of the neck, and in the armpit and groin. The belly is cream-coloured, and the tail has 10-12 dark, paired, semicircular marks. The gular pattern consists of a coarse blue-grey reticulation on a cream-white background. The cheeks and lips of males are bright blue to green. **Biology:** A solitary and shy species that lives in small tunnels excavated at the base of a bush. When disturbed, it usually huddles flat to the ground, relying on its effective camouflage to avoid detection. Its diet consists mainly of beetles and termites. **Habitat:** Prefers arid salt pans. **Range:** The Makgadikgadi spiny agama is restricted to the Nata and Makgadikgadi salt pans in NE Botswana.

## Kirk's Rock Agama
*Agama kirkii* **(Pl. 77)**

*SVL 80-100 mm; max. SVL 115 mm.*
A large agama with a flattish body and long limbs. The back scales are about the same size as those on the belly, are strongly keeled (although less so in females), and directed obliquely inwards towards the backbone. There are 99-114 scale rows at midbody. The ventrals are smooth. A dorsal crest, which is well developed on the nape of adult males, is present and extends onto the tail. The tail is almost twice as long as the head and body. There is a single row (and occasionally two) of 10-14 preanal pores in males. Breeding males have a vermilion to yellow head, and a purple body with a whitish vertebral crest and adjacent scales. The hind limbs and tail are light blue-green with narrow, white rings. Breeding females have a blue-green head, and a maroon body with blue-grey blotches. The limbs and tail are grey. In winter, juveniles and adults are camouflaged in mottled grey-black. **Biology and breeding:** Rock-loving; lives on granite and paragneiss outcrops. Diet consists almost exclusively of ants and termites, although beetles are occasionally taken. They are shy creatures and difficult to approach, and are often seen stationed at the base of a fig tree, browsing off the constant stream of ants that are attracted to the fruit. The female lays about 10 soft-shelled eggs in a hole in the ground or beneath a rock slab. **Habitat:** Prefers arid and mesic savannah. **Range:** Found in E. Botswana, through Zimbabwe and Mozambique to Malawi and Zambia.

## Mozambique Agama
*Agama mossambica* **(Pl. 107)**

*SVL 80-100 mm; max. SVL 115 mm.*
This large agama is very similar to Kirk's rock agama, *A. kirkii* (above), but the scales on the back are larger than those on the belly, there are fewer (69-94) scale rows at midbody, and breeding males have blue heads. The ventrals are keeled (but only faintly so in some populations). Breeding males have a pinkish or grey-brown body, and a broad blue-white vertebral band. The belly is suffused with pink, and the throat has a large blue patch. Breeding females are brilliant orange on the back, but otherwise similar to Kirk's rock agama. In winter, adults have an olive to dark brown head with a reddish bar across the forehead, a large reddish spot just above the shoulder, and sometimes a row of 4-5 brick-red to blackish spots on the flanks. In juveniles the dorsal spots are distinct and interspersed with smaller yellow spots, and the vertebral streak is yellowish. **Biology:** Equally at home in trees and on the ground, these agamas will climb rapidly up the nearest tree when disturbed. The diet consists mainly of ants, but is supplemented with beetles, other insects and millipedes. **Habitat:** This agama prefers lowland savannah and forest fringe. **Range:** It is found in E. Zimbabwe, extending through adjacent Mozambique to Malawi and Tanzania.

## Namibian Rock Agama
*Agama planiceps* **(Pl. 77)**

*A.p. planiceps*

*SVL 80-100 mm; max. SVL 112 mm.*
A large, graceful agama with a small, flat head and a pointed snout. The ear openings are large, and the tympanums are visible. The body is flattened with long limbs and toes. The large, feebly keeled back scales are directed obliquely inwards towards the backbone. There are 63-76 scale rows at midbody. The ventrals are small and smooth. The dorsal crest is weakly developed on the nape and absent on the back, but forms a crest

on the tail in males. The tail is much longer than the head and body. Males have a single row of 8-14 preanal pores. Breeding males have a dull blue-purple, almost metallic, back. The head, neck and throat are coral to orange-red, sometimes with scattered dark and yellow spots. The tail is olive-yellow at the base, changing to orange-red at the tip. The belly is dull purple to blue-black. Females and juveniles have a greyish to olive-brown body, with pale blotches and dark purple-brown infusions. There is a bright orange blotch behind the shoulder, and a pale dorsal streak is sometimes present. The head has symmetrical lemon-yellow blotches. **Biology and breeding:** Live in groups of up to 11 on rock outcrops and boulder-strewn hills, and are very active and difficult to approach. Form social groups in which dominant males defend a territory containing a harem of females, all of whom he will mate with. During the breeding season he will not tolerate other males in this territory. The diet includes leaves and seeds, as well as beetles and insects. A small clutch of 5-10 eggs, usually 6-7, (up to 20 mm long) are laid in soil in a rock crack or beneath a slab. They hatch in 45-50 days; hatchlings are 70-80 mm TL. Predators include hornbills and rock kestrels. Up to 30% of adults have broken tails. **Habitat:** Semi-desert and arid savannah. **Range:** Damaraland and Kaokoveld in northern parts of Namibia. **Subspecies:** Two races recognized, but only the typical race occurs in the region. Replaced in Angola by *A.p. schacki*.

## Tree Agamas    *Acanthocerus*

Large agamids that lack an enlarged occipital scale. Sometimes placed in *Stellio*, but this generic name is unavailable. There are about 20 species, only one of which enters the northern parts of the subcontinent.

### Southern Tree Agama    *Acanthocerus atricollis* (Pl. 76)
*SVL 120-150 mm; max. SVL 167 mm male, 135 mm female.*

A very large agama with a broad head (particularly in males, which also grow larger) that lacks an occipital scale. The ear openings are larger than the eyes, and the tympanums are visible. The scales on the body are small, rhomboidal and keeled, with those along the back larger and mixed with scattered enlarged, spiny scales. There is no vertebral crest. There is a strong fold across the throat. The ventrals are smooth. There are two (and sometimes three) rows of 10-12 preanal pores in males. Breeding males have a dull blue to bluish back, with bright blue (anteriorly) to straw-yellow (posteriorly) spines. The head is coppery-green to brilliant ultra-marine on top, blue-green on the sides and peacock-blue on the throat. There is a large black spot on each side above the shoulder, and a broad, blue-green to yellowish vertebral stripe. The tail is dull green to olive-brown. Females and non-breeding males are olive to green-brown, marbled with black above, with a black shoulder spot. Juveniles have a similar ground colour with dark X-shapes surrounded by white blotches along the sides. The tail is banded with dark brown-black. **Biology and breeding:** Frequently seen nodding their heads in display while clinging to a tree trunk. Come to the ground only to cross to another tree and occasionally to eat (especially flying ants and termites). Their diet is supplemented with caterpillars, grasshoppers and beetles. When threatened, they retreat around the tree trunk, always keeping it between themselves and danger. They gape the mouth widely, showing the bright orange mouth lining, and deliver a painful bite if caught. Contrary to popular belief, they are not poisonous. They sleep at night in a hollow branch or under

*A.a. atricollis*

218

peeling bark. Breeding males have more massive heads than females, and also develop swollen, scarred tail bases from fighting. The female lays 5-14 oval, soft-shelled eggs (10-21 x 22-28 mm) in a hole dug in moist soil. These hatch after 90 days. Hatchlings measure 70-80 mm TL; they triple in size in their first year, but growth slows thereafter. They become sexually mature in their second year. **Habitat:** Open savannah, particularly with *Brachystegia* and *Acacia* trees. **Range:** Ethiopia, through E. Africa to north-eastern parts of the subcontinent, reaching southern limits in coastal KwaZulu-Natal, E. Botswana (Lobatsi) and Ovamboland. **Subspecies:** Possibly up to six races in E. and central Africa, but all poorly defined. Only the typical race, *A.a. atricollis*, occurs on the subcontinent.

# Chameleons
## FAMILY CHAMAELEONIDAE

Chameleons are unmistakable, and look unlike any other lizards. Their scales are small, do not overlap and lack bony plates. The head and body are compressed and the neck is not defined. Limbs are always present, with the toes usually bound together and opposed. The tail is usually prehensile and cannot be shed or regenerated. The protruding eyes can move independently. The hearing is very poor, the middle ear cavity and external opening being absent. The tongue is telescopic and can be shot further than the body length to capture prey. Preanal and femoral pores are absent. Males are characterized by their bright coloration, and often have horns and other ornamentation on the head.

Chameleons are primarily arboreal, which explains many of their unusual features. Their colour, compressed bodies, crests and casques serve as camouflage; the prehensile tail and opposable toes, bound in uneven bundles, clasp swaying branches; the turreted eyes move separately, scanning for food and danger; and the unique tongue captures prey at a distance in flimsy foliage. Social displays and sexual dimorphism are well developed. Both males and females are asocial, maintaining their exclusive territories by ritualized combat which includes head-butting, inflating the throat pouch, and rapid colour changes. They rarely fight, but will bite if an intruder fails to withdraw. Colour varies to match the surroundings. The most dramatic darkening occurs when they are stressed, and the colour is most intense when they are aroused, either in territorial disputes with other males or when courting females. Most are oviparous, laying large clutches of soft-shelled eggs, but some montane and temperate species are viviparous.

This family has about 130-140 species in six genera, and is restricted mainly to Africa and Madagascar. At present, there are three genera with at least 18 species in the region; 15 species are endemic.

### KEY TO THE SOUTHERN AFRICAN GENERA IN THE CHAMAELEONIDAE
1 - Toes with single claw; tail prehensile; soles of feet smooth:     go to 2
   - Toes with bicuspid claws (small, secondary cusp directed downwards); soles of feet spiny; tail feebly prehensile; lungs simple; oviparous:
      *Rhampholeon* (Leaf chameleons, page 228)
2 - Parietal narrow and compressed; lungs with elongate sacs; oviparous:
      *Chamaeleo* (Common chameleons, page 227)
   - Parietal broad, with lateral processes; lungs simple; viviparous:
      *Bradypodion* (Dwarf chameleons, page 228)

# Dwarf Chameleons    *Bradypodion*

These are small chameleons. The tail is prehensile. The parietal forms a large plate over the temporal region. The lungs are simple and lack diverticula. The skin has scattered large tubercles, particularly on the flanks and limbs. Gular and dorsal crests are present and are usually composed of scaly flaps; ventral crests, tarsal spurs and occipital flaps are absent. The head lacks protuberances, but often has a well-developed casque, and adult males have a larger gular crest. Adult males develop intense breeding colours, while juveniles and females are camouflaged in mottled brown and grey-green.

They are often found in small, localized colonies that seem to undergo regular cyclic changes, with populations exploding and crashing in numbers. Fecundity is high, and the females give birth to two, rarely three, clutches, each of 5-20 minute babies, every season. Growth is rapid, and sexual maturity is reached in 1-2 years, sometimes sooner in captivity. Adult males become intensely coloured when defending their territories against other males or when courting females. They engage in well-developed ritual displays; the head is bobbed and the gular region expanded to reveal the brightly coloured interstitial skin. All are arboreal, although some small species live in low vegetation. They prey on small insects. Water is required regularly and is licked from dew or raindrops on foliage. They have many predators, particularly snakes (for example the boomslang and spotted bush snake) and birds (for example the fiscal shrike). They climb into the top of vegetation in the morning to bask in the sun and retreat at night into bushes, often quite low to the ground, where they turn pale grey-white (rendering them easy to locate with a torch). *Bradypodion* means 'slow foot', which describes well their deliberate, jerky gait.

These chameleons are usually considered endemic to the subcontinent, but some researchers also place a number of East African species in the genus. This is controversial, has not gained universal acceptance, and is deferred here pending fuller validation. The taxonomy of some southern African groups is also very confused as the scattered populations are characterized by slight differences in scalation and male breeding colour. The previous treatment of these groups as subspecies of a single, wide-ranging species, was an oversimplification. However, exaggerated claims of over 40 new taxa are unjustified without supporting morphological analysis. The relationships of the many isolated populations along the escarpment mountains of Mpumalanga and N. Province are very confused, and up to seven new species may be involved. The only described species from the region, *B. transvaalensis*, has a restricted distribution; other populations are listed under this species, but with the understanding that some will certainly be elevated to full species in the future. Conversely, some Cape species (for example *B. gutturale* and *B. karrooicum*) may best be considered regional variants (perhaps races) of the wide-ranging southern dwarf chameleon (*B. ventrale*). Within the genus two general groups can be recognized. The first, composed of the larger species, is associated with montane forests in KwaZulu-Natal (for example *B. thamnobates*), the southern Cape (for example *B. damaranum*) and Mpumalanga escarpment (for example *B. transvaalense*), but occurs in a wider variety of habitats in the Cape (for example *B. pumilum* and *B. ventrale*). The second group is restricted to coastal or fynbos vegetation and consists of small species (for example *B. taeniabronchum*, *B. setaroi* and *B. melanocephalum*). The evolutionary relationships of the groups remain unknown.

Species are often difficult to distinguish; there are few diagnostic features, and these are often only fully developed in adult males. However, few species are sympatric, so if the locality is known, with few exceptions they should be easy to identify. Given these limitations, 14 dwarf chameleon species are recognized at present, with at least ten new populations under investigation. All are endemic to the subcontinent.

### Transkei Dwarf Chameleon     *Bradypodion caffrum* (Pl. 94)

*(Endemic) SVL 50-65 mm; max. SVL 68 mm.*
A medium-sized dwarf chameleon. The flanks have rough granules, with a few scattered tubercles that may form an irregular row on the upper flanks. The head has an obvious, elevated, pointed and laterally compressed casque and moderate cranial crests. The gular region has 2-4 shallow throat grooves. There is a well-developed gular crest, with the anterior scaly flaps broader than they are long, and overlapping. The dorsal crest consists of large, compressed tubercles and extends well onto the tail in males, but fades out over the lumbar region in females. The tail is slightly longer than the body in males, and equal to or shorter than the body in females. The body is mottled brown, olive and cream, with an irregular pale cream lateral stripe that extends onto the temporal region and may intensify to orange in display. The gular region is pale cream, with white throat grooves. **Habitat:** Usually prefers low coastal forest. **Range:** Transkei dwarf chameleons are found in the immediate vicinity of Port St Johns, E. Cape, with an isolated population in Oribi Gorge in S. KwaZulu-Natal.

### Kentani Dwarf Chameleon     *Bradypodion kentanicum*

*(Endemic) SVL 45-55 mm; max. SVL 60 mm.*
A medium-sized dwarf chameleon. The gular crest is composed of simple tubercles, whilst the dorsal crest is composed of a continuous series of compressed, triangular tubercles; these do not extend much onto the tail. There are a few, scattered, slightly enlarged tubercles on the flanks. The casque is pointed, but not extended posteriorly. The coloration of live specimens is not known. **Biology:** A very poorly known species with an apparently restricted distribution. Previously confused with the black-headed chameleon, *B. melanocephalum*, to which it is probably similar in biology and behaviour. **Habitat:** Prefers low coastal thicket. **Range:** Kentani dwarf chameleons are found in the immediate vicinity of Kentani, E. Cape.

### Knysna Dwarf Chameleon     *Bradypodion damaranum* (Pl. 94)

*(Endemic) SVL 60-70 mm; max. SVL 79 mm male.*
A medium-sized dwarf chameleon. The flanks have granular scales with a few scattered, flattened tubercles and two longitudinal rows of enlarged tubercles. There is an oval patch of smooth skin around each forelimb. The head has a well-developed, narrow casque that is elevated and some-what recurved posteriorly. The cranial crests, which are prominent, consist of large, convex tubercles that surround large, polygonal, smooth temporal scales. The gular crest consists of 8-13 large, scaly flaps that are broader than they are long and overlap strongly. The dorsal crest consists of 35-50 low, interrupted tubercles that extend almost to the end of the tail, and are largest over the base of the tail. The tail is longer than the head and body in both sexes. Males are brilliant emerald-green often with a dark

blue-green, blue-maroon or rust patch on the flanks, bordered with smooth yellow skin around the base of each forelimb. The cranial crests are yellow to dark blue, with the temporal scales pale blue-grey and sometimes light maroon when the animal is excited. The interstitial skin of the gular region is pale yellow, with light blue tubercles. Females, juveniles and unaroused males are mottled in green and yellow-brown. **Biology and breeding:** This chameleon may climb high into the canopy, and often sleeps in the centre of tree ferns, where its long, coiled tail resembles a young fern frond. Hot berg winds may drive it from the canopy to seek shelter in the forest understorey. Several broods of 6-20 young are born during the summer months. **Habitat:** Usually prefers wet coastal forest; sometimes enters low secondary bush in clearings and gardens. **Range:** Occurs in the coastal regions of the W. and E. Cape provinces, from George to Witelsbos; despite its scientific name, this species is not found in Damaraland.

### Drakensberg Dwarf Chameleon

*Bradypodion dracomontanum* (Pl. 93)
*(Endemic) SVL 60-70 mm; max. SVL 77 mm.*
The flanks of this chameleon have fine granular scales and a few small, scattered, convex tubercles. The head has a medium-sized, recurved casque and distinct cranial crests. The gular crest is composed of 10-18 small, abutting scaly flaps that are longer than they are broad. The dorsal crest has 39-49 small, conical scales that extend onto the tail, which is longer than the head and body. Males have a green-blue body with dark blue blotches on the anterior flanks, and white tubercles. The belly and gular region are infused with bright yellow. The female is mottled in green, brown and white, sometimes with a faint, pale lateral stripe. **Habitat:** Prefers evergreen kloof forests and alpine veld between 1 500 and 2 500 m above sea level. **Range:** This dwarf chameleon is found in the southern and central parts of the KwaZulu-Natal Drakensberg, to extreme NE Free State.

### Black-headed Dwarf Chameleon

*Bradypodion melanocephalum* (Pl. 95)
*(Endemic) SVL 50-65 mm; max. SVL 71 mm.*
A small dwarf chameleon. The flanks are covered in granules, with scattered tubercles that may form 2-3 irregular rows. The head has a feeble, narrow, slightly recurved casque and a weak cranial crest. The gular region has 2-3 shallow throat grooves and a weak crest of 12-22 simple, small, conical tubercles. The dorsal crest is composed of 31-55 small, compressed tubercles and extends well onto the tail. The tail is slightly longer than the body in males, and shorter in females. The body is brown-green, with a pale brown area on the flanks that extends onto the temporal region and is interrupted or constricted by 2-3 dark-edged, irregular, brownish blotches. There are two brighter orange regions between the cranial crests. The gular region is off-white with white throat grooves. **Biology and breeding:** This dwarf chameleon has adapted well to urban gardens. Up to 12 tiny young are born during the summer months. **Habitat:** Coastal bush and reed beds around vleis. **Range:** Restricted to N. KwaZulu-Natal coast (below 30 m), from Mount Edgecombe to Nqwazi River, with isolated populations around Pietermaritzburg and Greytown.

## Zululand Dwarf Chameleon — *Bradypodion nemorale* (Pl. 95)

*(Endemic) SVL 55-75 mm; max. SVL 80 mm.*
A medium-sized dwarf chameleon. The flanks have fine, granular scales and a row of slightly enlarged tubercles. The head has a recurved, prominent casque and moderate cranial crests. The gular crest is composed of 8-10 scaly, non-overlapping flaps that are longer than they are broad. The dorsal crest consists of 10-29 well-spaced, triangular scales and usually extends onto the tail. The tail is shorter than the body. Males have dirty green flanks with large, irregular, rust-coloured blotches that intensify during display. The tubercles on the flanks are orange, and those on the dorsal crest are reddish-brown. The gular region is pale green with white throat grooves (SA RDB, Restricted). **Habitat:** Forest. **Range:** Qudeni and Nkandla forests in N. KwaZulu-Natal.

## Cape Dwarf Chameleon — *Bradypodion pumilum* (Pl. 93)

*(Endemic) SVL 65-80 mm; max. SVL 82 mm.*
A large dwarf chameleon. The flanks are covered with granules and have 1-2 rows of enlarged, rounded, convex tubercles. The head has a moderate, narrowed and pointed casque and well-developed cranial crests. The gular region has 3-4 shallow grooves that are not separated by the enlarged tubercles. The gular crest is composed of 12-17 elongate, scaly flaps that do not overlap. The dorsal crest extends along two-thirds of the tail and is composed of small, separate, conical tubercles. The tail is longer than the body. Coloration is uniform leaf-green usually with an orange to rust-red lateral stripe. The temporal region is red-orange, sometimes with wine-coloured cranial crests. The gular region is pale green to yellow. **Biology and breeding:** May be less territorial than other species, and can reach high densities (200 specimens per hectare), with 5-6 adults inhabiting a single bush. Lives in low coastal bushes and reed beds. May produce up to three litters per year; litters born in December consist of more babies (5-12) than those born in April (3-6). Foetal membranes stick to the foliage, whereupon the young wriggle free. Like all lizards, they fend for themselves from birth. **Habitat:** Vleis and along river courses. **Range:** SW Cape, with isolated populations around Clanwilliam and Bredasdorp. Introduced to Alexander Bay and Walvis Bay, Namibia.

## Setaro's Dwarf Chameleon — *Bradypodion setaroi* (Pl. 95)

*(Endemic) SVL 45-50 mm; max. SVL 59 mm.*
A small dwarf chameleon. The flanks have fine granular scales and an irregular series of enlarged, flattened tubercles bordering the backbone. The head has a pronounced, elevated, narrow casque and moderate cranial crests. The gular crest is composed of 13-23 weakly developed, irregular scaly flaps that are longer than they are broad. There are 2-4 shallow throat grooves. The dorsal crest is reduced, is composed of l0-18 low tubercles, and does not reach the hind body. The tail is longer than the body in males and shorter in females. The body is light grey-brown, with an irregular orange stripe on the flanks, which may have 2-3 darker orange blotches. The lateral stripe is bordered with vermiculated grey-green that also occurs as bars on the tail and speckles on the head. The gular region is light green, with white throat grooves. **Breeding:** Eight babies (39-42 mm TL) are born in late April. (SA RDB, Restricted.) **Habitat:** Low coastal dune forest, entering urban gardens. **Range:** Maputaland, probably into adjacent Mozambique.

**Smith's Dwarf Chameleon** *Bradypodion taeniabronchum* **(Pl. 95)**
*(Endemic) SVL 45-55 mm; max. SVL 58 mm.*
A small dwarf chameleon. The flanks are finely scaled with a few scattered, flattened tubercles that may form an irregular row on the dorsal surface. The head has a small, pointed, indistinct casque and weakly developed cranial crests. The gular region has two deep grooves. The gular crest is small, with 18-22 tiny, conical tubercles in an interrupted series. The dorsal crest is composed of 30-45 small conical tubercles and reaches to the base of the tail. The tail is shorter than the body. Coloration ranges from grey-green to pale green (sometimes with a pale lateral stripe). The belly and gular region are paler. The throat grooves are black. Occasional specimens are rust-red, with deep maroon throat grooves.
**Biology and breeding:** Lives in protea bushes, feeding on insects that are attracted to the flowers. Shelters at night among dead flower heads. Much of its habitat has been destroyed for pine plantations (SA RDB, Endangered). Gives birth to up to 13 minute babies (35-40 mm TL) in summer. An unreceptive female will reject the male's advances by taking an open-legged stance, gaping her mouth to reveal the bright yellow-orange lining and black throat grooves, and rocking from side to side. **Habitat:** Mountain fynbos. **Range:** Apparently isolated populations on Vanstadensberg near Port Elizabeth, around Churchill Dam and Kareedouw and on N. slopes of Tsitsikammaberg, near Misgund in Langkloof, E. Cape.

### Natal Midlands Dwarf Chameleon
*Bradypodion thamnobates* **(Pl. 93)**
*(Endemic) SVL 60-80 mm; max. SVL 103 mm.*
A large dwarf chameleon. The flanks have granular scales and 1-2 rows of enlarged, convex tubercles on the upper surface, and similar tubercles scattered over the lower sides and tail. The head has a strongly elevated, recurved casque and very distinct cranial crests composed of horn-coloured, conical tubercles. The gular crest has 10-18 scaly lobes, usually overlapping and longer than they are broad. The pronounced dorsal crest is composed of 26-43 elongate, conical tubercles, and extends onto the tail which is longer than the head and body in males, but shorter in females and equal in juveniles. Males are dark blue-green on the back, with an elongate, cream, bright yellow or red-brown lateral patch, and a light blue-green belly and limbs. The tubercles on the limbs and flanks are reddish-cream to horn-coloured. The cranial crests are horn-coloured, sometimes with dark blue-black blotches. There are scattered red tubercles on the temporal region and the eyes. The chin, throat and base of the forelimbs are white to cream with white interstitial skin in the throat grooves. Females and juveniles are mottled in grey and brown, and some individuals are uniform green. **Biology and breeding:** A very hardy species that prefers open thicket and adapts well to suburban situations. From 8-20 babies are born in a litter, the young measuring 40-42 mm TL. Growth is very fast, and in captivity sexual maturity can be reached in only 9 months. (SA RDB, Restricted.) **Habitat:** Lowland forest and bush. **Range:** KwaZulu-Natal midlands, from Mooi River to Howick and Bulwer.

**Transvaal Dwarf Chameleon** *Bradypodion transvaalense* **(Pl. 94)**
*(Endemic) SVL 50-75 mm; max. SVL 82 mm female, 68 mm male.*
A large dwarf chameleon. The flanks have granular scales and scattered tubercles over the back; these are sometimes confined to 1-2 longitudinal

rows. The head has a moderate casque that is curved slightly upwards, and prominent cranial crests. The gular crest has 10-16 (usually 13) well-developed, rounded, scaly flaps, the anterior ones overlapping and broader than they are long. The dorsal crest is prominent and extends onto the first third of the tail. The tail is slightly longer than the head and body. Coloration is varied. Aroused males have a prominent, elongate, pale yellow-mustard stripe that is bordered with dark maroon, and extends from the temporal region onto the flanks. The gular is cream-coloured and the belly often infused with rust. Females and juveniles are mottled in brown and cream. The back is dark and the flanks cream-coloured with a number of large dark-edged, irregular blotches that may form vertical bars. The edge of the casque is bright mustard. **Biology and breeding:** Although mainly a forest species, it does adapt to forest fringes and even well-wooded gardens. From 7-17 young are born at the end of winter to early spring. The young measure 43-49 mm TL. **Habitat:** Wet forest of escarpment kloofs. **Range:** This species is restricted to the vicinity of Haenertsburg and Woodbush Forest Reserve, N. Province escarpment. Isolated populations of other dwarf chameleons occur along the Mpumalanga and N. Province escarpment, from Barberton north to the Soutpansberg, and extending into adjacent Swaziland (shown as stippled areas on the map). As many as nine taxa may occur, forming two groups. Those that occur north of the Olifants River have males with yellow and black coloration, and 20-29 (mostly 22-27) tubercles in the vertebral crest. The males belonging to the group that occurs south of the Olifants River are pale blue and white in colour, with a little black, and have 27-43 (mostly 30-35) vertebral tubercles.

### Southern Dwarf Chameleon — *Bradypodion ventrale* (Pl. 93)

*(Endemic) SVL 65-80 mm; max. SVL 85 mm male, 79 mm female.*

A large dwarf chameleon. The flanks have small granules and scattered, flattened to convex tubercles, the largest ones forming 2-4 rows on the upper flanks. The head has a moderate, slightly raised casque and cranial crests. The gular region has 3-5 irregular grooves separated by rows of enlarged tubercles. The gular crest has 12-17 scaly flaps, the first 4-7 being broader than they are long and overlapping. The dorsal crest is composed of 35-45 conical tubercles running in an interrupted series to near the end of the tail. The tail is shorter than the body in both sexes, and relatively longer in males. Unaroused males, females and juveniles are predominantly mottled in grey, olive, cream and brown, and occasionally have three dark-edged, irregular bands on the back. An elongate, pale yellow to cream patch extends from the temporal region onto the forebody. The enlarged tubercles on the flanks are dark brown. The skin behind the casque is sometimes mustard-yellow. The gular region is pale yellow-green, with white grooves. Excited males are blue-black, with a bright rust stripe surrounding orange flank tubercles. **Biology and breeding:** When threatened, this chameleon rapidly loses its bright colours and retreats so as to position a branch between itself and danger. It may drop to the ground and hide among the leaf litter if escape or concealment in the foliage is impossible. One or two litters, each of 10-22 young (up to 43 mm TL), are born during summer. Predators include snakes (particularly the boomslang and sometimes even herald snakes), birds (the fiscal shrike and Burchell's coucal) and golden orb spiders. **Habitat:** Mesic thicket, rarely entering fynbos. **Range:** Found in E. Cape, from Uniondale, and possibly the eastern Little Karoo, to Hogsback. **Subspecies:** No races are recognized, however, the Karoo and Robertson dwarf chameleons (below) may be local races, and a number of isolated populations in the Little Karoo, Swartberg and Franschhoek may also be related.

### Robertson Dwarf Chameleon    *Bradypodion gutturale* (Pl. 94)

*(Endemic) SVL 65-75 mm; max. SVL 84 mm male, 79 mm female.*
A medium-sized dwarf chameleon. The flanks are rough, and have fine granules and scattered, very large tubercles that form one (and sometimes two) obvious row on the sides. The head is covered with very rough tubercles and well-developed cranial crests, and has a prominent, pointed casque. The gular region has irregular grooves and scattered, large tubercles. The gular crest is prominent, with numerous scaly, sometimes conical, flaps that are longer than they are broad and that overlap at the front. The dorsal crest is well developed, with 36-55 elongate tubercles that are largest over the shoulder region and extend over half the length of the tail. The tail is usually shorter than the body. This chameleon is blue-grey, with rust-coloured lateral tubercles and a dorsal crest of the same colour, becoming light orange-red anteriorly and on the cranial crests. The gular region has light orange scales and blue-grey interstitial skin. **Breeding:** Several clutches of 10-20 babies (40 mm TL) are born between September and February. **Habitat:** Low montane fynbos scrub. **Range:** Vicinity of Worcester and Robertson in SW Cape, extending to Anysberg in the Little Karoo. **Subspecies:** Perhaps only a local race of the southern dwarf chameleon, *B. ventrale.*

### Karoo Dwarf Chameleon    *Bradypodion karrooicum* (Pl. 94)

*(Endemic) SVL 65-72 mm; max. SVL 75 mm male, 73 mm female.*
A medium-sized dwarf chameleon. The flanks have granular scales and scattered, convex tubercles that form 2-4 irregular, longitudinal rows on the upper flanks. The head has a well-developed casque that is feebly elevated, and shallow cranial crests. The gular region has 3-5 irregular throat grooves and a row of small tubercles. The gular crest is composed of elongate, and sometimes pointed, scaly lobes that are longer than they are broad and do not overlap. The dorsal crest is composed of prominent conical tubercles, interrupted by smaller tubercles and granular skin, and extends over most of the tail. The tail is shorter than the head and body in both sexes. The body is mottled in ash-grey and cream-brown, tinged with olive-green, and with 2-3 diffuse, dark-edged blotches. One or two rows of rust-orange flank stripes and chrome-yellow interstitial skin in the gular region may develop. **Biology and breeding:** This species is similar in habits and behaviour to the southern dwarf chameleon, *B. ventrale* (page 225). **Habitat:** Sparse thorn bushes along river courses; adapting to urban gardens. **Range:** S. and E. Karoo, with introduced populations in the Free State and Gauteng. **Subspecies:** Perhaps only a local race of the southern dwarf chameleon, *B. ventrale.*

### Namaqua Dwarf Chameleon    *Bradypodion occidentale* (Pl. 93)

*(Endemic) SVL 70-80 mm; max. SVL 91 mm female, 86 mm male.*
A large dwarf chameleon. The narrow casque is well developed and extends backwards. The dorsal crest is prominent, with conical tubercles in a continuous series extending well onto the tail. The gular crest is composed of large scaly lobes that are much longer than they are broad

and overlap extensively. The throat grooves are conspicuous and extend almost to the forelimbs. The flank has a longitudinal row of very large, flattened tubercles, surrounded by scattered smaller tubercles. The tail is shorter than the head and body, particularly in females. Adults and juveniles have ash-grey bodies that are mottled with dark grey and black. The coloration of breeding males is unknown. **Biology and breeding:** This large dwarf chameleon favours low coastal bush, where it is well camouflaged among the lichen-covered branches. The diet comprises mainly stink bugs, moths and caterpillars, but beetles are also taken. Up to 20 babies are born in summer. **Habitat:** Strandveld in the north and dry coastal fynbos in the south. **Range:** W. Cape coastal regions, almost as far south as Cape Town, with remnant populations near Stellenbosch and Vredendal in the south, Steinkopf and Kamiesberg in the north, and with an isolated, possibly introduced population at Lüderitz in S. Namibia. **Subspecies:** Previously treated as a western race of the southern dwarf chameleon, *B. ventrale.*

## Common Chameleons  *Chamaeleo*

These are medium to large chameleons with prehensile tails, a narrow, compressed parietal bone, and diverticulate lungs. Males of some central African species have bizarre horns and crests that are used in display.

Found mainly in forest or well-wooded savannah, some species enter montane grassland or semi-desert. Most lay eggs, although some small, montane E. African chameleons (for example *Chamaeleo bitaeniatus*) are viviparous.

There are about 45 species in the genus, which is restricted mainly to Africa, with isolated populations surrounding the Mediterranean and extending east to S. India and Ceylon. Madagascan species have been transferred to the genera *Caluma* and *Furcifer*. The Kenyan Miocene fossil *C. intermedius*, which is 14 million years old, is very similar to the Namaqua chameleon, *C. namaquensis* (page 228). Two species, neither of which is endemic, occur on the subcontinent.

### Flap-neck Chameleon  *Chamaeleo dilepis* (Pl. 96)

*SVL 120-140 mm; max. SVL 150 mm.*

A large chameleon with a continuous crest of small, white, triangular tubercles on the throat and belly, a prehensile tail that is as long as the body, and occipital flaps (these are large in western populations, but small or rudimentary in the east). Coloration is varied, from pale yellow through green shades to brown. The belly crest is white, and there is usually a pale bar and several white spots on the sides. The interstitial skin of the male throat pouch is orange. **Biology and breeding:** Common in suitable habitat. The diet consists of insects, particularly grasshoppers and beetles. When threatened, it inflates its body, distends its throat, raises the occipital flaps and opens its mouth wide to expose the red-orange lining. It will bite readily. It is greatly feared by many tribal people, and is the subject of much folklore, but is not poisonous. It is easier to find at night, when it turns blue-white in colour. Predators are mainly snakes (particularly the boomslang and twig snakes), but also include monkeys and birds (for example the crowned hornbill). Mating and egg-laying are energetic. In spring the male's gular skin turns pearl-white, and the female permits approach. Introductions are minimal, and the female is taken more or less by storm. Mating may last for up to an hour. Egg development takes 3-4 months. The female becomes bloated with 25-50 (max. 65) small eggs (13-15 x 8-9 mm); during this times, she is dull-coloured and very aggressive. She constructs a tunnel (150-300 mm long) in damp soil, in which to lay her eggs in late summer (March-May in Maputaland). She may take up to 24 hours to complete laying. The eggs take approximately 150 days to hatch in captivity (27°C), but may take up to 377 days in the wild when development is slowed during winter. Hatchlings measure about 45-50 mm TL. **Habitat:** This chameleon prefers savannah woodland, entering coastal forest in Maputaland in N. KwaZulu-Natal. **Range:** Found in tropical Africa, southwards to KwaZulu-Natal, Mpumalanga, northern provinces, N. and E. Botswana, to N. Cape and N. Namibia. **Subspecies:** There is a great controversy over the races; 5-6 races have been described, but only *C.d. ruspolii* from Somalia is well-defined. Southern African populations are sometimes referred to *C. quilensis*, but this has not gained wide acceptance.

### Namaqua Chameleon      *Chamaeleo namaquensis* (Pl. 96)
*SVL 120-140 mm; max. SVL 160 mm female, 145 mm male.*

A large, ungainly chameleon with a robust head and a big mouth. The dorsal crest is composed of 12-14 very large, knob-like tubercles that decrease in size towards the tail. There is no gular or ventral crest. The tail is much shorter than the head and body, and is feebly prehensile. The body is dull green-grey to pinkish-maroon, with scattered dark spots and a row of 4-5 larger pale spots on the upper flanks. **Biology and breeding:** Mainly terrestrial; lives in some of the hottest, most desolate regions. On very hot days it climbs into bushes or onto rocks, facing head up into the sun, to keep cool. It eats anything that is small enough to swallow, including locusts, crickets, lizards, and even snakes (for example Péringuey's adder). It has a big appetite, and may eat up to 200 beetles a day. A nasal salt gland rids the body of excess salt, allowing the chameleon to forage at the coast. Territories are defended initially with display (side-to-side head bobs), but a fight will break out if the transgressor does not retreat. Two or three clutches per year, each of 6-30 soft-shelled eggs (10-13 x 16-20 mm), are laid in a burrow 200-250 mm deep. A preferred site is at the foot of a windward slope of a large dune, and is defended by the female. Clutches laid in spring contain fewer but larger eggs than those laid in winter. The eggs take 90-100 days to hatch (and up to 115 days if they are laid in winter). Newly hatched males are smaller (45-50 mm TL) than females and reach maturity later (males at about 210 days, females at about 150). The young, which often hatch at night, have more dorsal tubercles than adults and climb bushes more readily. **Habitat:** Sandy regions (including coastal dunes) with scrub vegetation. **Range:** Western karroid areas, through Namaqualand and Namib Desert to S. Angola.

## African Leaf Chameleons     *Rhampholeon*
These dwarf chameleons inhabit evergreen montane forests. The tail is short, and at most feebly prehensile. The parietal forms a broad plate over the temporal region. The lungs are simple, without diverticula. They are mainly terrestrial, searching the forest leaf litter for small insects. At night they climb into low vegetation to sleep. They are oviparous.

Eight species are recognized from East and southern Africa, but only two endemic species occur on the subcontinent. Some were previously placed in the genus *Brookesia*, which is now restricted to Madagascar.

## Marshall's African Leaf Chameleon
### Rhampholeon marshalli (Pl. 95)
*(Endemic) SVL 30-60 mm; max. SVL 73 mm female, 60 mm male.*

A tiny chameleon with a short (50-75% of the body length), prehensile tail, a rostral appendage, a vertebral series of enlarged tubercles arranged in clumps, bicuspid claws, and feet with spinose soles. It does not have a gular or ventral crest, nor occipital flaps. In colour, the male is shades of brown, grey or olive-green, contrasting with the bright blue-green to black ventrum, and with a prominent row of pale tubercles along the chin, the sides of the lower body and most of the tail. Females are light green. **Biology and breeding:** This relatively sedentary chameleon lives on undergrowth in montane forests, feeding on small beetles, flies, etc. It resembles a small, dead leaf, and is therefore well camouflaged. It excavates a hole in leaf-litter in which it lays 10-18 eggs (13 x 8 mm) in late summer. The embryos are well developed and hatch in only 35-60 days. Hatchlings measure about 32 mm TL, and mature in two years. **Habitat:** Wet montane evergreen forests. **Range:** Eastern border of Zimbabwe and probably into adjacent Mozambique. **Subspecies:** None recognized; *R. gorongosae* is now treated as a separate species.

## Gorongoza African Leaf Chameleon   *Rhampholeon gorongosae*
*(Endemic) SVL 30-60 mm; max. SVL 71 mm female, only 31 mm male.*

A tiny chameleon with a very short (44-53% of the body length), prehensile tail, an elongate rostral appendage in males (tiny in females), a vertebral series of enlarged tubercles arranged in clumps, a curved row of tubercles between the eyes, bicuspid claws, and feet with smooth soles. It does not have a gular or ventral crest, nor occipital flaps. The male is light brown to buff in colour, and the female light green to olive. The belly is only slightly paler than the back. **Biology and breeding:** Similar to Marshall's leaf chameleon (above), inhabiting undergrowth or leaf litter on the forest floor. The small male, which is half the size of the female, has been found riding on the female's back, probably to discourage other suitors. A large female contained 11 eggs (9,5 x 5,5 mm) in late November. **Habitat:** Wet submontane evergreen forests. **Range:** Restricted to Gorongoza Mountain in central Mozambique.

# Geckos
### FAMILY GEKKONIDAE

This family of unusual lizards has an amazing array of feet and eyes. The toe-tips of many species have groups of scales with minute hairs. These unique scales are arranged in rows or paired pads called scansors that allow them to 'stick' to seemingly smooth surfaces. Many species also have claws, which in some species are retractile between the scansors. The different species and genera are easily identified by their feet. Their eyes are usually large, with complicated pupils that dilate widely at night and close to pin-pricks during the day. Most lack movable eyelids; these have become fused and transparent so that each eye is covered by a spectacle. To keep this clean, they lick it with the long, fat tongue. Preanal and femoral pores are usually present in males.

Although a few geckos are diurnal, most are nocturnal. They can withstand much lower temperatures than most other lizards, and live in a large variety of different habitats, including cool mountain tops and temperate regions; they are most common in deserts, which may become very cold at night. Many have adapted well to urbanization and live in homes and factories, and have spread around the world by hiding in goods and ships. All are oviparous (the viviparous New Zealand geckos are now placed in a different family), and usually lay two, relatively large, hard-shelled eggs. A single egg is laid by some geckos, particularly the American sphaerodactylines. Many species lay several clutches during a breeding season, and utilize communal egg-laying sites. They store calcium for the egg shells in special neck glands called endolymphatic sacs. Some all-female species reproduce parthenogenetically. Many live in colonies and have developed a range of different sounds to allow them to communicate in the dark. With the exception of a few colourful diurnal groups (for example *Phelsuma*) most are drably coloured in buffs, greys and browns.

Typical geckos are among the most diverse lizards and are widely distributed throughout the world. The primitive geckos are now placed in separate families (Eublepharinae and Diplodactylinae) and do not occur in southern Africa. Two gekkonid subfamilies are now recognized: the Teratoscincinae, which includes a single genus consisting of five species that are restricted to the near East; and the Gekkoninae which is distributed throughout the tropical regions and includes about 760 species in 67 genera. Geckos are the most diverse family in southern Africa, with 89 species (68 of which are endemic) in 15 genera (six of which are endemic) occurring in the subregion.

### KEY TO THE SOUTHERN AFRICAN GENERA IN THE GEKKONIDAE

1 - Hindfeet webbed:     *Palmatogecko* (Web-footed geckos, page 263)
  - Hindfeet without webs:     go to 2
2 - Toes not dilated, lacking enlarged terminal scansors:     go to 3
  - Toes dilated, with enlarged terminal scansors:     go to 5
3 - Toes short, cylindrical, covered with minute scales, clawless in males, with minute claw in females:
    *Chondrodactylus* (Giant ground gecko, page 237)
  - Toes elongate and strongly clawed:     go to 4
4 - Head and body flattened; toes not fringed; diurnal:
    *Narudasia* (Festive gecko, page 249)
  - Head short, body cylindrical; toes fringed; nocturnal:
    *Ptenopus* (Barking geckos, page 265)
5 - Toes with large claws:     go to 6
  - Toes clawless, or with minute, usually retractile claws:     go to 12
6 - Toe-tips dilated and with single series of scansors:
    *Homopholis* (Velvet geckos, page 244)
  - Toe-tips with paired series of scansors:     go to 7
7 - Toe-tips dilated and with paired scansors separated by groove:     go to 8
  - Toe-tips hardly dilated and with oblique, paired scansors:     go to 11
8 - Toes with single pair of scansors:     go to 9
  - Toes with 2-3 pairs of scansors:     *Afroedura* (Flat geckos, page 231)
9 - Small; pupil with straight edges, back with enlarged keeled tubercles:
    *Cryptactites* (Péringuey's gecko, page 239)
  - Medium to large; pupil wavy-edged; usually no enlarged tubercles (if present these are smooth):     go to 10
10 - Rostral with crease in midline; males with preanal pores:
    *Goggia* (Dwarf leaf-toed geckos, page 239)

- Rostral entire; males without preanal pores:
  *Afrogecko* (African leaf-toed geckos, page 236)
11 - First toe well-developed; pupils vertical; nocturnal:
  *Hemidactylus* (Tropical house geckos, page 242)
- First toe rudimentary; pupils round; diurnal:
  *Lygodactylus* (Dwarf geckos, page 245)
12 - Some toes much longer than others; diurnal:  go to 13
- Toes more or less equal in size; nocturnal:  go to 14
13 - First toe small; scansors at toe-tip divided; no femoral pores; nostrils tubular, each pierced between three nasals:
  *Rhoptropus* (Namib day geckos, page 266)
- First toe rudimentary; scansors at toe-tip undivided; long row of femoral pores; nostrils not tubular:  *Phelsuma* (Day geckos, page 264)
14 - Three or more scansors at toe-tip:
  *Pachydactylus* (Thick-toed geckos, page 249)
- Two scansors at toe-tip:  *Colopus* (Kalahari ground gecko, page 238)

# Flat Geckos  *Afroedura*

These geckos are characterized by a large pair of adhesive scansors beneath the dilated toe-tip, separated by a small gap from 1-2 pairs of smaller scansors. Claws that are retractile between the scansors are present in both sexes. The head and body are flattened, and the eyes are large with vertical pupils. The back is covered with small, flat, smooth granular scales. Preanal pores are present in males, and the tail is usually segmented at the base and slightly longer than the body.

They are nocturnal, usually sheltering under exfoliating flakes on hard rock outcrops (for example granite, gneiss and some sandstones) from sea level to the mountain tops. Some species are communal, and may be found in large aggregations (10-20 individuals) in a suitable crack. They lay two hard-shelled eggs, often in a communal egg-laying site. The eggs are slightly soft and sticky when first laid, but harden later and adhere together and to the rock.

The taxonomy of many populations remains confused and a number of new species await description, particularly in the escarpment region of Mpumalanga and the N. Province. Currently there are 15 species in the genus and all occur on the subcontinent; only two are not endemic.

### African Flat Gecko  *Afroedura africana* (Pl. 88)
*(Endemic) SVL 50-60 mm; max. SVL 64 mm.*
A large flat gecko with an elongate flattened body that is covered with small granules. The nasals are in contact behind the rostral. The toe-tips have three pairs of scansors. The back is pale yellow to buff with 5-6 wavy dark brown bands, and is indistinctly banded (but regenerated tails are not banded). The belly is white-yellow. The dorsal bands are faint or replaced by blotches in the southern races. The tail is segmented. Males have 8-15 preanal pores in an angular series. **Biology and breeding:** Live under thin, exfoliating flakes on the shaded, overhanging surfaces of large granite boulders, where they are protected from the midday heat. Occasionally found under bark on large *Acacia* trees in dry riverbeds. Two thin-shelled eggs (12-13 x 8-9,5 mm) are laid in rock cracks; these hatch in approximately 100 days. Predators include snakes (the spotted house snake and western keeled snake). **Habitat:** Rocky desert and succulent karroid veld. **Range:** Isolated populations in central and S. Namibia and

■ *A.a. namaquensis*

☐ *A.a. tirasensis*

▦ *A.a. africana*

Little Namaqualand. **Subspecies:** Three races are recognized: *A.a. africana* does not have enlarged gular scales, and has 11-15 preanal pores; it occurs in SW Damaraland. In *A.a. tirasensis* the mental and adjacent lower labials are elongate but the adjacent gular scales are not enlarged, and there are 9-10 preanal pores; it is found in Bethanie district of Namibia. *A.a. namaquensis* has enlarged gular scales and 8-10 preanal pores: it is found in Little Namaqualand.

### Amatola Flat Gecko
*Afroedura amatolica* (Pl. 88)

*(Endemic) SVL 50-58 mm; max. SVL 60 mm.*
This medium-sized species is very similar to the mountain flat gecko, *A. nivaria* (page 233). The body is short and flattened. The nasals are not in contact behind the rostral, which enters the nostril. The scales on the back are flattened and overlapping. The back is brownish-grey, with 7-8 wavy, zig-zagging dark brown bands that may be broken up into scattered, irregular blotches. The belly is off-white. The tail is segmented, and there are three pairs of scansors on the toe-tips. Males have 10-12 preanal pores in an angular series. **Biology and breeding:** Up to 10 geckos may be found in a suitable crack on a granite outcrop. They hibernate in deep cracks to escape the snow that covers the mountains in winter. Two eggs (10-12,5 x 7,5-9,5 mm) are laid in a rock crack and 10-30 eggs may be found in a communal site. Hatchlings appear in January-February, and measure 40-44 mm TL. **Habitat:** Rock outcrops in montane grassland and dry thicket. **Range:** Amatola and Katberg Mountains, south to the Fish River valley in E. Cape.

### Kaokoveld Flat Gecko
*Afroedura* cf. *bogerti*

*SVL 40-50 mm; max. SVL 50 mm.*
This small species has a flattened body and broad, segmented tail. The nasals are not in contact behind the rostral, which is excluded from the nostril. The scales on the back are flattened and overlapping, and in about 75 midbody rows; the back is brownish grey, with 7-8 wavy, zig-zagging dark brown bands that may be broken up into scattered, irregular blotches. The belly is off-white. Males have about 8 preanal pores in an angular series. **Habitat:** Rock outcrops in arid savannah. **Range:** It may be an Angolan species. Found in extreme N. Kaokoveld, N. Namibia. The taxonomic status of this population has still to be resolved.

### Hawequa Flat Gecko
*Afroedura hawequensis* (Pl. 88)

*(Endemic) SVL 60-80 mm; max. SVL 83 mm.*
A large flat gecko with a stout flattened body that is covered with small granules. The nasals are not in contact behind the rostral. There are three pairs of scansors on all toes except the first. The back has 5-6 irregular dark brown bands over a light grey-brown background, with scattered yellow spots at the edges of the dark bands and along the flanks. The belly is creamy white. The tail is segmented (leaf-like when regenerated). Males have 30-32 preanal pores in a curved series. **Biology and breeding:** These geckos live in narrow cracks in sandstone boulders, preferring shady positions. Living communally, up to five individuals may be found in the same crack, and they may share this with the smaller marbled African leaf-toed gecko, *Afrogecko porphyreus* (page 237). Two large eggs (14 x 17 mm) are laid in November-December. **Habitat:** Fynbos vegetation. **Range:** Cape fold mountains in SW Cape.

## Karoo Flat Gecko

*Afroedura karroica* **(Pl. 88)**

*(Endemic) SVL 40-50 mm; max. SVL 54 mm.*
A small flat gecko with a short, flattened body. The rostral is separated from the nostril, there are no enlarged chin shields, and the nasals are in contact behind the rostral. The scales on the back are flattened and granular, and the back is light grey-brown to beige, with numerous pale flecks and scattered, dark brown blotches that may rarely form irregular bands. The belly is off-white. The tail is segmented, and there are three pairs of scansors beneath the toes. Males have 6-8 preanal pores. **Biology and breeding:** It prefers small rock outcrops in broken ground, and does not live in large aggregations, but can be very common in suitable habitat. The diet comprises ants and small beetles. A number of two-egg clutches are laid during summer, and communal egg sites are used. **Habitat:** Sandstone outcrops in montane grassland. **Range:** Inland mountains of E. Cape. **Subspecies:** At present no races are recognized.

## Hall's Flat Gecko

*Afroedura halli* **(Pl. 107)**

*(Endemic) SVL 50-60 mm; max. SVL 58,3 mm female, 64,2 mm male.*
A medium-sized flat gecko with well-separated nasorostrals and a rostral that is excluded from the nostril. There are no enlarged chin shields. The scales on the back are flattened, granular and juxtaposed, and the back is light grey-brown to beige with 6-7 irregular, wavy dark brown crossbands. The top of the head and the limbs bear numerous scattered dark brown flecks. The belly is off-white. The tail is segmented, and is marked with dark crossbands, (the regenerated tail is irregularly blotched). There are three pairs of scansors beneath the toes, and males have 6-7 preanal pores. **Biology and breeding:** Often only a single individual or a pair is found under a suitable rock flake, but it may also be communal. Preferred flakes are those on the west side of large overhanging boulders of weathered sandstone that catch the evening sun and are protected from seeping water. The female lays clutches of two oval eggs (12-16 x 10-12 mm) in summer under a thin rock flake in a sunny position. These may hatch in 5-6 weeks and hatchlings measure approximately 44 mm TL. **Habitat:** This gecko prefers large sandstone rock faces on mountain summits in montane grassland. **Range:** Found in W. Lesotho and adjacent NE Cape and Free State.

## Mountain Flat Gecko

*Afroedura nivaria* **(Pl. 107)**

*(Endemic) SVL 50-55 mm; max. SVL 58,8 mm male, 59,6 mm female.*
A medium-sized flat gecko that closely resembles Hall's flat gecko, *A. halli* (page 233), but in which the rostral borders the nostril. The nasorostrals are not in contact behind the rostral. The scales on the back are granular, rounded and juxtaposed, and the back is light brown, with darker mottlings that may form irregular, wavy, transverse bands. The belly is off-white. The tail is segmented, and marked with vague bars or blotches. There are three pairs of scansors below the toes. Males have 9-15 preanal pores in an angular series. **Biology and breeding:** These geckos live in rock cracks and under loose boulders lying on bedrock at altitudes well above the snowline (2 750 m). They eat beetles and grasshoppers. Two eggs (13 x 10 mm) are laid in January-March. Communal sites have been found with the weathered remains of 16 layers of old egg shells. **Habitat:** Montane grassland. **Range:** Drakensberg Mountains of Lesotho, entering adjacent KwaZulu-Natal and Free State.

## Pondo Flat Gecko
*Afroedura pondolia* **(Pl. 89)**

*(Endemic) SVL 45-50 mm; max. SVL 50 mm.*
A small gecko with a slightly flattened, unsegmented and tapering tail. The nasorostrals are separated by a granule, and the rostral enters the nostril. A dark stripe extends from the nostril, through the eye to the side of the neck. The dorsal scales are flattened and almost overlap. The top of the head is mottled with brown. The back is greyish-white with six irregular or broken dark brown bands. The tail has dark brown crossbands and the belly is dirty white. Males have an angular series of 13-15 preanal pores. **Biology and breeding:** Common in natural habitat, but displaced from suburban situations by more aggressive tropical house gecko, *Hemidactylus mabouia* (page 243). Diet includes moths and flies. Clutches of two eggs (8 x 9 mm) laid in summer under bark or in rock cracks. They hatch after 105-114 days; hatchlings measure 45 mm TL. **Habitat:** Rocky outcrops and coastal cliffs, entering houses. **Range:** Coastal and lowland areas of KwaZulu-Natal and Transkei (E. Cape). **Subspecies:** None.

## Marley's Flat Gecko
*Afroedura marleyi* **(Pl. 107)**

*(Endemic) SVL 25-35 mm; max. SVL 36 mm, female, 34 mm male.*
A small flat gecko with an unsegmented and tapering tail that is longer than the head and body. The nasorostrals are separated by a granule, and the rostral enters the nostril. A dark brown stripe extends from the nostril, through the eye, almost to the shoulder. The dorsal scales are rounded and juxtaposed. The top of the head is mottled with brown. The back is pale brown with broken, irregular dark brown bands, and a vertebral series of whitish spots. The flanks are spotted and blotched with dark brown. The belly is dirty white, and the tail has up to 11 dark brown crossbands and a pinkish tip. Males have an angular series of 10-14 preanal pores. **Biology and breeding:** Usually found singly or in pairs, and sometimes in association with spotted gecko, *Pachydactylus maculatus*, and Van Son's gecko, *P. vansoni*. Shelters under bark, in dead aloe stems, or under rock slabs on bedrock. Two small eggs (7-8 x 6,1-6,2 mm) are laid under bark or in a dead log. Hatchlings are tiny; measure only 31-32 mm TL. **Habitat:** Varied, including coastal dune forest, mesic savannah and rocky outcrops. **Range:** N. KwaZulu-Natal, into Swaziland, and probably S. Mozambique.

## Giant Swazi Flat Gecko
*Afroedura major* **(Pl. 89)**

*(Endemic) SVL 60-70 mm; max. SVL 76 mm male, 74 mm female.*
A large flat gecko with a faintly segmented and tapering tail that is longer than the head and body. The nasorostrals are usually separated by a granule (sometimes in contact), and the rostral enters the nostril. A thin dark band extends from the nostril, through the eye, to form a W-mark on the back of the head. The dorsal scales are hexagonal, juxtaposed and keeled. The back is grey with six wavy, irregular dark crossbands, that have pale blotches along their posterior margins. There are 6-7 dark crossbands on the tail, which has a bluish sheen. Males have an angular series of 18-19 preanal pores. **Biology and breeding:** It lives in large boulders and rock faces, often along rivers, where it often runs around on the ceilings of wide horizontal cracks. It may bask close to the entrance of a crack. Clutches of two large eggs are laid during summer. **Habitat:** Granite boulders in broad-leaf savannah and grassland. **Range:** Restricted to the highveld and middleveld regions of Swaziland, from Nkomati Bridge and vicinity of Black Umbelusi and Mantenga Falls.

### Lowveld Flat Gecko
*Afroedura langi* (Pl. 89)

*(Endemic) SVL 35-40 mm; max. SVL 44 mm male, 45,5 mm female.*
A small gecko with a slender, faintly segmented and tapering tail that is longer than the head and body. The nasorostrals are in broad contact and the rostral enters the nostril. A dark streak extends from the nostril to the eye. The dorsal scales are round, flat and juxtaposed. The back is brown to pinkish-grey with six dark blackish-brown, irregular wavy crossbands. The belly is pinkish-white, and there are 6-7 dark crossbands on the tail. Males have an angular series of 14-17 preanal pores. **Biology and breeding:** Rupicolous; usually found singly or in pairs. Clutches of two eggs (8 x 5,6 mm) deposited under stones and in sun-warmed crevices. **Habitat:** Schist outcrops in mixed deciduous woodland. **Range:** Restricted to vicinity of Olifants river valley, N. Province. Isolated populations related to this species, inhabiting granite and sandstone outcrops in the N. Province, also known from Leolo mountains, Soutpansberg, Waterberg and at Mica. Their taxonomic status must still be resolved.

### Woodbush Flat Gecko
*Afroedura multiporis* (Pl. 107)

*(Endemic) SVL 50-60 mm; max. SVL 63 mm male, 67 mm female.*
Large, with a faintly segmented and tapering tail that is longer than the head and body. The nasorostrals are usually separated by a granule (sometimes in contact, see Subspecies), and the rostral enters the nostril. A dark streak extends from the nostril, through the eye, to fuse with the first crossband behind the head. The dorsal scales are round, juxtaposed or slightly overlapping, bluntly-keeled or conical. The back is greyish, greyish-brown to olive-brown in colour and marked with six wavy, irregular blackish crossbands with pale blotches along their posterior margins. The belly is whitish. The tail is greyish and speckled below, and marked with about nine dark crossbands. Males have an angular series of preanal pores (see Subspecies). **Biology:** Rupicolous, sheltering under exfoliating rock flakes, and usually found singly or in pairs (the race *A.m. haackei* may be semi-communal). **Habitat:** Rock outcrops in open woodland to montane forest. **Range:** Escarpment of Mpumalanga and N. Province. **Subspecies:** Two recognized, with another awaiting description. Typical *A.m. multiporis* is the largest and restricted to vicinity of Woodbush and Wolkberg; has nine lower labials, a single internasal, 94-101 midbody scale rows, and 16-17 preanal pores. *A.m. haackei* is smaller (max. SVL 50-52 mm), has 8-9 lower labials, 87-95 midbody scale rows, and 24-28 preanal pores; restricted to lowveld of S. Mpumalanga around White River and Nelspruit. Undescribed race found around Abel Erasmus Pass and Blyde River Canyon, is medium-sized (max. SVL 56 mm female, 62 mm male) and has 7-8 lower labials, 87-95 midbody scale rows and 20-24 preanal pores.

*A.m. multiporis*
*A.m. haackei*

### Tembo Flat Gecko
*Afroedura tembulica*

*(Endemic) SVL 50-55 mm; max. SVL 53 mm male, 57 mm female.*
Medium-sized, very similar to Amatola flat gecko, *A. amatolica* (page 232). The body is short and flattened, and covered with small granules. The nasals are not in contact behind the rostral, which enters the nostril. The back is greyish-brown with darker mottlings and the belly is creamy-white. The tail is segmented. There are three pairs of scansors beneath the toes. Males have 6-9 preanal pores in an angular series. **Biology and breeding:** Similar to that of Amatola flat gecko. **Habitat:** Rocky montane grassland. **Range:** Mountains around Queenstown in E. Cape.

### Transvaal Flat Gecko

*Afroedura transvaalica* (Pl. 88)

*(Endemic) SVL 55-60 mm; max. SVL 73 mm male, 70 mm female.*
A medium-sized flat gecko with a slender flattened body that is covered with small granules. The nasals are in contact behind the rostral, which enters the nostril. The chin shields are not enlarged. The back is pale grey-brown, with faint irregular dark crossbands, and the belly is white. The tail is segmented. There are two pairs of scansors below the toes. Males have 5-10 (up to 8 south of the Limpopo River) preanal pores arranged in an angular series. **Biology and breeding:** These geckos are often found in large aggregations (up to 50) beneath rock flakes on granite and sandstone outcrops. The diet includes bugs, beetles and grasshoppers. Clutches of two eggs are laid in communal sites under rock flakes. Hatchlings emerge in December and measure about 48 mm TL. **Habitat:** Mesic savannah. **Range:** Isolated populations from N. Province to Zambezi River. **Subspecies:** None; *A. loveridgei* is now treated as a full species.

### Loveridge's Flat Gecko

*Afroedura loveridgei*

*SVL 40-50 mm; max. SVL 59 mm male, 54 mm female.*
A smallish flat gecko that resembles the Transvaal Flat Gecko (above), but differs in having a rostral that is excluded from the nostril. The nasals are in contact behind the rostral, and the chin shields are not enlarged. The back is pale grey, mottled with grey-brown, and marked with faint, irregular, broad dark crossbands on the body and tail. The belly is uniform white, and the tail is segmented and has a blackish tip with narrow pale bands. There are two pairs of scansors below the toes. Males have 6-11 pre-anal pores that are arranged in an angular series. **Biology and breeding:** Common beneath flakes on rock outcrops. Preys on a variety of insects, including beetles and grasshoppers. Clutches of two eggs are laid in communal sites under rock flakes. **Habitat:** Paragnesis and sandstone outcrops in arid savannah. **Range:** Both banks of the Zambezi River around Tete, Mozambique, north to the Malawi border.

# African Leaf-toed Geckos *Afrogecko*

These medium-sized to large geckos have a small, retractile claw on each foot plus a pair of distinctive leaf-shaped scansors under each toe-tip. It has vertical pupils with wavy edges. The body is usually covered with small, smooth, granular scales (although one species has enlarged, non-keeled tubercles). Preanal pores are absent in males, and there is no midline crease in the rostral.

They are nocturnal and usually rupicolous (although the habits of two Angolan species are poorly known).

This newly-described genus contains three species, two endemic to South Africa and one from central Angola (*A. ansorgii*). Another Angolan species awaits description. The species were previously placed in *Phyllodactylus*, which is now restricted to the New World.

### Swartberg African Leaf-toed Gecko

*Afrogecko swartbergensis* (Pls. 3 and 108)

*(Endemic) SVL 63-77 mm; max. SVL 70 mm male, 77 mm female.*
A large, heavy-bodied, leaf-toed gecko with enlarged but smooth tubercles on the back, which are separated by smaller granules and arranged in irregular rows. The large eyes have pupils with wavy margins. The back, upper surface of the limbs and the top of the head are grey to pinkish and

mottled in tans and creams, with irregular, diffuse dark blotches that may form vague bars over the rear, or an irregular zig-zag pattern on the forebody. The belly and lower limbs are uniform cream in adults, and blotched in juveniles. The tail tapers gently, and is slightly shorter than the head and body; the original tail is marked with 7-8 faint bands. Males lack pre-anal pores but have a single large cloacal spur on each hemipenial bulge. This gecko is more conspicuously mottled when active at night. **Biology and breeding:** A rare, rupicolous species that inhabits deep rock cracks on the sun-warmed northern slopes of mountain summits. Docile, it relies on immobility and camouflage to avoid detection. During the day it may bask next to its retreat, which may be shared by several individuals. Clutches of two, hard-shelled eggs (13,8-14,5 x 11,5-12,7 mm) are laid in summer in a soil-filled rock crack. **Habitat:** Large rock outcrops in dry mountain fynbos. **Range:** Restricted to Swartberg range in Cape fold mountains.

### Marbled Leaf-toed Gecko — *Afrogecko porphyreus* (Pl. 87)
*(Endemic) SVL 43-48 mm; max. SVL 51 mm.*

A medium-sized, gracile species with a flattened head and body. The back is smooth and covered with small granules. There are no enlarged central chin shields, and the first upper labial does not enter the nostril, which is pierced between the rostral and three nasal scales. The rostral has no cleft in its centre. There is often a dark stripe through the eye. The back is grey-ish to light brown, rarely plain, sometimes with a prominent, pale dorsal stripe, but usually mottled in reddish-brown to dark brown. The belly is off-white to cream, and sometimes speckled on the sides. The tail is round, unsegmented and longer than the body. **Biology and breeding:** Nocturnal, they live in varied habitats, including cracks in rock outcrops, under bark on dead trees, and in rotting logs. They are common on houses in Cape Town and along the S. Cape coastal region, where they are often seen around outdoor lights, feeding on insects. They are often transported to new regions with cargo. This gecko is not territorial, and as many as 24 individuals may live in the same retreat. Two hard-shelled eggs (9-11 x 7-8 mm) are laid beneath tree bark or in a rock crack, or sometimes even among rubbish. Communal sites may contain up to 30 eggs. These hatch in 50-60 days; hatchlings are 30-40 mm TL. Growth is rapid, and the young mature in about two years. **Habitat:** Coastal and montane fynbos; also entering cold evergreen forest and urban areas. **Range:** W. and S. Cape, from Nieuwoudtville to Cape St Francis. Introduced to most west coast offshore islands, Port Elizabeth, Grahamstown and even St Helena Island in mid-Atlantic Ocean.

## Giant Ground Gecko — *Chondrodactylus*
This large terrestrial, padless gecko is closely related to the thick-toed geckos, *Pachydactylus* (page 249). The genus consists of a single species, which is endemic to the subcontinent.

### Giant Ground Gecko — *Chondrodactylus angulifer* (Pl. 79)
*(Endemic) SVL 70-90 mm; max. SVL 113 mm male, 98 mm female.*
This large gecko has a stout cylindrical body, and a big head with a short snout and prominent bulging eyes with vertical pupils. The back has scattered, enlarged, keeled tubercles. The feet are wide, with short toes that are not flared and lack scansors. Minute fine claws are present in females, and males lack femoral and preanal pores. The tail is segmented

■ *C.a. angulifer*

□ *C.a. namibensis*

(each segment bearing a transverse row of evenly spaced, enlarged tubercles), swollen and shorter than the body. Males grow larger than females and have a prominent hemipenial bulge. Coloration is varied. The back is pale orange to red-brown, with irregular, dark reticulations, overlaid with a variety of different patterns (see Subspecies). The belly is pink-white. Juveniles are darker and do not develop dorsal white spots until 3-4 months old. **Biology and breeding:** These terrestrial, nocturnal geckos spend the day in their retreat, usually a short burrow that they dig afresh each night, or an old scorpion burrow that they have widened. At night they emerge to hunt and can often be found slowly stalking the sand flats. The diet is varied and includes termites, moths, beetles and spiders, and also other small geckos. The female lays 1-2 large, almost round (18 x 16 mm), hard-shelled, fragile eggs in a chamber that she digs in sand. Gravid females are found in the wild from October to January, and hatchlings from December to April. In captivity, eggs can be laid at 14 to 40-day intervals and it is probable that more than one clutch is laid per season in the wild. In captivity, the eggs hatch in 45-60 days, but probably take up to 90 days in the wild. Hatchlings are about 70 mm TL and weigh 2-3 g. Growth is fast and sexual maturity may be reached in 12 months. Males fight each other. Predators include the horned adder, owls, bat-eared foxes and suricates. When alarmed, these geckos stand stiff-legged with the tail arched scorpion-like, over their back. They hiss and lunge and will bite if necessary. Although considered poisonous in some regions, they are quite harmless. **Habitat:** Gravel plains, interdune spaces and sandy flats. **Range:** Through Namib Desert, S. Namibia and karroid regions of Cape. **Subspecies:** Two races are recognized: *C.a. angulifer* is smaller (SVL 101 mm male, 92 mm female), has stout limbs, ventral scales that increase in size on the sides, and a dorsal pattern consisting of 4-5 pale, dark-edged chevrons that extend as bars onto the tail and are more conspicuous in females (particularly on the shoulder region), but fainter in males (which usually have the pale bars reduced to a series of prominent white dorsolateral spots); it occurs in S. Namibia into karroid areas of Cape. *C.a. namibensis* has slender limbs, ventral scales that decrease in size on the sides, and a pale dorsal pattern with enlarged white-tipped tubercles that is the same in both sexes; it occurs in the Namib Desert, from Lüderitz Bay to W. Kaokoveld.

# Kalahari Ground Gecko *Colopus*

This small, terrestrial, almost padless gecko is closely related to the thick-toed geckos, *Pachydactylus* (page 249), and is restricted to the Kalahari region. The genus is monotypic.

### Kalahari Ground Gecko *Colopus wahlbergii* (Pl. 80)

*(Endemic) SVL 45-50 mm; max. SVL 52 mm male, 61 mm female.*
A small, pretty gecko with an elongate slender body and granular overlapping scales on the back. The toes are small, with two undivided scansors and minute claws on the hind feet of females. The prominent eyes have vertical pupils that each close to four pinholes. The nostrils are not tubular. The tail is stout and cylindrical and almost equal in length to the body. Preanal and femoral pores are absent. Coloration is varied. The back is light orange to brown, usually with a complicated dorsal pattern (see Subspecies). The belly is chalky white. **Biology and breeding:** These geckos are found under cover or in short burrows. The diet consists

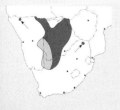

C.w. *wahlbergii*

C.w. *furcifer*

mainly of small insects (termites, grasshoppers, etc.). The female lays two hard-shelled eggs. Predators include snakes, owls and small carnivores. **Habitat:** Flat sandy plains with scattered vegetation. **Range:** Kalahari region of Botswana, extending into N. Cape, Namibia, and near Victoria Falls in SW Zimbabwe and Soutpansberg, N. Province. Has not been recorded from Angola or SW Zambia, although it reaches the Caprivi Strip and may be expected to occur further north. **Subspecies:** Two recognized: *C.w. wahlbergii* has a rounded head and a dorsal pattern that consists of a vertebral series of large, pale, dark-edged spots that may fuse; it occurs in the Kalahari region, from N. Cape to the Caprivi Strip. *C.w. furcifer* has a more pointed head, and a dark-edged, pale vertebral line on the back, that divides on the neck; it is found in the dunes of W. and SW Kalahari.

# Coastal Leaf-toed Gecko  *Cryptactites*

A small, gracile leaf-toed gecko with keeled scales and straight-edged pupils; males lack preanal pores. This recently-described genus contains only a single species that is endemic to South Africa. For over 80 years it remained a herpetological mystery, and was known from only two specimens. It was rediscovered in 1992 in coastal salt marshes, a unique habitat for geckos. It was previously placed in the genus *Phyllodactylus*, which is now restricted to the New World.

### Péringuey's Coastal Leaf-toed Gecko

*Cryptactites peringueyi* **(Pl. 108)**

*(Endemic) SVL 20-25 mm; max. SVL 27,8 mm male, 28,3 mm female.*

A very small species with a long neck, pointed snout and rounded body that is covered with scattered, large, keeled tubercles on the back. The nostril pierces a small nasal (or lies between the rostral and nasal in some specimens). The rostral lacks a median cleft, and preanal pores are absent. Coloration is varied and may change with maturity and sex. Males are often striped, the pale brown body bearing a light golden brown vertebral stripe (sometimes black-edged) that is bordered by various other stripes on the flanks. Females and juveniles are usually uniform brown; the colour may darken in gravid females. The throat and belly are dirty cream with faint dark speckling. **Biology and breeding:** Nocturnal, lives in thick vegetation in salt marshes or other coastal vegetation. Climbs in grass and restio clumps, and feeds on insects. Two eggs (7-12 x 5-6 mm) are laid, usu-ally within mulch of dead stems about 30 cm up from base of restio clumps. Hatchlings measure 23-24 mm TL. **Habitat:** Coastal salt marshes, adjacent salt-tolerant vegetation. **Range:** Restricted to coastal and estuarine zones from Chelsea Point near Port Elizabeth east to Kromme estuary, E. Cape.

# Dwarf Leaf-toed Geckos  *Goggia*

These very small geckos have a pair of distinctive leaf-shaped scansors under each toe-tip plus a small, retractile claw on each foot. The pupils are vertical with wavy edges, and the rostral has a crease in the middle. The body is covered with small, smooth, granular scales. A small series of preanal pores are present, but femoral pores are absent.

They are nocturnal and usually rupicolous, although one species is terrestrial or lives under tree bark. They are common in suitable habitats. They lay two hard-shelled eggs, and the female often has very large endolymphatic sacs on the sides of the neck where calcium is stored for egg-shell production.

This newly-described genus contains eight species, all endemic to the subcontinent. They were previously placed in *Phyllodactylus*, which is now restricted to the New World.

### Braack's Dwarf Leaf-toed Gecko — *Goggia braacki* (Pl. 87)

*(Endemic) SVL 25-30 mm; max. SVL 34 mm male, 34,6 mm female.*
Almost identical to Hewitt's dwarf leaf-toed gecko, *G. hewitti*, but geographically isolated. A very small gecko with a flattened head and body. There is no mental cleft, usually only one nasorostral scale, and 9-12 scales between the nostril and front of the eye. Scales on the back are smooth and uniform, and in 79-88 midbody rows. The back is light brown-tan with dark brown markings forming scalloped or reticulate patterns. The belly is pale cream with faint dark stippling. The original tail is slightly longer and paler than the body, with up to 12 vague dark cross-bands (absent from regenerated tails). Males have 4 preanal pores. **Biology and breeding:** Nocturnal and rupicolous, sheltering in thin cracks on dolerite outcrops. Two small eggs are laid under sun-warmed rock flakes. Hibernates in deep cracks when winter snows carpet the escarpment. **Habitat:** Dolerite outcrops in *Merxmuellera disticha* grassland at over 1 900 m. **Range:** Restricted to eastern plateau of Nuweveldberg, W. Cape.

### Essex's Dwarf Leaf-toed Gecko — *Goggia essexi* (Pl. 108)

*(Endemic) SVL 20-25 mm; max. SVL 27,5 mm male, 28,4 mm female.*
A very small species with a flattened head and body, and 78-84 midbody scale rows. There is no mental cleft, 0-2 nasorostral granules, and 9-12 scales between the nostril and front of the eye. The central chin shields are not enlarged. The back is greyish to pink-brown, with 5-6 pale spots that are bordered anteriorly by dark brown and may fuse to form 8-10 irregular scalloped bars. The pattern in some specimens is obscured by heavy mottling that may extend onto the white belly. The original tail is slightly longer than the body. Males have four preanal pores. **Biology and breeding:** Lives on small rock outcrops, under thin flakes or under boulders. Very alert and difficult to catch. Communal sites under sun-warmed rocks used for egg-laying. **Habitat:** Sandstone and shale outcrops in Karroid thicket and grassy fynbos (Suurberg). **Range:** Upland areas in the Albany region, E. Cape, from the Suurberg to the Great Fish River.

### Richtersveld Dwarf Leaf-toed Gecko — *Goggia gemmula* (Pl. 108)

*(Endemic) SVL 20-25 mm; max. SVL 27,7 mm male, 30 mm female.*
A very small, gracile species with a flattened head and body, and 70-86 midbody scale rows. There is no mental cleft or enlarged tubercles on the back. The top of the head is mottled light brown with a vague dark brown stripe running from the nostril, through the eye and onto the side of the neck. The back is mottled brown above with 5-7 more-or-less paired pale yellow spots on either side of the backbone. Small yellow blotches on the sides may align with the large dorsal spots. The belly is cream with a dark stipple on the sides. The original tail is slightly longer than the body. Males have four, rarely five, preanal pores. **Biology and breeding:** Shelters under granite flakes on isolated boulders, and emerges at night to feed on termites and small insects. Very localized; rarely more than one or two individuals on a boulder. Two small eggs are laid in a rock crack. **Habitat:** Small rocky outcrops in arid succulent Nama Karoo. **Range:** Restricted to the Richtersveld and adjacent S. Namibia.

### Hewitt's Dwarf Leaf-toed Gecko    *Goggia hewitti* (Pl. 108)

*(Endemic) SVL 28-35 mm; max. SVL 34,6 mm male, 37,5 mm female.*
Almost identical in appearance to Braack's dwarf leaf-toed gecko, *G. braacki*, but geographically isolated. A very small gecko with a flattened head and body. There is no mental cleft, usually only one nasorostral scale, and 10-13 scales between the nostril and front of the eye. Scales on the back are smooth and uniform, and in 77-91 midbody rows. The back is a light tan-brown with seven irregular dark brown markings forming pale-centred scallops or a reticulate pattern. The belly is pale cream with faint dark stippling. The original tail is slightly longer than the body, and is paler than the body with up to 15 vague dark crossbands (absent from regenerated tails). Males have only 4 preanal pores. **Biology and breeding:** Strictly rupicolous, and found singly or in pairs beneath small rocks or under rock flakes. Clutches of two eggs (9 x 5-6 mm) are laid during summer under rock flakes. **Habitat:** Usually inhabits summit sandstone outcrops in mountain fynbos, but enters shale bands in karroid brokenveld in the valleys of the E. Little Karoo. **Range:** Cape fold mountains, from Witberge and Anysberg in the west to Kammanassieberg and Baviaanskloofberge in the east, but absent from the coastal ranges.

### Cedarberg Dwarf Leaf-toed Gecko    *Goggia hexapora* (Pl. 108)

*(Endemic) SVL 25-32 mm; max. SVL 33,7 mm male, 35,3 mm female.*
A very small gecko with a flattened head and body. There is no mental cleft, usually only one nasorostral scale, and 8-13 scales between the nostril and front of the eye. A fine dark line runs from the nostril, through the eye and onto the side of the head. Scales on the back are smooth and uniform, and in 75-91 midbody rows. The back is light tan-brown and either heavily stippled in dark brown, or with 5-6 irregular dark brown markings forming pale-centred scalloped or reticulate patterns. The belly is pale cream with faint dark stippling. The original tail is slightly longer and paler than the body, with up to 12 vague dark cross-bands. Regenerated tails are light brown-orange with scattered dark flecks. Males have six preanal pores, sometimes five. **Biology and breeding:** Similar to Hewitt's dwarf leaf-toed gecko. Predators include large scorpions. **Habitat:** Sandstone outcrops in mountain fynbos and coastal renosterveld. **Range:** W. Cape fold mountains, from Bokkeveldberge in north, through the Cedarberg and adjacent mountain ranges to Ceres.

### Striped Dwarf Leaf-toed Gecko    *Goggia lineata* (Pl. 87)

*(Endemic) SVL 25-30 mm; max. SVL 30,1 mm male, 31,8 mm female.*
A very small, variably coloured species, with a cylindrical body, rounded snout and short, deep head. The first upper labial enters the nostril, the rostral has a cleft in its centre, and there are 7-10 scales between the nostril and front of the eye. The anterior chin shields are enlarged. The back is covered with small, flattened, partly overlapping, smooth scales in 64-84 midbody rows. The tail is cylindrical, not segmented, and is the same length as the body. Males usually have 5 preanal pores. Coloration is varied; the back is light grey usually with a dark striped pattern, although sometimes with dark, pale-centred scallops. The belly is off-white, and finely stippled in grey. **Biology and breeding:** Terrestrial and nocturnal, this gecko shelters in a retreat during the day in dead aloes, rubble or rubbish piles, or under dead bark. It emerges at sunset to hunt small insects, particularly termites. Two round, hard-shelled eggs (7-8 mm long)

are laid under bark or in debris. Several clutches may be laid during a season. **Habitat:** Coastal fynbos, and succulent and transitional karroid veld. **Range:** Low-lying areas of W. and N. Cape to S. Namibia. **Subspecies:** No races are now recognized; all raised to full species.

### Small-scaled Leaf-toed Gecko      Goggia microlepidota (Pl. 87)
*(Endemic) SVL 50-60 mm; max. SVL 68,7 mm male, 68,4 mm female.*
A large, very attractive leaf-toed gecko covered with minute, granular scales, that are flattened along the backbone. The central chin shields are not enlarged, and the first upper labial enters the nostril. The rostral has a median, sometimes Y-shaped, cleft. The back is grey to slate, with a blackish, reticulate pattern. The belly is off-white, and the tail is round, not segmented, and just longer than the body. Males have a continuous row of 4-9 preanal pores, and 4-6 enlarged cloacal spurs. **Biology:** Restricted to mountain summits; lives in large rock cracks in sandstone outcrops or under the bark of dead Clanwilliam cedar trees. **Habitat:** Montane fynbos. **Range:** W. Cape fold mountains, from Cedarberg to Ceres.

### Namaqualand Dwarf Leaf-toed Gecko   Goggia rupicola (Pl. 112)
*(Endemic) SVL 20-25 mm; max. SVL 28,2 mm male, 31,5 mm female.*
Small and variably coloured with a sharp snout, flat head and flattened body. The first upper labial enters the nostril, and the rostral has a cleft in its centre. There are two nasorostral scales, and 10-12 scales between the nostril and front of the eye. A dark eye-stripe extends from the nostril onto the side of the head. The anterior chin shields are enlarged. The back is covered with small, smooth scales that are flattened and partly overlapping, and arranged in 80-90 midbody rows. The back is light pink-brown, with a conspicuous scalloped pattern consisting of a transverse series of 5-6 pale spots, with dark brown anterior margins that may fuse to form wavy bands. The belly is off-white with fine stippling on the sides. The tail is cylindrical, not segmented, and is the same length as the body. The original tail is orange-pink and bears up to 18 fine dark bands. Males usually have 4 preanal pores. **Biology:** Rupicolous; shelters under fine granite flakes. Can be very common, and several can be found under the same shelter. Feeds on ants and termites on warm nights. **Habitat:** Granite outcrops and bedrock in succulent Nama Karoo. **Range:** Restricted to upland areas of Namaqualand, from Aninaus Pass in north to Kliprand in south.

## Tropical House Geckos     *Hemidactylus*
These medium-sized geckos have large, flared toes, with large, retractile claws and prominent scansors that are usually arranged in pairs. The eyes are large, with vertical pupils and distinct upper eyelids. Scalation on the back is variable, and preanal and femoral pores are usually present.

Geckos belonging to this genus are nocturnal and occur in a wide range of habitats. The genus includes terrestrial, arboreal and rock-living species. All lay two hard-shelled eggs, but there are some all-female species that reproduce parthenogenetically. They have complicated behaviours, and most species vocalize. Territories are usually defended vigorously. Many species have adapted well to urban development, and have become commensal, sharing living space with humans.

This genus is distributed widely throughout the Pacific region, S. Europe, Asia, central America and Africa. Some species have, and continue to spread through the tropical regions as a result of their association with man and his goods. The genus contains over 70 species, only four of which occur in southern Africa, and only one of which is endemic to the subregion.

## Moreau's Tropical House Gecko *Hemidactylus mabouia* (Pl. 89)
*SVL 55-65 mm; max. SVL 66 mm male, 68 mm female.*

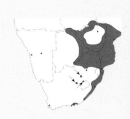

A medium-sized gecko with a flattened head and body, and large eyes with vertical pupils. The toe-tips are flared, with strong, retractile claws and 6-7 paired scansors. The back is covered with granular scales, with 10-18 irregular rows of small, weakly-keeled tubercles, and is pale grey to grey-brown, plain or with 4-5 faint, irregular, dark crossbands that fade if exposed to light for prolonged periods. The belly is cream. The tail is stout and cylindrical but flattened below, with transverse rows of six enlarged tubercles; it is marked with about 10-12 dark bars. There are 22-40 preanal pores. **Biology and breeding:** Mainly arboreal and common under tree bark and in the hollows of baobab trees. It frequently enters homes, and emerges in the evening to catch moths, beetles and cockroaches. Large specimens may eat small lizards. The males are very territorial, and fight vigorously; few have unbroken tails. They are normally silent, but can emit a quiet 'tik-tik-tik' (7-8 times). The eggs (8-10 x 10-13 mm) are adhesive and are often laid singly in nooks and crannies. Communal deposits of 50-60 eggs may be found. Hatchlings measure 30-32 mm TL. **Habitat:** Varied; wet and dry savannah, and coastal bush. **Range:** Coastal regions of KwaZulu-Natal, through lowveld, Mozambique, and border regions of Zimbabwe and E. Botswana. There is an old isolated record in N. Namibia, and introduced colonies have been discovered in various E. Cape coastal towns, and inland in Pietermaritzburg, Bloemfontein, Pretoria and Gariep Dam. Elsewhere, known from Madagascar and other islands in Indian Ocean, and east coast of S. and central America. **Subspecies:** None; Tasman's gecko (below) is now treated as a full species.

## Tasman's Tropical House Gecko
### *Hemidactylus tasmani* (Pls. 89 and 110)
*(Endemic) SVL 65-75 mm; max. SVL 73 mm male, 78 mm female.*

A medium-sized gecko with a flattened head and body, and large eyes with vertical pupils. The toe-tips are flared, with strong, retractile claws and 6-7 paired scansors. The back is covered with granular scales, with 12-18 irregular rows of small, strongly keeled tubercles, and is pale grey to grey-brown, plain or marked with 4-6 conspicuous dark crossbands. The belly is cream. The tail is stout and cylindrical but flattened below, with transverse rows of six enlarged tubercles; it is marked with about 10-12 dark bars. There are 26-50 preanal pores. **Biology and breeding:** Mainly rock-living, sheltering in rock cracks and caves but also entering houses. The eggs (9-10 x 11-13 mm) are adhesive and are usually laid in pairs in a sun-warmed rock crack. **Habitat:** Granite outcrops in mesic savannah. **Range:** Central and eastern districts of Zimbabwe.

## Long-headed Tropical House Gecko
### *Hemidactylus longicephalus* (Pl. 110)
*SVL 55-60 mm; max. SVL 64 mm male, 59 mm female.*

A medium-sized gecko with a flattened head and body, and large eyes with vertical pupils. The toe-tips are flared, with strong, retractile claws and 8-11 paired scansors. It has a single internasal granule. The back is covered with granular scales, with 14-18 irregular rows of small, strongly keeled tubercles, and is uniform greyish, with indistinct darker and lighter markings, and occasionally a light dorsolateral line. The tail may be barred, is stout and cylindrical but flattened below, with transverse rows of six enlarged tubercles. The belly is whitish, and there are only 4-8 preanal pores. **Biology:** Rock-living but also sheltering under dead palm fronds on sandy soil. **Habitat:** Rock outcrops in mesic savannah. **Range:** Angola, north to Cameroon and east to Lake Tanganyika, and just entering N. Namibia near Epupa Falls.

### Flat-headed Tropical House Gecko

*Hemidactylus platycephalus* **(Pl. 89)**
*SVL 80-90 mm; max. SVL 94 mm male, 90 mm female.*

A large house gecko with a stout, flat head and body. The eyes are large and have vertical pupils. The toe-tips are flared, with strong, retractile claws and 6-7 paired scansors. The back is covered with granular scales, with 8-12 irregular rows of small, conical tubercles, and is pale grey to grey-brown, plain or with 4-5 faint, dark chevrons. The belly is uniform cream or pale yellow. The tail is stout and cylindrical but flattened below, with transverse rows of six enlarged tubercles, and 10 vague bars. There are 45-57 preanal pores. **Biology and breeding:** Prefer higher rainfall areas and are abundant on the trunks of baobab trees, but occasionally inhabit rock crevices and enter houses. The eggs (10-13 mm long) are cemented together in pairs in rock cracks or under bark. **Habitat:** Mopane and miombo woodland at low altitudes. **Range:** E. Africa, entering S. Mozambique and E. Zimbabwe.

## Velvet Geckos   *Homopholis*

These are medium-sized to large, arboreal geckos. Their skins are soft and covered with small, granular scales. The toe pads are dilated, and have 8-12 undivided, chevron-shaped scansors, and small claws. The tail is relatively short and thick. Male velvet geckos have a pair of enlarged preanal scales with pores.

There are four species in the genus. *H. boivini* is restricted to Madagascar; *H. fasciata* occurs in E. Africa (with *H.f. erlangeri* restricted to Ethiopia and Somalia); and two species are endemic to the subcontinent.

### Wahlberg's Velvet Gecko

*Homopholis wahlbergii* **(Pl. 90)**
*(Endemic) SVL 90-110 mm; max. SVL 123 mm female (227 mm TL), 108 mm male.*

A large velvet gecko with small dorsal scales that overlap and are in 80-107 scale rows at midbody. There are 26-30 scales between each eye and the anterior ear border. Males' preanal pore-bearing scales are enlarged and are usually separated by 2-3 small scales. The back is light to dark grey-brown, usually with irregular pale and dark crossbars, and often with a series of pale vertebral blotches. The snout lacks a black band. The belly is cream and is sometimes lightly spotted. Many specimens (particularly males) have a pair of broad, black dorsolateral stripes. **Biology and breeding:** Active during the day and night, but forages away from its retreat only at night. Shelters under bark, in holes in baobab trees, on hut roofs, and even in empty swallows' nests in caves and rock overhangs. Rock fissures, particularly on overgrown koppies and river banks, are favoured spots. Preys on large insects, particularly grasshoppers and cockroaches, but also eats termites and millipedes. A pair of large (15-19 x 11-17 mm), hard-shelled eggs are laid in a rock crack or under bark. Bites and squeals when first caught, and readily sheds its tail. Despite this, settles well in captivity and makes a fine pet. **Habitat:** Varied; coastal bush and mesic and arid savannah. **Range:** Zimbabwe and S. Mozambique, into adjacent Zululand, N. Province and E. Botswana.

### Muller's Velvet Gecko

*Homopholis mulleri* **(Pl. 90)**

*(Endemic) SVL 65-75 mm; max. SVL 81 mm female, 71 mm male.*
A small velvet gecko with small dorsal scales that do not overlap, and are in 65-72 rows at midbody. There are 18-20 scales between each eye and the anterior ear border. The head is white, with minute black spotting. The upper labials are also white, and bordered from eye to eye by a black band. The back is dark grey to light brown, with three large, silvery blotches on the forebody, followed by four white, black-margined chevrons. The flanks have 5-6 silvery blotches. The belly is white, with small dark spots and lines. The preanal pore-bearing scales in males are enlarged and usually in contact, but are sometimes separated by a small, wedge-shaped scale. **Biology and breeding:** A rare and poorly known species that probably resembles Wahlberg's velvet gecko, *H. wahlbergii* (above), in habits and behaviour. It usually shelters under bark, and in holes in marula and knob-thorn trees. **Habitat:** Open, mixed mopane veld. **Range:** Restricted to a small area between Soutpansberg and Limpopo River, N. Province.

# Dwarf Geckos   *Lygodactylus*

Geckos that belong this genus have a rudimentary inner toe, while the other toes have a large retractile claw and scansors that are paired and oblique. The snout is short and rounded, and the eyes prominent with round pupils and distinct eyelids. The body is short and cylindrical and is covered with small, granular scales. The tail, which is equal in length to the body, is cylindrical and has modified scales at the tip which serve as a fifth scansor. Males have preanal pores, but femoral pores are absent.

These delightful dwarfs are very common in suitable habitat. They are diurnal and usually arboreal, although some species are rock-living. The adult male usually commands a shrub, low tree or boulder, sharing it with a number of females and subadults. They are well camouflaged; when threatened they freeze or quickly run around a trunk, branch or rock, keeping it between themselves and danger. They feed on ants and termites, and often can be seen stationed next to their trails, picking off victims. Two hard-shelled eggs are laid under bark or in a suitable cranny.

This ancient genus is distributed throughout sub-Saharan Africa and Madagascar, with two species also occurring in South America. There are about 60 species in the genus, 12 species (seven of which are endemic) occur in southern Africa.

### Angola Dwarf Gecko

*Lygodactylus angolensis*

*SVL 25-30 mm; max. SVL 33 mm male, 31 mm female.*
A small dwarf gecko that resembles the Cape dwarf gecko, *L. capensis* (page 246). There is a pair of lateral clefts in the mental, and no soft spines above the eyes. The back is olive-brown, usually with a series of pale spots on the upper flanks, and the belly and throat are cream. Males have 7-10 preanal pores. **Biology and breeding:** Similar in behaviour to

the Cape dwarf gecko. **Habitat:** Mixed dry deciduous woodland and grassland. **Range:** Zambezi drainage basin, from Mozambique through W. Zimbabwe, N. Botswana, Caprivi Strip and NE Namibia, to E. Angola.

### Bernard's Dwarf Gecko
*Lygodactylus bernardi* (Pl. 90)
*(Endemic) SVL 30-38 mm; max. SVL 39 mm male, 40 mm female.*
A gecko of robust build, with a pair of lateral clefts in the mental. There is a series of 4-7 soft spines above each eye. The back is olive-brown with pale spots. The throat is bluish-white, the belly yellow, and the tail orange to orange-brown below. Males have 7-10 preanal pores. **Biology and breeding:** Live in cracks of sun-split boulders on hillsides. Two small eggs (7,5-8 x 6-6,5 mm) are laid in a rock crack. Large communal egg sites may contain the remains of hundreds of eggs. **Habitat:** Rock outcrops in montane grassland. **Range:** Inyanga district of E. Zimbabwe. **Subspecies:** None; *L. bonsi* from Mulanje Mountain, Malawi, is a full species.

### Bradfield's Dwarf Gecko
*Lygodactylus bradfieldi* (Pl. 91)
*SVL 25-30 mm; max. SVL 30 mm.*
This small gecko is very similar to the Cape dwarf gecko, *L. capensis* (below), and was previously treated as a western race of that species. The subcaudal scales are irregular in size. The throat often has dark spots, the back is grey-brown with a pair of pale stripes, bordered by narrow, black lines on the flanks, and the belly is cream. There are 4-7 preanal pores in males. **Biology and breeding:** Mainly arboreal. In Richtersveld, favours the open stems of tree aloes, but in the north occurs on dead logs and branches in mopane scrub. Clutches of two eggs (7,2 x 5,3 mm) are laid under bark and in hollow stems. **Habitat:** Arid savannah and succulent desert. **Range:** Western part of subcontinent, from N. Cape to S. Angola, reaching Tuli Circle area in NE Botswana and adjacent SE Zimbabwe.

### Cape Dwarf Gecko
*Lygodactylus capensis* (Pl. 91)
*SVL 35-40 mm; max. SVL 39 mm male, 43 mm female.*
A large dwarf gecko with a pair of lateral clefts in the mental, and no soft spines above the eyes. A postnasal is present. The throat is usually stippled with grey or dark brown, and the belly is cream. The back is grey-brown, with a dark streak from the snout to the shoulder that sometimes extends onto the flank, and a pale dorsolateral band that may break up into a series of light spots towards the tail. There are three subcaudal scales per tail segment. Males have 4-7 preanal pores that develop with sexual maturity. **Biology and breeding:** These geckos prefer to forage in low scrub and on dead trees, but also tolerate urban situations. They feed almost exclusively on ants and termites. Sexual maturity is reached in only eight months, and they usually live 15-18 months. Breeding is continuous, and communal egg sites are common. The hard-shelled eggs (5-6 x 6,5-7 mm) are usually laid in pairs (but sometimes singly) in rock cracks or under loose bark. They may take 2-5 months to hatch; hatchlings are approximately 25 mm long. **Habitat:** Well-wooded, savannah and subtropical thicket. **Range:** Eastern half of the subcontinent, from S. Transkei (E. Cape) to E. Africa. May become commensal, and introduced colonies are known from Port Elizabeth, Grahamstown, Bloemfontein, etc. **Subspecies:** Three races are recognized, but only the typical form occurs on the subcontinent. It is replaced in Tanzania and N. Mozambique by *L.c. grotei*, and on Pemba Island by *L.c. pakenhami*.

*L.c. capensis*

246

**Chobe Dwarf Gecko**           *Lygodactylus chobiensis* **(Pl. 91)**

*SVL 30-35 mm; max. SVL 42 mm male, 38 mm female.*
A large dwarf gecko with a mental that lacks lateral clefts. The rostral is
excluded from the nostril, and there are no soft spines above the eyes.
The back is blue-grey, with large pale dorsal spots that extend onto the
head and neck. Males' throats may be all-black or pale yellow with two
dark chevrons, which are faint or absent in females. The belly is yellow.
Males have 7-11 preanal pores. **Biology and breeding:** These geckos
prefer to forage high in trees, and are common on acacia, baobab and
mopane trees, and occasionally on houses. They feed on ants and
termites. They are relatively short-lived, growing to maturity, breeding
and dying in 18 months. Two hard-shelled eggs (5 x 6,5 mm) are laid
under bark, in disused termite mounds, etc. Females reach sexual maturity
in 8-9 months, and breed continuously, laying clutches at seven- to eight-
week intervals. Incubation lasts approximately 125 days; hatchlings
measure 30-32 mm TL. Males reach sexual maturity in 9-10 months.
**Habitat:** Moist savannah. **Range:** Okavango Basin, extending along
Zambezi Valley to Tete, and on to Zimbabwe plateau and adjacent Zambia.

**Granite Dwarf Gecko**          *Lygodactylus graniticolus* **(Pl. 109)**

*(Endemic) SVL 34-38 mm; max. SVL 39,5 mm male.*
A medium-sized gecko with no lateral clefts in the mental or soft spines
above the eyes. The scales on the back are smooth. A row of pale-centred
spots runs along the upper flanks, from behind the eye to the base of the
tail. Other pale spots also occur on the flanks. The throat is speckled with
grey, and the belly is white to creamy, becoming speckled on the tail.
A grey-brown to brownish band extends from the snout to the tail. The
toe-tips are heart-shaped with four pairs of scansors. Males have 8-9
preanal pores. **Biology and breeding:** Rock-living, sheltering in cracks
in granite outcrops. Two egg clutches (5,4-5,6 x 8,1 mm) are laid in
summer. **Habitat:** Moist savannah. **Range:** Restricted to Percy Fyfe
Nature Reserve and surrounding area in N. Province.

**Lawrence's Dwarf Gecko**        *Lygodactylus lawrencei* **(Pl. 109)**

*SVL 30-32 mm; max. SVL 34 mm.*
A small dwarf gecko that resembles the spotted dwarf gecko, *L. ocellatus*
(page 248). It has a large mental that lacks lateral clefts. The rostral is well
separated from the nostril, and there are no soft spines above the eyes.
The throat has two dark chevrons, and the belly is white. The back is
ashy-grey, with numerous thin, broken darkish stripes, and often with a
pale chestnut lateral stripe that extends from the neck onto the anterior
half of the tail. There are no transversely enlarged subcaudals. Males have
two well-developed preanal pores. **Habitat:** Rocky, dry savannah. **Range:**
Kaokoveld in N. Namibia, extending into S. Angola.

**Methuen's Dwarf Gecko**         *Lygodactylus methueni* **(Pl. 91)**

*(Endemic) SVL 35-38 mm; max. SVL 42 mm.*
A large dwarf gecko with a large mental that lacks lateral clefts. There
are eight enlarged chin shields, the rostral is in contact with the nostril,
and there are no soft spines above the eyes. The back is olive to olive-grey
with rows of well-defined pale-centred, reddish-brown spots, that are
occasionally absent or fused into an irregular band. The belly is yellow,
and more intensely coloured towards the rear and under the tail.

There are no transversely enlarged subcaudals, and males have 9-11 preanal pores. **Biology and breeding:** A threatened species (SA RDB, Vulnerable), as much of its habitat is now under exotic pine plantations. They forage on the trunks of trees and adjacent rock outcrops. Two eggs are laid under stones or loose bark. **Habitat:** Remnant montane forest. **Range:** Endemic to Woodbush Forest, N. Province.

### Black-spotted Dwarf Gecko  Lygodactylus nigropunctatus (Pl. 109)
*(Endemic) SVL 29-35 mm; max. SVL 38 mm.*

☐ *L.n. incognitus (a)*

■ *L.n. montiscaeruli (b)*

▦ *L.n. nigropunctatus (c)*

A medium-sized dwarf gecko that lacks lateral clefts in the mental but has a series of 10-12 soft spines above the eyes. Two postnasals are present. There are four pairs of scansors beneath the toes and four subcaudal scales per tail segment. Males have 7-11 preanal pores that develop with sexual maturity. The dorsal coloration is variable (see Subspecies); a dark streak runs from the snout, through the eye to the shoulder, and a series of dark dorsolateral blotches is usually present (always indistinct in one race). The throat is usually speckled. The belly is off-white to yellowish and speckled, sometimes heavily, on the sides. **Biology and breeding:** Rock-living, sheltering in rock crevices or under loose rocks. Occasionally climbs trees. Usually solitary, although small groups occur. Well camouflaged and difficult to spot. Females grow slightly larger than males, and lay two egg clutches (7,0-8,8 x 4,5-6,9 mm) during summer. **Habitat:** Wet and dry savannah and subtropical thicket. **Range:** Central N. Province, Soutpansberg and Blouberg. **Subspecies:** The three races are morphologically poorly-defined. Typical form (c) is widespread in the central regions of N. Province; it is distinguished by conspicuous dorsolateral spots and up to 11 preanal pores; *L.n. incognitus* (a) is restricted to Soutpansberg, N. Province, and has indistinct dorsolateral spots and only 7-9 preanal pores; *L.n. montiscaeruli* (b), restricted to Blouberg and adjacent Makgabeng Hills, is of similar coloration to the typical race, but has only 7-8 precloacal pores.

### Spotted Dwarf Gecko  Lygodactylus ocellatus (Pls. 91 and 110)
*(Endemic) SVL 26-32 mm; max. SVL 35 mm.*

■ *L.o. ocellatus*

☐ *L.o. soutpansbergensis*

This small species is similar to Lawrence's dwarf gecko, *L. lawrencei* (page 247). The large mental lacks lateral clefts. The rostral is in contact with the nostril and there are no soft spines above the eyes. There are 2-3 enlarged chin shields. The top of the head is heavily flecked, and the back is grey to greyish-brown, irregularly marked with numerous pale-centred dark spots (solid black in some Soutpansberg specimens) that extend onto the limbs. The belly is whitish, and the tail is grey to orange-brown with black speckling. There are no transversely enlarged subcaudals, and there are four pairs of scansors beneath the toes. Males have 6-10 preanal pores (usually 6-8 in the typical race). **Biology and breeding:** These geckos live among rocks and stones on exposed hillsides. Two oval, hard-shelled eggs (6,9-7,4 x 5,1-6,2 mm) are deposited under stones and in rock crevices. Hatchlings measure 25-28 mm TL. **Habitat:** Prefers rocky outcrops above 1 500 m. **Range:** Found in the N. Province, Mpumalanga and Swaziland. **Subspecies:** *L.o. soutpansbergensis* is restricted to the Soutpansberg. It differs from the typical race in having a flatter, more pointed snout, three rather than two enlarged chin shields, 7 rather than 6 upper labials, and usually 8-9 preanal pores in males. Its colour is more variable, and the pale spots may be absent. The typical race is always spotted and occurs over the rest of the range.

**Stevenson's Dwarf Gecko**  *Lygodactylus stevensoni* **(Pl. 91)**
*(Endemic) SVL 30-35 mm; max. SVL 40 mm male, 37 mm female.*
A stout dwarf gecko with one pair of lateral clefts in the mental and no
soft spines above the eyes. The back and flanks are blue-grey to brownish,
with large, irregularly scattered, black spots. The throat bears dark chevrons,
and the belly is off-white. Males have 6-9 preanal pores. **Biology:** Mainly
rock-living, but also shelters under the bark of dead trees, and enters
buildings. The bark snake is a major predator. **Habitat:** Well-wooded
granite hills. **Range:** S. Zimbabwe and extreme N. Kruger National Park.

**Waterberg Dwarf Gecko**  *Lygodactylus waterbergensis* **(Pl. 110)**
*(Endemic) SVL 34-38 mm; max. SVL 40 mm.*
Similar to the granite dwarf gecko, *L. graniticolus* (page 247). A large dwarf
gecko with no lateral clefts in the mental. The soft spines above the eyes
are small or absent. Scales on the back are conical. The back and flanks are
grey, with irregular rows of dark blotches and interrupted bars. The throat
is speckled with grey, and the belly and tail are off-white and speckled on
the sides. The tail has evenly-spaced dark, white-edged, wavy crossbars.
The lower surface of the thighs is brownish to straw-yellow. The toe-tips
are rounded with four pairs of scansors. Males have 9 preanal pores.
**Biology:** Mainly rock-living, sheltering in cracks in sandstone boulders.
**Habitat:** Well-wooded granite hills. **Range:** Restricted to the Waterberg
escarpment in N. Province.

# Festive Gecko  *Narudasia*
This very small gecko has long slender, clawed toes that lack adhesive
scansors. The genus contains a single species, which is endemic to central
and S. Namibia. It is related to the small thorny-eyelidded geckos
(*Quedenfeldtia* sp.) of the Sahara.

**Festive Gecko**  *Narudasia festiva* **(Pl. 90)**
*(Endemic) SVL 25-30 mm; max. SVL 31 mm.*
A very small gecko with a flattened head and body. The eyes are large
with vertical pupils. The back is covered with small, granular scales, and
is grey-purple to chestnut-brown, with scattered white and cream spots,
and a series of 5-6 narrow, zig-zagging, black bands that are pale-edged
posteriorly. The belly is dirty white to yellow. The tail is cylindrical and
slightly longer than the body, and is often brightly coloured (yellow-
orange) and barred in black (but uniform grey when regenerated). Preanal
and femoral pores are absent. **Biology and breeding:** This very agile,
diurnal gecko forages in the early morning and evening for ants and flies
on the rock walls and boulders of mountain ravines and rocky slopes. It
may shelter beneath exfoliating flakes. The female lays two hard-shelled
eggs (7,6 x 6 mm) in rock cracks. **Habitat:** Prefers arid mountain slopes.
**Range:** Found in S. Namibia, from the northern bank of the Orange
River to Damaraland.

# Thick-toed Geckos  *Pachydactylus*
This is a large, ancient group of geckos that are characteristic of the
southern African subregion. Their toes have a series of undivided (rarely
divided) scansors under the tips, and there are usually minute claws on the
toes of the hind limbs. Many of the other geckos in the region (for example
the giant ground gecko, page 237; the Namib day geckos, page 267;

the web-footed geckos, page 263, and the Kalahari ground gecko, page 238) are closely related to the thick-toed geckos, as are the Moorish geckos (*Tarentola* sp.) of N. Africa and S. Europe.

Their bodies are covered with small, granular, non-overlapping scales, and many species also have scattered tubercles, that are enlarged and keeled, on the back, tail and limbs. The prominent eyes have vertical pupils, and non-functional eyelids that are distinct, forming a ridge around each eye. Femoral pores are absent, and preanal pores are present in only two species. Thick-toed geckos are usually camouflaged in buffs, browns and greys, with speckled, blotched or banded patterns. Juveniles are often more brightly coloured, and in some species have very different colour patterns (for example the velvety and Brandberg geckos, pages 251 and 258). Males have swollen hemipenial pouches at the base of the tail that are often adorned on the sides with 2-6 enlarged spines.

These geckos occupy a wide variety of habitats, but are most common in the arid western parts of the subregion. All the species are nocturnal, although some of the bigger, rock-living species are often found at the entrance to their rock cracks during the day, waiting for prey to come within their range. At night they forage away from the safety of their retreats. All lay two hard-shelled eggs, and it is probable that they lay several clutches during a season. A few species have been reported to call in the wild, but most are silent, although they may give a distress call when handled.

There are 33 species in the genus, and possibly more. All but one species are found in southern Africa; 25 of these are endemic.

### Transvaal Thick-toed Gecko     *Pachydactylus affinis* (Pl. 82)

*(Endemic) SVL 30-40 mm; max. SVL 44,5 mm male, 46,5 mm female.*
This small gecko has a slightly flattened head and body. The top of the head is spotted but bears no distinctive mark. A dark stripe extends from the nostril, though the eye, to the side of the head (onto the shoulder in the east). The back bears numerous tubercles that are in contact or separated by large irregular granules. It is pale brown to brown in adults with numerous dark brown to blackish spots and flecks, and usually also with scattered, smallish, white spots. The belly is white. Juveniles are purple-brown above, with 5-6 narrow, dark-edged, yellow-white cross-bands. The bars may become disrupted. There are 4-5 lamellae under the fourth toe. **Biology and breeding:** Mainly rupicolous but often also found in dead termite nests. Common in houses and gardens. A vocal species that produces a sharp creak when handled. Clutches of two small eggs (8,5-11 x 6-8 mm) are laid in termite nests, under bark, or under a boulder. Several clutches may be laid during summer and the hatchlings measure 33-36 mm TL. **Habitat:** Rocky outcrops and dead termite nests in Highveld grassland. **Range:** Restricted to the four northern provinces of S. Africa and possibly adjacent Free State and SE Botswana.

### Austen's Thick-toed Gecko     *Pachydactylus austeni* (Pl. 82)

*(Endemic) SVL 30-40 mm; max. SVL 47 mm male.*
A small gecko with a cylindrical body and a short snout. The rostral does not enter the nostril, which is pierced between two nasals. The scales on the back are of uniform size, and lack enlarged tubercles. The middle row of scales below the toes and above the scansors is not enlarged. There are 3-4 scansors beneath the middle toes. The tail is cylindrical, unsegmented

and slightly shorter than the body in adults. Coloration is very varied. A dark stripe may extend from the snout through the eye, and the upper eyelid may be bright yellow. The back may be pale grey, red-brown or dark brown, and patterned with either scattered white spots that may form irregular crossbands or large diffuse dark blotches. The belly is uniform white. **Biology and breeding:** The habits of these common geckos are similar to those of the web-footed gecko, *Palmatogecko rangei* (page 263). They are terrestrial and nocturnal, sheltering during the day in a small burrow that they dig in loose sand. In spring they lay two hard-shelled eggs in a hole dug in sand; these hatch in December. The Namaqua dwarf adder is a common predator. **Habitat:** Sparsely vegetated coastal dunes. **Range:** Coastal areas of W. Cape to Little Namaqualand.

### Velvety Thick-toed Gecko      *Pachydactylus bicolor* (Pl. 85)
*(Endemic) SVL 30-40 mm; max. SVL 40 mm male.*

A beautiful, small gecko with a flattened head and body. The rostral, which is much broader than it is deep, does not enter the nostril. The nasorostrals are in contact. The scales on the back are uniform, granular and abutting, and lack enlarged tubercles. The middle row of scales below the toes and above the scansors is enlarged. There are five scansors beneath the middle toe. The tail is hardly segmented and lacks bands of enlarged scales. Coloration is varied. Juveniles have a jet-black body bordered with white bands on the hips and neck, with those on the neck extending onto the lips; the head and tail are dusky brown. Adults have a light buff body with irregular brown blotches and bars, and adjacent yellow-brown blotches; the tail is yellow-brown, with faint dark spots, and the belly is yellow-white. Subadults turn dusky chocolate with scattered small, white spots adjacent to darker blotches. **Biology and breeding:** These geckos are nocturnal and rock-living, favouring thin cracks in small, shattered rock outcrops. Two eggs (9,2 x 6 mm) are laid in a rock crack. **Habitat:** Prefers rocky semi-desert. **Range:** Found in NW Damaraland and Kaokoveld in Namibia.

### Bibron's Thick-toed Gecko      *Pachydactylus bibronii* (Pl. 84)
*(Endemic) SVL 70-90 mm; max. SVL 100 mm male, 90 mm female.*

A large, stout gecko with very large, strongly keeled tubercles that are separated by granular scales on the back. The rostral is separated from the nostril, which is directed upwards and outwards. The scales bordering the mental are very small (diameter of five approximately half width of dorsal tubercle). The middle row of scales below the toes and above the scansors is not, or is only feebly, enlarged. There are 10-12 scansors beneath the middle toes. The tail, which is about the same length as the body, has a fat base and is segmented, with regular transverse rows of strongly keeled (almost spiny) scales. The back is dark buff to grey-brown or purplish-black with 4-5 indistinct, dark, wavy crossbands and scattered, white tubercles. The belly is white, and the tail has 8-10 dark bands that are prominent in juveniles but fade in adults. **Biology and breeding:** One of the most common Karoo geckos, they live on rock outcrops, under loose tree bark and on houses. They are gregarious and often live in dense colonies. As befits their appearance, they are pugnacious and ever-willing to bite. Despite this they make excellent long-lived pets. A wide variety of prey is eaten, including grasshoppers, ants, termites, beetles, and even poisonous centipedes and smaller lizards. Two eggs (16 x 14 mm) are laid

in a rock crack, under bark, etc. **Habitat:** Karroid veld and semi-desert. **Range:** Now mainly restricted to the Cape provinces, just extending into adjacent Free State and Namibia.

### Cape Thick-toed Gecko — *Pachydactylus capensis* (Pl. 83)

*(Endemic) SVL 40-60 mm; max. SVL 61 mm male, 67 mm female.*
A small to medium-sized gecko with a robust body, and 16-24 rows of enlarged, strongly keeled tubercles that are separated by granular scales on the back. The nostril is well separated from the rostral. The middle row of scales below the toes and above the scansors is not enlarged. There are five scansors beneath each middle toe. The original tail is slightly longer than the body, slightly flattened and distinctly segmented, with 4-6 scale rows per segment. Each segment has a transverse row of 6-8 enlarged, keeled tubercles. Regenerated tails lack tubercles, are carrot-shaped, and are rarely longer than the body. The back is typically light brown to grey-brown above, flecked with small black and white spots. The belly is white. **Biology and breeding:** Terrestrial, they are commonly found under calcrete blocks (in the Kalahari), rotting logs and in disused termitaria, but occasionally inhabit low rock cracks and houses. At night they emerge to forage for small insects. Clutches of two eggs (11-14 x 9-10 mm) are laid in old termitaria or under stones in September-December. Incubation takes 90-110 days, and hatchlings (35-50 mm TL) are found in November-January. They have many predators, including snakes and small carnivores. **Habitat:** Varied; karroid veld, grassland, and mesic savannah. **Range:** Cape provinces, through most of the subcontinent. **Subspecies:** None; previous races are now treated as full species.

### O'Shaughnessy's Thick-toed Gecko
*Pachydactylus oshaughnessyi* (Pl. 83)

*SVL 45-55 mm; max. SVL 58 mm.*
A small to medium-sized gecko with a robust body, and 18-24 rows of enlarged, but weakly keeled tubercles that are separated by granular scales on the back. The nostril is well separated from the rostral. The middle row of scales below the toes and above the scansors is not enlarged. There are four scansors beneath each middle toe. The original tail is slightly longer than the body, and weakly segmented with 3 scale rows per segment. The scales are large and feebly keeled and there are no enlarged tubercles. Regenerated tails are carrot-shaped and are rarely longer than the body. The top of the head is pale. A dark stripe extends from the nostril, through the eye, and fuses with a yellow, black-bordered band across the neck. From 2-7 (see Subspecies) similar crossbands occur on the back. The belly is white (grey-brown on sides in juveniles), and pale brown beneath the tail. Juveniles are more brightly coloured, the dark markings being purple-brown to black. **Biology:** This beautiful gecko is terrestrial, sheltering under boulders, logs, coconut palm fronds, etc. They may enter houses. **Habitat:** Prefers mesic savannah. **Range:** Found in N. Zimbabwe, adjacent W. Mozambique, into Malawi and Zambia, with an isolated race occurring in the E. Democratic Republic of Congo (former Zaïre). **Subspecies:** The typical race (*P.o. oshaughnessyi*) has 3-4 yellow cross-bands (4-5 in Zambia); it occupies most of the range. An isolated race (*P.o. katanganus*) occurs in the Shaba Province of the Democratic Republic of Congo. It has 6-8 thin yellow bands on the body and larger, keeled tubercles on the back.

*P.o. oshaughnessyi*

## Western Cape Thick-toed Gecko
*Pachydactylus labialis* **(Pl. 82)**
*(Endemic) SVL 30-40 mm; max. SVL 44 mm male, 46 mm female.*
This gecko has 16-18 rows of enlarged, keeled tubercles, separated by granular scales on the back. The rostral does not enter the nostril, and the nasorostrals are separated by a granule. The middle row of scales below the toes and above the scansors is not enlarged. There are five scansors beneath the middle toes. The tail, which is slightly longer than the body, is cylindrical and segmented, with transverse rows of six enlarged, keeled tubercles. Adults are orange-brown to dark greyish-brown, with large, diffuse paler blotches. The tubercles are often dark-tipped. The belly is creamy-white, and the tail is usually barred with dark brown. Juveniles are often dark brown, with paler tubercles. **Biology:** They live under stones on sandy soil. **Habitat:** Succulent karroid veld. **Range:** W. Cape, from Little Namaqualand to Calvinia.

## Angolan Banded Thick-toed Gecko
*Pachydactylus caraculicus* **(Pl. 111)**
*SVL 30-40 mm; max. SVL 41 mm male, 40 mm female.*
A small gecko with a flattened body and short, stout limbs. Each nostril is pierced between the three nasals, and the nasorostrals are in contact. The scales on the back are uniform, with a broad band of small, feebly keeled scales down the back, and smooth and larger scales on the sides. The toes are feebly dilated and have three scansors. The tail is cylindrical, distinctly segmented and tapers to a fine point; it is slightly longer than the body. Juveniles are purple-brown above, with five ivory-white or yellow, dark-edged bands, and a pale yellow tail with narrow brown crossbars; the belly is plain white. In adults, the white bands become less distinct and may become dusted with fine dark speckles; the tail develops white bars above and becomes dark. In southern populations only the neck band remains distinct, the bands on the body breaking up into white spots. **Biology and breeding:** Prefers rocky areas, sheltering in basalt rock cracks and under boulders. Hatchlings (28-30 mm TL) emerge in May. **Habitat:** Bushy Karoo-Namib shrubland. **Range:** SW Angola, entering N. Kaokoveld.

## Banded Thick-toed Gecko
*Pachydactylus fasciatus* **(Pl. 86)**
*(Endemic) SVL 40-50 mm; max. SVL 52 mm male, 56 mm female.*
A medium-sized, slender, flattened gecko with 16-18 irregular rows of enlarged, rounded and keeled tubercles that are separated by granular scales on the back. The nasorostrals are in contact. The middle row of scales below the toes and above the scansors is enlarged. There are 5-7 scansors beneath the middle toes. The tail, which is longer than the body, is thin, segmented and has transverse rows of six enlarged, keeled tubercles. The back is light brown to yellowish-brown in colour, with three regular, dark brown crossbands on the body and a brown stripe that encircles the head. The belly is dirty white, and the tail has 8-10 dark bands. Juveniles are more distinctly marked than males. **Biology and breeding:** A terrestrial species that lives in small tunnels, often dug beneath calcrete boulders on sandy soils. Clutches of two eggs (11-12 x 9 mm) are laid in soil beneath cover in summer. Hatchlings (measuring 21-25 mm SVL) appear in April-May. **Habitat:** Prefers arid mopane and *Acacia* savannah. **Range:** This gecko is found in N. Damaraland and also adjacent Kaokoveld, N. Namibia.

## Ocellated Thick-toed Gecko · · · · · · · · · · · · · · *Pachydactylus geitje* (Pl. 82)

*(Endemic) SVL 30-35 mm; max. SVL 39 mm male, 45 mm female.*

A small gecko with a short, cylindrical body, and uniform, granular scales on the back. The rostral does not enter the nostril, and the nasorostrals are separated. The middle row of scales below the toes and above the scansors is enlarged. There are 4-5 scansors beneath the middle toes. The tail is cylindrical, unsegmented and covered with smooth, slightly over-lapping scales; regenerated tails are fat and covered with irregular scales. Coloration is varied. A dark brown stripe runs from the snout through the eye. The back may be greyish-brown to dark brown, with small, scattered, dark-edged, white or yellow spots that are sometimes arranged in rows. The belly is white, and sometimes speckled with brown, particularly on the sides. Inland populations often lack the typical ocelli, having instead diffuse, pale blotches. **Biology and breeding:** These secretive, gentle geckos hide among debris and under stones, and feed at night on small insects. They appear to require moist conditions. When at rest, they curl the fat tail around their bodies like a contented cat; when disturbed, they stand stiff-legged with the head and tail held high. Two eggs (8-9,5 x 7-8 mm) are laid among debris and hatch in 60 days, but may take much longer (up to 122 days) if incubated at low temperatures. Hatchlings measure 30 mm TL. **Habitat:** Varied; coastal strandveld, fynbos and rocky grassland associated with inland escarpment. **Range:** SW Cape, extending along Cape fold mountains to Port Elizabeth and inland along the escarpment mountains to Cradock.

## Koch's Thick-toed Gecko · · · · · · · · · · · · · · *Pachydactylus kochii* (Pl. 80)

*(Endemic) SVL 40-50 mm; max. SVL 51 mm male, 54 mm female.*

A long, slender gecko with long limbs and uniform, granular scales on the back. The nasorostrals are in contact. There are three scansors beneath the middle toes. The tail is unsegmented and slender, and tapers to a fine point. The body is greyish-white above, with a slight lavender tinge, and with five bright reddish-brown crossbands. The belly is chalky white, and the tail has 12 red-brown bars. **Biology and breeding:** Little is known about this thick-toed gecko, but it is probably very similar to its close relative, the Marico gecko, *P. mariquensis* (page 256). The first specimens were collected at night under quartz lumps, or while they were moving slowly over open sand. **Habitat:** Usually prefers open sandy plains with scattered boulders. **Range:** Found in the vicinity of Cape Cross in Namibia.

## Turner's Thick-toed Gecko · · · · · · · · · · · · · · *Pachydactylus turneri* (Pl. 84)

*SVL 65-85 mm; max. SVL 95 mm male, 86 mm female.*

This large, stout gecko has very large, smooth or keeled tubercles that are separated by granular scales on the back. It is easily confused with Bibron's gecko (page 251), but the scales bordering the mental are larger (diameter of five approximately equal to width of dorsal tubercle). The rostral is separated from the nostril, which is directed almost vertically upwards. The middle row of scales below the toes and above the scansors is not, or is only feebly, enlarged. There are 10-12 scansors beneath the middle toes. The tail, which is shorter than the body, has a fat base, is segmented, and has regular, transverse rows of strongly keeled (almost spiny) scales. The back is pale creamy-olive to olive grey-brown in colour, with 3-4 dark, wavy crossbands, usually edged posteriorly with bright white spots. The belly is white. **Biology and breeding:** This species is very similar in habits and behaviour to Bibron's gecko, *P. bibronii* (page 251), but is not as common or as social, and is restricted to rock outcrops (although occasionally found on houses). The female lays 2-3 clutches, each consisting of two large eggs (18-20 x 14-16 mm), in a small hole dug in the sand (possibly also in rock cracks) in August-December. Incubation takes 60-80 days, and the hatchlings (60-65 mm TL) appear in December-March. **Habitat:** Semi-desert and arid savannah, entering moist habitats in NE. **Range:** Widely distributed; absent from most of the Cape provinces, although extending along the Orange River valley; occurs through Namibia, Botswana, into the western Free State, NW and N. Provinces, N. KwaZulu-Natal, and via Zimbabwe to Angola and Tanzania. **Subspecies:** None are now recognized. Through much of its northern range it was previously confused with Bibron's gecko.

### FitzSimons' Thick-toed Gecko    *Pachydactylus fitzsimonsi* (Pl. 84)

*SVL 65-85 mm; max. SVL 90 mm male, 81 mm female.*
This large, stout gecko has large, smooth, irregular and juxtaposed scales on the back and head, that are not separated by granules. It is easily confused with Bibron's gecko (page 251) and Turner's gecko (page 254), but the scales bordering the mental are large (diameter of five approximately twice the width of dorsal tubercle). The rostral is separated from the nostril, which is directed almost vertically upwards. The middle row of scales below the toes and above the scansors is not, or is only feebly, enlarged. There are 10-12 scansors beneath the middle toes. The back is olive yellow, with 4-5 dark, wavy crossbands, usually edged posteriorly with bright white spots. The belly is white. **Biology and breeding:** Very similar in habits and behaviour to Turner's gecko, *P. turneri* (page 254). Restricted to rock outcrops, although occasionally found on houses. **Habitat:** Semi-desert and arid savannah. **Range:** Restricted to Damaraland in Namibia, just entering S. Angola.

### Spotted Thick-toed Gecko    *Pachydactylus maculatus* (Pl. 81)

*(Endemic) SVL 35-45 mm; max. SVL 48 mm male, 58 mm female.*
A small, gentle gecko with a fat body and a rounded snout. The naso-rostrals are usually separated by 2-4 granules. The enlarged tubercles on the back are small and conical, and only slightly larger than the few surrounding granular scales. The back is grey to greyish-brown, with four rows of elongate, blackish spots that are not white-edged and occasionally fuse into irregular crossbands. The belly is off-white, and usually extensively flecked with brown. The tail is cylindrical, unsegmented and grows fat (particularly when regenerated); original tails are slightly longer than the body, while regenerated tails are shorter. There are 3-4 scansors beneath the middle toes. **Biology and breeding:** They are terrestrial, occasionally entering rocky areas, but normally found under debris, in rotting logs, old termitaria, or under loose bark on dead trees. A favoured retreat in Cape coastal regions is the empty shell of a giant land snail. Up to 10 geckos may pack into a single shell during winter. They feed at night on small insects and spiders. Predators are numerous, and include the large Natal hunting spider, which often takes only the shed tail. These geckos live for 3-4 years, and most adults lose their tail at least once, but sometimes up to three times, which emphasizes its usefulness in defence. Sexual maturity is reached within a year. Females are gravid from

September-February and lay 2-3 clutches, each consisting of two hard-shelled eggs (8 x 10 mm), in dry sand at the base of grass clumps in well-drained areas, or in crannies in debris or dead logs. Communal egg sites containing up to 12 eggs have been found in old land snail shells. Incubation takes 100-120 days in the wild (80-90 days in captivity); hatchlings are 30-35 mm long. **Habitat:** Varied; fynbos and coastal bush to arid karroid veld. **Range:** Inland escarpment of Cape from Sutherland, and coastal region from Knysna through E. Cape, KwaZulu-Natal, to Swaziland and extreme SE Mpumalanga; one record from adjacent Mozambique.

### Golden Spotted Thick-toed Gecko

*Pachydactylus oculatus* **(Pl. 81)**
*(Endemic) SVL 35-45 mm; max. SVL 47 mm male, 53 mm female.*
A small gecko with a fat body and a slightly pointed snout. The nasorostrals are usually separated by 1-2 granules. The enlarged tubercles on the back are of varied sizes, conical, and are larger than the many surrounding granular scales. The back is pale brown to beige, with four rows of rounded, brown to reddish-brown spots that are distinctly white-edged and largest along the backbone. The belly is white. Juveniles are more intensely coloured, and the dark dorsal spots are black-edged, not white-edged. The tail is cylindrical, unsegmented and grows fat (particularly when regenerated); original tails are slightly longer than the body, while regenerated tails are shorter. There are 3-4 scansors beneath the middle toes. **Biology and breeding:** This species is very similar to the spotted gecko, *P. maculatus* (page 255), but is found only on rock outcrops, favouring horizontal cracks in small boulders or flat rocks lying on exposed bedrock. Predators include snakes and larger lizards. Two hard-shelled eggs (10-11 x 8-9 mm) are laid in a rock crack. **Habitat:** Karroid veld, occasionally entering montane grassland and fynbos. **Range:** Inland escarpment of W. and E. Cape to S. Free State.

### Marico Thick-toed Gecko

*Pachydactylus mariquensis* **(Pl. 80)**
*(Endemic) SVL 40-50 mm; max. SVL 52 mm male, 57 mm female.*
A small, slender, thin-legged gecko with a short snout. The rostral does not enter the nostril, which is pierced between the three nasals. The back is covered with uniform, granular scales that lack enlarged tubercles. The middle row of scales below the toes and above the scansors is not enlarged, and there are 3-4 scansors beneath the middle toes. The tail is cylindrical, unsegmented and thin, and usually slightly shorter than the body. The back is grey to pinkish-buff in colour, with 5-6 wavy, reddish-brown, dark-edged crossbands. These may break up into irregular, vague, pale and dark blotches, particularly on the flanks. The belly is creamy white, and sometimes pink-tinged. The original tail has 5-7 dark-edged, brown crossbands (regenerated tails are grey-brown, with scattered black flecks). **Biology and breeding:** They are terrestrial, living on sandy, flat plains, and sheltering during the day under stones or in old scorpion holes. They emerge at night to forage for small insects. Most activity occurs on warm spring nights, when the males look for mates. At this time they vocalize, giving a short, slow pulse of clicks ('wek,wek ... wek'). The female lays 1-2 clutches, each consisting of two hard-shelled eggs (10 x 7,5 mm), in sandy soil, sometimes under a rock slab, in October-March. **Habitat:** Flat sandy plains with sparse vegetation. **Range:** Western arid

*P.m. mariquensis*

*P.m. latirostris*

region of South Africa, with scattered populations in S. and central Namibia. **Subspecies:** There are two races, both occurring in the region. In *P.m. mariquensis*, the nasorostrals are in contact, and the scales on the back are granular and abutting; it occurs in E. Cape (Addo), north to S. Free State and west to Ceres and Little Namaqualand. In *P.m. latirostris* the nasorostrals are separated by granular scales, and the scales on the back are flattened and slightly overlapping; it occurs in central and N. Karoo to Great Namaqualand, with an isolated population in Namibia around Spitzkoppe and south-west of Brandberg.

### Namaqua Thick-toed Gecko *Pachydactylus namaquensis* (Pl. 110)

*(Endemic) SVL 70-80 mm; max. SVL 82 mm male, 85 mm female.*

A large, stout gecko with rough but delicate skin. The rostral enters the nostril. The ear opening is rounded, 7-11 granules border the mental, and the supralabial is usually excluded from the nostril. The enlarged dorsal tubercles are twice the diameter of surrounding granular scales. The back is usually light olive-grey, with indistinct, paler and darker markings. The belly is creamy white to yellowish-white. The tail, which is slightly shorter than the head and body, has a fat base, and bears enlarged, spine-like scales along the sides. The cloacal spines are large. The middle row of scales beneath the toes is slightly enlarged, and there are 10-11 scansors beneath the middle toes. **Biology:** These geckos live in rock cracks, usually on large outcrops but also on isolated boulders. They are active mainly at night when they hunt grasshoppers, beetles, and moths and their caterpillars. **Habitat:** Large rock outcrops in karroid succulent veld. **Range:** Namaqualand, from the Kamiesberge to the Richtersveld, with a single S. Namibia specimen from the Huib-Hoch Plateau.

### Thin-Skinned Thick-toed Gecko
### *Pachydactylus klaroderma* (Pl. 84)

*(Endemic) SVL 65-75 mm; max. SVL 86 mm male, 80 mm female.*

A large, stout thick-toed gecko with rough but delicate skin. The rostral enters the nostril. The ear opening is a slit, 3-6 granules border the mental, and the supralabial usually enters the nostril. The dorsal tubercles on the back are rarely twice the diameter of the surrounding granules. The back is dark grey-brown, with vague blotches forming a series of six irregular bands that are wider towards the head. The belly is grey, and the skin beneath the head, throat, chest and lower surfaces of the limbs and tail is lighter than the belly. The original tail is banded, but irregularly blotched when regenerated. It is slightly shorter than the head and body, has a fat base, but does not bear enlarged, spine-like scales along the sides. The cloacal spines are small. The middle row of scales beneath the toes is slightly enlarged, and there are 10-11 scansors beneath the middle toes. **Biology:** These geckos live in rock cracks, usually on large outcrops or summit rock bands. They often bask at the crack entrance during the day, but are also active at night. They eat various large insects, including grasshoppers and beetles. They have a startling defence: when gripped, they twist violently, tearing off large bits of their skin, and often manage to slip away. The flayed gecko is a frightening sight but the skin is quickly regenerated. **Habitat:** Prefers large rock outcrops in karroid and succulent veld. **Range:** Occurs in an arc, from the inland Cape escarpment on the Nuuweveldberg, through to the rocky western Karoo and on to the southern Cape fold mountains.

## Haacke's Thick-toed Gecko   *Pachydactylus haackei* (Pl. 110)
*(Endemic) SVL 70-80 mm; max. SVL 85 mm male, 84 mm female.*
A large, stout gecko with rough but very delicate skin. The ear opening is round to squarish, 3-10 granules border the mental, and the rostral enters the nostril (the supralabial rarely does). The dorsal tubercles on the back are rarely twice the diameter of the surrounding granules. The back is pink-grey with vague blotches that form a series of seven irregular bands that are wider towards the head. The belly is cream, and the skin beneath the head, throat, chest and lower surfaces of the limbs and tail is lighter than the belly, with vague dark reticulation on the sides. The original tail is banded, but irregularly blotched when regenerated. The tail, which is equal to or slightly longer than the head and body, has a fat base, but does not bear enlarged, spine-like scales along the sides. The cloacal spines are small. The middle row of scales beneath the toes is slightly enlarged, and there are 10-11 scansors beneath the middle toes. **Biology and breeding:** They shelter in large rock cracks, where several individuals may be found, particularly when not breeding. They may bask at the crack entrance during the day, but are also active at night. Large insects, particularly beetles, form the main diet. Two large, round, hard-shelled eggs (16 mm dia.) are laid in a rock crack. Communal egg sites may contain many eggs. Like the previous species (*P. kladeroderma*) the skin is very fragile and easily torn when gripped. **Habitat:** Large rock outcrops on the upper and lower slopes of mountains in desert and succulent veld. **Range:** S. Namibia, just entering the Richtersveld.

## Kaokoveld Thick-toed Gecko   *Pachydactylus oreophilus* (Pl. 85)
*(Endemic) SVL 40-50 mm; max. SVL 54 mm male, 57 mm female.*
A medium-sized, flattened gecko with a large head and 16-18 rows of feebly keeled, enlarged tubercles that are separated by granular scales on the back. The head is pinkish-grey, with dark brown lips with 11-12 upper labials, and two dark, curved lines running from the eye around the back of the neck. The back is grey-brown, with irregular, dark blotches that are concentrated on either side of the backbone. The belly is mainly white. The tail is longer than the body and is segmented, with transverse rows of strongly keeled tubercles above. The lower forelimbs lack keeled tubercles, and there are 6-7 scansors beneath the middle toes. **Biology:** At night they emerge from rock cracks and under exfoliating flakes to forage on vertical rock faces. **Habitat:** Semi-desert. **Range:** From Brandberg in Namibia to S. Angola.

## Brandberg Thick-toed Gecko   *Pachydactylus gaiasensis* (Pl. 111)
*(Endemic) SVL 50-60 mm; max. SVL 68 mm male, 65 mm female.*
A medium-sized, flattened gecko with a large head and 14 rows of strongly keeled, enlarged tubercles that are separated by granular scales on the back. The lower forelimbs have bluntly keeled tubercles, and females have minute claws on the toes. There are 6-8 scansors beneath the middle toes. The tail is shorter than the body and is segmented, with transverse rows of strongly keeled tubercles above, and enlarged, smooth scales below. Adults are light grey above, with mauvish-brown, irregular blotches that may form vague crossbars, and a thin, grey vertebral stripe. The belly is greyish-white. Juveniles have a brown head and jet-black body and forelimbs, bordered at the front and back by well-defined, white bands. The belly is brownish-white, and the tail and hind limbs are greyish-

brown. **Biology:** These terrestrial geckos emerge at night from underneath sandstone boulders to forage slowly on the sand. **Habitat:** Arid, sandy veld. **Range:** Vicinity of Brandberg in Namibia.

### Speckled Thick-toed Gecko   *Pachydactylus punctatus* (Pl. 81)
*SVL 25-35 mm; max. SVL 38,5 mm male, 38 mm female.*

A small gecko that is both gentle and beautiful. It has small, granular, flattened and overlapping scales on the back, and lacks enlarged tubercles. The rostral does not enter the nostril. The middle row of scales below the toes and above the scansors is enlarged, and there are 3-4 scansors beneath the middle toes. The tail is cylindrical, unsegmented and covered with large, overlapping scales. Coloration is very varied. There is usually a dark streak from the nostril through the eye, which is edged with white-yellow. The back may be pale grey to purple-brown, with numerous dark spots that are sometimes pale-centred, or at other times marked only with scattered, light spots. The belly is creamy white, and the tail sometimes flecked. **Biology and breeding:** These terrestrial geckos are very common in suitable habitat. They live on sandy soils, sheltering in tunnels beneath rotting logs, stones, or under suitable cover, and emerge at night to hunt for small invertebrates. Two eggs (8-9 x 6-7 mm) are laid in midsummer, and hatchlings measure 20 mm SVL. **Habitat:** Varied; arid desert, but preferring dry savannah. **Range:** Found through much of the northern parts of the subregion, from Mpumalanga to N. Botswana and Zimbabwe, throughout Namibia, to Angola and Katanga in the north and Richtersveld in the south.

### Schertz's Thick-toed Gecko   *Pachydactylus scherzi* (Pl. 111)
*(Endemic) SVL 25-35 mm; max. SVL 33 mm male, 35 mm female.*

A small gecko, previously confused with the speckled thick-toed gecko, *P. punctatus* (page 259). It has small, granular, flattened and overlapping scales on the back, and lacks enlarged tubercles. The rostral does not enter the nostril, and the first upper labial usually borders the nostril. The middle row of scales below the toes and above the scansors is enlarged, and there are 3-4 scansors beneath the middle toes. The back is dark brown, typically with characteristic dark-edged, pale crossbars, that may be interrupted in the middle. In western coastal populations the crossbars may disrupt into large pale blotches. The belly is creamy white, and the tail is slender and sometimes barred. **Biology:** Poorly known; apparently rupicolous, living in rock cracks or under stones on bedrock. **Habitat:** Rocky outcrops in arid savannah and desert. **Range:** Restricted to the inland escarpment and coastal plain of Namibia, from the Brandberg north to the Kaokoveld.

### Rough Thick-toed Gecko   *Pachydactylus rugosus* (Pls. 83 and 111)
*(Endemic) SVL 45-60 mm; max. SVL 51 mm male, 65 mm female.*

An unusual, small, round-bodied gecko, usually with irregular rows of very enlarged tubercles that are separated by granular scales on the back. The middle row of scales below the toes and above the scansors is not enlarged, and there are five scansors beneath the middle toes. The tail is shorter than the body and is segmented, with a transverse series of 8-10 enlarged tubercles and spiny subcaudals (southern races lack spiny subcaudals). Coloration is varied (see Subspecies). Juveniles of all races are more brightly coloured. **Biology:** The typical race is usually found in dry

*P.r. rugosus*
*P.r. barnardi*
*P.r. formosus*

riverbeds, under the loose bark of dead tees. The other races often occur on rock outcrops, sometimes in horizontal rock cracks, but often in dead twigs and debris accumulated around stones on granite bedrock. When threatened, they arch the tail over the back. **Habitat:** Semi-desert and succulent karroid veld. **Range:** W. Cape to Kaokoveld in Namibia. **Subspecies:** Three races are recognized, but it is probable that all are valid species. All occur in the region. The back of *P.r. rugosus* is covered with very large tubercles, and the scales on the belly are rough. The back is olive green-brown in colour, with four wavy, cream to yellow-brown crossbands, and the side of the head is sometimes marked with a white stripe. The belly is greyish-white, with small brown flecks, and the tail has narrow white bars and scattered white tubercles. It is found in the inland regions of Namibia, through N. Cape to Calvinia. *P.r. formosus* also has large tubercles on the back, but the belly scales are smooth. The upperparts are brown to reddish-brown in colour, with five wavy, pale yellowish, dark-edged crossbands, the first completely encircling the head. The belly is off-white and finely speckled with brown, and the tail is broadly banded. It is found in the W. Cape, from Ceres to Little Namaqualand. *P.r. barnardi* is similar to *P.r. formosus*, but the dorsal crossbands disrupt into paired blotches. It is intermediate in colour and pattern between the other two races as befits its geography; it occurs in Little Namaqualand.

### Large-scaled Thick-toed Gecko  *Pachydactylus scutatus* (Pl. 85)
*SVL 30-40 mm; max. SVL 42 mm male, 40 mm female.*

A small, round-bodied gecko, with large and strongly keeled scales on the back, except for a strip of smaller, smoother scales along the backbone. The rostral enters the nostril. The middle row of scales below the toes and above the scansors is enlarged, and there are 5-7 scansors beneath the middle toes. The tail is cylindrical and segmented, with transverse rows of 4-8 keeled tubercles, and is slightly longer than the body. Adults are light greyish-brown above, with a few, scattered, dark blotches. A dark, pale-centred stripe runs from each nostril through the eye and around the back of the head. The belly is dirty white. Juveniles are paler than adults, lack the dark spots on the back, and have an olive-yellow tail. **Biology and breeding:** These geckos are nocturnal and terrestrial, living under rocks and occasionally under exfoliating flakes on low boulders. The white, oval eggs (7-8 x 5-6 mm) are laid in pairs under rock flakes. The species was once reported to lay four eggs, but this is improbable. **Habitat:** Arid veld. **Range:** Restricted to N. Namibia, extending into S. Angola.

### Western Spotted Thick-toed Gecko

*Pachydactylus serval* (Pls. 86 and 112)

*(Endemic) SVL 35-40 mm; max. SVL 41 mm male, 45 mm female.*
A small gecko with a flattened head and body. The scalation on the back is variable (see Subspecies). The rostral, which is only slightly broader than it is deep, enters the nostril, and the nasorostrals are in contact. The middle row of scales below the toes and above the scansors is enlarged, and there are 5-6 scansors beneath the middle toes. There are no large tubercles on the hind limbs. The tail is cylindrical and segmented, with transverse rows of 6-8 spinose tubercles, and is slightly longer than the body. Coloration is varied. The back is pale olive to greyish-brown, with dark brown blotches (small and scattered in the southern race, larger and fusing in the typical race). The belly is white, and the tubercles on the tail

■ *P.s. serval*

□ *P.s. purcelli*

▦ *P.s. onscepensis*

are golden. Populations along the lower Orange River are light orange-brown, with diffuse darker crossbands and golden tubercles on the body and tail. **Biology and breeding:** These geckos are found in isolated populations, where they are usually very common. They live in small, hard-rock cracks (granite, sandstone and dolerite) and under exfoliating flakes. Two small, hard-shelled eggs (9-11 x 6-7 mm) are laid in rock cracks. Hatchlings measure 25-27 mm TL. **Habitat:** Semi-desert and succulent karroid veld. **Range:** S. Karoo (Rietbron) to lower Orange River and to Great Namaqualand; absent from W. Cape and Little Namaqualand. **Subspecies:** Three races; all occur in the region. *P.s. serval* has scattered, enlarged tubercles on the back, that are not keeled or raised; it is found in S. Namibia. The back of *P.s. purcelli* is covered with granular scales and lacks enlarged tubercles; it is found in the karroid areas of South Africa, entering the W. Little Karoo in the south and stretching northwards into SE Namibia. *P.s. onscepensis* has scattered, raised keeled tubercles on the back; it occurs along the lower Orange River valley.

### San Steyn's Thick-toed Gecko *Pachydactylus sansteyni* (Pl. 112)
*(Endemic) SVL 35-45 mm; max. SVL 48 mm male, 48 mm female.*

A small, slender gecko with 6-7 irregular rows of small tubercles that are separated by granular scales on the back. The rostral enters the nostril and there are 10-12 upper labials. The middle row of scales below the toes and above the scansors is enlarged, and there are 4-5 scansors beneath the middle toes. The hind limbs have enlarged, conical keeled tubercles. The tail is segmented, with transverse rows of 4-6 spinose tubercles, and is shorter than the body. Adults are mauvish-brown above, with irregular, dark brown spots and blotches. A dark brown stripe runs through the eye from the snout to the ear. The belly is off-white. Juveniles have finer spotting on the body, and the tubercles are inconspicuous. **Biology:** A terrestrial species that lives under sandstone boulders on sandy soil, and emerges at night to feed on small insects. Juveniles may enter rock cracks. **Habitat:** Semi-desert. **Range:** Vicinity of Kuidas, S. Kaokoveld in Namibia, north to Cunene River mouth.

### Tete Thick-toed Gecko        *Pachydactylus tetensis*
*SVL 70-90 mm; max. SVL 100 mm male, 87 mm female.*

Unlike all other southern African *Pachydactylus* species, the male has 8-14 preanal pores. The back of this very large gecko is covered with enlarged, strongly-keeled tubercles, which are separated by granular scales, and may form four irregular rows on either side of the backbone. The back is uniform pale grey above, and the belly is white. The tail has a pair of slightly enlarged scales. There are 11-14 scansors beneath the middle toes. **Biology:** Usually found in wide, shaded rock cracks, but occasionally also inhabits hollow baobab trunks. Gregarious, with several specimens often found side by side in a crack. When grasped, their thin skin tears easily. **Habitat:** Mopane woodland. **Range:** Lower Zambezi valley.

### Tiger Thick-toed Gecko        *Pachydactylus tigrinus* (Pl. 82)
*(Endemic) SVL 40-50 mm; max. SVL 51 mm male, 53 mm female.*

A small gecko with a very flattened body that is covered with small, scattered tubercles on the back; the tubercles are flattened, feebly keeled and separated by granular scales. The rostral does not enter the nostril. The middle row of scales below the toes and above the scansors is not enlarged, and there are 4-5 scansors beneath the middle toes. The tail is strongly segmented, and lacks enlarged tubercles; regenerated tails are carrot-shaped. Coloration is varied. Juveniles are purple-brown to black above, with 5-6 narrow white or yellow crossbands (these may disrupt into spots in northern populations); adults from N. Province retain the juvenile 'tiger' pattern; in SW Zimbabwe the ground colour is lighter, and the white crossbands are dark-edged occasionally breaking up into lines of white spots with dark spots between them; and in N. Zimbabwe and the Matopos, the pale markings are obscured by numerous large, black blotches. The belly is brownish in southern populations and usually white in the north. **Biology:** Rock-living; inhabits narrow crevices in granite and sandstone outcrops, often sharing them with the Transvaal flat gecko, *Afroedura transvaalica* (page 236). **Habitat:** Mesic savannah. **Range:** Zimbabwe and adjacent N. Province, E. Botswana and W. Mozambique.

### Tsodilo Thick-toed Gecko    *Pachydactylus tsodiloensis* (Pl. 112)
*(Endemic) SVL 45-55 mm; max. SVL 58,5 mm male, 60 mm female.*

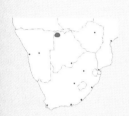

A medium-sized, flattened gecko with a similar colour pattern to Weber's gecko (page 263). The rostral does not enter the nostril, and the nasorostrals are in contact behind the rostral. There are 14 upper labials, the last forming a large oval scale at the angle of the jaw. The back is covered with granular scales, with 18 rows of enlarged tubercles. The middle row of scales below the toes and above the scansors is enlarged, and there are seven scansors beneath the middle toes. The tail is swollen at the base and segmented, with transverse rows of eight enlarged keeled tubercles; it is slightly longer than the body. Adults are light greyish-brown above, with 5-6 off-white, brown-edged crossbars. The head is marked with dark brown spots and vermiculations, with a pale dark-edged stripe starting from behind each nostril, running through the eyes, and fusing on the top of the head. The belly is white. In some specimens the crossbars are indistinct. Juveniles are similar to adults, but the head is unmarked. **Biology:** A nocturnal gecko that inhabits quartzite and dolomitic limestone outcrops. It rarely leaves the rock to cross the sandy flats. Feeds mainly on ants and other small insects. **Habitat:** Prefers moist savannah. **Range:** Endemic to Tsodilo Hills in N. Botswana.

### Van Son's Thick-toed Gecko    *Pachydactylus vansoni* (Pl. 83)
*(Endemic) SVL 40-50 mm; max. SVL 55 mm male, 59 mm female.*

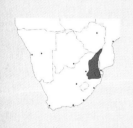

This attractive, medium-sized gecko has a somewhat flattened body, and the back is covered with 10-17 (mostly 13-15 on the Highveld) rows of enlarged, strongly keeled, sometimes trihedral tubercles that are separated by granular scales. The nostril is well separated from the rostral. The middle row of scales below the toes and above the scansors is not enlarged, and there are 4-5 scansors beneath each middle toe. The original tail is slightly longer than the body, slightly flattened and distinctly segmented, with 3-4 scale rows per segment. Each segment has a transverse row of 6-8 flattened, weakly-keeled tubercles. Regenerated tails lack tubercles, are carrot-shaped and are rarely longer than the body. The back is grey-brown to red-brown, sometimes with irregular dark brown blotches, but mostly with 5-8 white crossbands (which may be absent or staggered), and 1-2 semicircular white lines behind the head. The belly is white, and the original tail has black and white crossbands. **Biology and breeding:** Mainly terrestrial; shelters in a tunnel beneath a rock or dead log.

Highveld populations are totally rupicolous, living in rock cracks. Two egg clutches (10-11 x 7-9 mm) are laid in rock cracks or under bark. Incubation takes 41-61 days and hatchlings measure 37-42 mm TL. They may live for up to 8 years. **Habitat:** Mesic and arid savannah. **Range:** N. KwaZulu-Natal and adjacent Free State, through Mpumalanga and E. Northern Province to SE Zimbabwe and adjacent Mozambique.

**Weber's Thick-toed Gecko**      *Pachydactylus weberi* **(Pl. 86)**
*(Endemic) SVL 35-45 mm; max. SVL 49 mm male, 48 mm female.*

A small, slender, flattened gecko with 22 irregular rows of small tubercles that are separated by granular scales on the back. The rostral does not enter the nostril. The middle row of scales below the toes and above the scansors is enlarged, and there are 5-7 scansors beneath the middle toes. The tubercles on the hind limbs are enlarged. The tail, which is slightly longer than the body, is segmented, with regular, transverse rows of 6-8 enlarged keeled tubercles. In southern populations the juveniles are golden-brown, with four light brown to cream, dark-edged crossbands; the tail merges to white at the tip and has 10-12 black bands. Southern adults are dull brown, with irregular dark brown blotches, and golden tubercles that give a speckled appearance, particularly on the tail. In northern populations, the dark edges to the juvenile crossbands are greatly expanded to form a rich reddish-brown body with three golden cross-bands (the first on the back of the neck); the tail is banded in light and dark brown, with rings of golden tubercles. Northern adults have wavy, dark brown blotches above that may form irregular crossbars, and the tail retains faint juvenile bands; the body and tail are speckled with golden tubercles. Populations from Great Namaqualand and central Namibia are intermediate between these phases. **Biology and breeding:** These very agile geckos live in cracks in hard rock (granite, sandstone, quartzite, etc.), and are active at night. They eat mainly moths and spiders. Two hard-shelled eggs (9-10 x 6-7 mm) are laid in a rock crack, and take 80-90 days to hatch; hatchlings measure 30-35 mm TL. Communal egg sites may contain up to 60 eggs. **Habitat:** Succulent karroid veld. **Range:** Central Namibia, through Namaqualand to W. Cape. **Subspecies:** Although some races have been described (for example *P.w. acuminatus, P.w. werneri,* etc.), none are currently recognized.

# Web-footed Geckos    *Palmatogecko*

Medium-sized, slender geckos that have large heads with jewel-like eyes. The body is covered with minute, granular scales, and the large hind feet are frog-like, with extensive webbing between the toes. Despite their appearance, they are closely related to the thick-toed geckos, *Pachydactylus* (page 249). The genus contains two species (with the inclusion of *Kaokogecko*), both of which are endemic to the Namib Desert.

**Web-footed Gecko**      *Palmatogecko rangei* **(Pl. 79)**
*SVL 60-65 mm; max. SVL 68 mm male, 78 mm female.*

A beautiful and bizarre gecko with an elongate, cylindrical body and thin legs. The large eyes, which appear bloodshot, have vertical pupils that each close to two pinholes in bright light. The nostrils are tubular. The toes of the forelimbs and hind limbs are joined with webbing, except for the toe-tips, which have a large, claw-like scale. There are no adhesive scansors. The tail is thin and unsegmented. The body is almost semi-

transparent. Males are slightly smaller than females, and have a prominent hemipenial bulge at the tail base which bears a row of 6-8 spines on the sides. The back is fleshy-pink to pink-brown with irregular, reticulated dark blotches that extend onto the tail. There is a dark brown band across the snout, and a blue-black patch above the eyes. The belly and sides are chalky white, and the other ventral regions are transparent pink. **Biology and breeding:** Terrestrial and nocturnal, these geckos spend the day in a tunnel (up to 50 cm long) that they dig in fine sand or silt. They emerge late, even on surprisingly cold nights, and despite their delicate appearance are active in strong winds. The diet comprises small insects, spiders, etc. They obtain all their moisture from condensing fog, and from their food. When threatened they adopt a raised stiff-legged posture, but do not squeak. Males may fight and bite one another in territorial disputes. The tail is rarely lost, and then always from near the base. It is readily regenerated. The skin is shed in pieces and then eaten. Predators include owls, snakes and the Namib golden mole (SA RDB Peripheral). Clutches of two large, fragile, hard-shelled eggs (21 x 10 mm) are laid from November-March in a small tunnel dug in sand. They hatch in about 90 days; hatchlings measure 30-35 mm TL. **Habitat:** Wind-blown sands of coast and desert. **Range:** Coastal Richtersveld to S. Angola.

### Kaoko Web-footed Gecko      *Palmatogecko vanzyli* (Pl. 80)
*SVL 50-55 mm; max. SVL 60 mm male, 66 mm female.*
This beautiful and unusual gecko has a slender body with a soft, semi-transparent skin. The head is flattened, with a pointed snout. The eyes are large, with vertical pupils. The back is covered with minute granular scales. All the toes have two small scansors at the tip, and the toes of the hind feet are webbed and clawed in both sexes. Preanal and femoral pores are absent. The tail is cylindrical, unsegmented and shorter than the body. The back is light brown, with a series of 9-12 large, light purple to brown-pink blotches along the back and tail, and is scattered with dark brown spots that are concentrated around the borders of the dorsal blotches. The belly is white. **Biology:** This terrestrial, nocturnal species constructs a short burrow for its daytime shelter. The hole is excavated with the clawed forefeet while the webbed hind feet push the loose sand to one side. During the day, the entrance to the burrow is closed with loose sand. In the early evening, they emerge to forage for food, often climbing nearby rocks. They eat termites and small beetles. **Habitat:** Gravel plains. **Range:** N. Namib Desert, just entering SW Angola.

## Day Geckos    *Phelsuma*
This group of geckos has reduced inner toes. All but the distal scansors on the toe-tips are undivided. The eyes are large and usually have round pupils. Males have femoral and preanal pores in a continuous series. These beautifully coloured geckos are diurnal and mainly arboreal. There are approximately 30 species in the genus, distributed throughout the islands of the Indian Ocean, particularly Madagascar, with a few species reaching the east coast of Africa. One isolated species is endemic to Namaqualand.

### Namaqua Day Gecko      *Phelsuma ocellata* (Pl. 90)
*(Endemic) SVL 30-40 mm; max. SVL 42 mm male, 35 mm female.*
A small day gecko with a small inner toe. The flared toe-tips have 7-8 undivided scansors and no claws. The nostrils are not tubular and each

pierces the first upper labial. The eyes are large, and have vertical pupils and prominent eyelids that cannot close and that form a continuous ring around the eye. The scales on the back are smooth and granular, but the belly scales are overlapping. Males have a long series of 24-31 femoral pores that are continuous across the preanal region. The back is light brown to greyish-brown, with scattered pale and dark spots. The belly is cream to blue-white, often tinged with pink. **Biology and breeding:** These very active geckos are found running and jumping between boulders on rocky hillsides and outcrops. They occasionally forage on succulent bushes or fig trees. They shelter under exfoliating rock flakes, where they are very well camouflaged. Small beetles, aphids and other insects are eaten. One to two small, hard-shelled eggs (8,5 x 6,5 mm) are laid under a rock flake in September. They may lay additional clutches later in the season. (SA RDB, Restricted). **Habitat:** Succulent karroid veld. **Range:** N. Little Namaqualand, through Richtersveld to SW Namibia.

## Barking Geckos   *Ptenopus*

These are small, unusual burrowing geckos that lack scansors on the toes but have a fringe of scales to aid digging. They are the only local geckos with slightly movable upper eyelids.

Terrestrial and nocturnal, they dig elaborate burrow systems with concealed escape holes. They live alone, but form diffuse colonies. At night they forage for insects, walking slowly across the sand and pausing often. Males call on summer nights at their burrow entrance, attracting mates and proclaiming their territory. The call is a chain of clicks ('ceek-ceek-ceek ...') that vary in number and pitch between the species. One or two hard-shelled, white eggs are laid in a shallow pit in spring. Predators include owls, snakes and meerkats. When caught, these geckos squeak and may bite. The genus contains three species, all of which are endemic. Two are restricted to the Namib Desert, while the other is widely distributed in the western arid regions.

### Carp's Barking Gecko   *Ptenopus carpi* (Pl. 79)

*(Endemic) SVL 50-55 mm; max. SVL 59 mm male, 60,4 mm female.*
A slender gecko, with long legs and weakly fringed toes. There are 105-140 scale rows at midbody. The nostrils are not swollen and lack valves. The back is creamy white, with fine, orange-brown speckles and reticulations. There are 3-5 dark brown crossbars on the back and 5-9 on the tail. The belly is white, with a yellow heart shape on the throat that is absent in juveniles and seasonal in females. Specimens from N. Namib Desert are darker. **Biology and breeding:** These geckos live in shallow burrows with a few side tunnels that they dig in very compact soil. They are very well camouflaged. If disturbed, they raise the body on stiff legs, puff out their yellow throat, hiss and may even bite. The call is a monotonous series of slow, low-pitched clicks (3-20, but usually 12). **Habitat:** Flat, barren gravel plains with an annual rainfall of less than 125 mm. **Range:** Central and N. Namib Desert, from Kuiseb River north to Rocky Point.

### Common Barking Gecko   *Ptenopus garrulus* (Pl. 79)

*(Endemic) SVL 45-60 mm; max. SVL 62 mm male, 62,6 mm female.*
A small barking gecko with swollen nostrils and strongly fringed toes. There are 110-190 scale rows at midbody. The back colour varies (see Subspecies). The belly is white. Males have an orange or yellow heart

■ *P.g. maculatus*

□ *P.g. garrulus*

shape on the throat. **Biology and breeding:** These geckos become active for a short period around sunset, and their calls signal sunset in the desert. They may also call on cool mornings. The call varies regionally from one to 13 clicks but usually consists of five. They do not inhabit mobile dunes. In rocky areas, they often live in a sand hummock trapped at the base of a bush. After dark they emerge and walk slowly in search of prey, which includes termites, ants and small beetles. If disturbed, they freeze and are effectively camouflaged. Their burrows are complex, with many blind passages, some running upwards and ending just beneath the surface. These serve as escape routes from predators such as small snakes and meerkats. **Habitat:** Desert and semi-desert on various soil substrates, preferring flat, stable, sandy soil with sparse vegetation. **Range:** Western arid regions of southern Africa, from Little Karoo to Kruger National Park, N. Province, and entering extreme S. Zimbabwe. **Subspecies:** Two races are recognized. *P.g. garrulus* is smaller (max. SVL 51-52 mm), has more than 160 scale rows at midbody, and is finely speckled in reddish-brown, sometimes with diffuse, darker spots; it occurs in Kalahari sands of Namibia, Botswana and adjacent regions. *P.g. maculatus* has fewer than 160 scale rows at midbody, and the colour varies with the substrate, but is usually greyish-yellow, with black crossbars, five pairs of pale spots on the flanks, and 5-10 dark bars on the tail; it is found in Namibia (including some areas in the Namib Desert), extending through Namaqualand to Great and Little Karoo.

### Koch's Barking Gecko

*Ptenopus kochi* (Pl. 79)

*(Endemic) SVL 50-60 mm; max. SVL 64,8 mm male, 62,8 mm female.*
A stout burrowing gecko, with large bulging eyes, swollen nostrils and minute body scales, in 187-222 rows at midbody. The flattened toes are fringed with elongate scales, and the body is slightly longer than the tail. The body is reddish-brown with dark speckles, particularly on the sides. An irregular row of light spots (which may be yellow in adult males) occurs on the flanks. The belly and inner surfaces of the limbs are white. The throat is white in females and juveniles, and sulphur-yellow in males. **Biology:** These geckos live in extensive, elaborate burrows that they dig in the fine sand of interdune spaces and silt of dry riverbeds. The burrows may be up to 90 cm long and 40 cm deep. **Habitat:** Desert. **Range:** South-central Namib Desert.

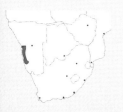

# Namib Day Geckos   *Rhoptropus*

These are medium-sized geckos with long legs. The feet have four long, thin toes (the fifth toe is small and rudimentary), with flaired tips that have a series of 5-13 undivided scansors, and sometimes a rudimentary claw. The body is squat and covered with small, granular scales. The head is distinct. The nostrils are swollen, and the eyes are large, with vertical pupils and immovable eyelids that form a complete ring around the eye. The lower jaw has elongate chin shields. Males lack femoral pores.

These diurnal geckos run around on vertical rock faces or on broken, rocky ground. They are sit-and-wait hunters, hiding in a shaded vantage point and attacking any insects that come within range. Two hard-shelled eggs are laid in a rock crack or in sand under a slab. Communal egg-laying sites are frequently used.

At present, the genus contains five species, all of which are found on the subcontinent. One is endemic.

## Common Namib Day Gecko

*Rhoptropus afer* **(Pl. 92)**

*SVL 35-50 mm; max. SVL 55 mm.*

A small species with relatively short, stout toes. There are 5-6 scansors under the middle toes. There are no preanal pores. The middle row of scales under the tail is not enlarged. The scales on the back are small and rounded. The back is light olive to grey-brown, with scattered red-brown and pale spots. The chest and belly are bluish-white. The tail is banded in dark brown and dirty yellow, and is slightly shorter than the head and body. The throat, anal region and lower surfaces of the limbs and tail are bright yellow. **Biology and breeding:** These small day geckos prefer dry gravel plains with sheet rock and exfoliating flakes. They are very active, darting rapidly between rock slabs, where they are perfectly camouflaged. In social display the tail is curled upwards to reveal the yellow undersurface. They live on the hottest Namib plains, sheltering in cracks from the midday sun. If there is a cool breeze, they climb up to a vantage point and lift the body high to cool in the wind. They feed on ants and small beetles. Two white, hard-shelled, oval eggs (10-12 x 6-8 mm) are laid under rock slabs. The eggs often stick to the stone, but may be found loose in the sand. **Habitat:** Prefers rocky desert. **Range:** This species is restricted to the coastal regions of the Namib Desert, from the Kuiseb River to extreme SW Angola.

## Barnard's Namib Day Gecko

*Rhoptropus barnardi* **(Pl. 92)**

*SVL 30-45 mm; max. SVL 49 mm.*

The smallest Namib day gecko, with long slender toes, the fourth bearing eight undivided scansors. Males have 4-7 preanal pores arranged in a row. The middle row of scales under the tail is not enlarged. The scales on the back are slightly keeled and tubercular. The tail is flattened and segmented at its base (but smooth when regenerated), and is slightly longer than the head and body. The back is pale grey to pinkish-brown, or dark brown with scattered pale and dark spots that may form irregular bands. The belly is pale bluish to white. **Biology and breeding:** This gecko lives in regions of higher rainfall than other Namib day geckos, preferring small rock outcrops and ridges of varied rock types. It is rarely found together with the larger, rupicolous species, possibly because of competition. The female lays clutches of two eggs (11-12 x 9-10 mm) in May-June in rock cracks. Communal nesting sites, containing up to 200 eggs, may be found. **Habitat:** Prefers semi-desert. **Range:** Occur mainly inland of the N. Namib Desert, from central Namibia to SW Angola; can be found inland as far as the Etosha Pan.

## Kaokoveld Namib Day Gecko

*Rhoptropus biporosus* **(Pl. 92)**

*SVL 40-50 mm; max. SVL 55 mm.*

Another small species, similar to Barnard's Namib day gecko, *R. barnardi* (page 267), but it has a slimmer build, a rounder snout, a thinner tail, and only two preanal pores. The toes are long and slender with 11 undivided scansors beneath the fourth one. The middle row of scales under the tail is not enlarged. The scales on the back are slightly tubercular. The tail is flattened and segmented at its base (but smooth when regenerated), and is slightly shorter than the head and body. The back is light grey to fawn in colour, with irregular spots and markings. The limbs and tail have indistinct, dark bars, and the belly is white to cream. **Biology:** This species is active on low rock outcrops and boulders, preferring flat

GECKOS

surfaces. **Habitat:** Prefers semi-desert. **Range:** Recorded only inland of N. Namib Desert, from extreme N. Namibia (vicinity of Orupembe in Kaokoveld) and into adjacent SW Angola.

### Boulton's Namib Day Gecko

*Rhoptropus boultoni* (Pl. 92)

*SVL 55-70 mm; max. SVL 74 mm.*
This largish, stocky species has long, slender toes, with 13 undivided scansors beneath the fourth toe. Males have 5-8 preanal pores arranged in a row. The middle row of scales under the tail is enlarged, at least on the distal half, and the scales on the back are smooth and only feebly tubercular. The tail is flattened, thick and segmented at its base, and slightly shorter than the head and body. The back is dark sooty-grey to olive-brown in colour, with large, irregular maroon to dull brick-red blotches. The belly is dull bluish-grey to slate. **Biology and breeding:** These day geckos forage on vertical granite and basalt boulders, and even Baobab trees, where they feed on ants, spiders and beetles. The males are pugnacious and defend their territories against intruders. Females contained two large eggs (11,5 x 8,5 mm) in June. Geckos seen on basalts appear darker than those on light granite rocks. **Habitat:** Prefers rocky desert regions. **Range:** Found in Damaraland in Namibia, and north to S. Angola. **Subspecies:** Three races are recognized, with only the typical race occurring on the subcontinent. It is replaced in Angola by *R.b. benguellensis* (in the Benguela Province) and *R.b. montanus* (in Huila).

*R.b. boultoni*

### Bradfield's Namib Day Gecko

*Rhoptropus bradfieldi* (Pl. 92)

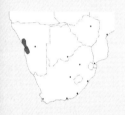

*(Endemic) SVL 50-65 mm; max. SVL 69 mm.*
This day gecko is related to the common Namib day gecko, *R. afer* (page 267), but has 11 undivided scansors beneath the fourth toe and the tail is slightly longer than the head and body. The back is sooty-brown to blackish in colour with faint traces of crossbands or narrow zigzags. The tail segments are edged with black. The belly is slate-grey to bluish, lacking the yellow infusion of the common Namib day gecko. **Biology and breeding:** During the heat of the day, these geckos hang on the shaded vertical surfaces of large, dark rocks, dashing out to seize any food that comes within range. Their dark coloration may help heat absorption in coastal regions where cool winds and fogs are common. The diet comprises ants, moths and beetles. Adults give high-pitched squeaks when approaching one another; it is possible that this is a territorial signal. Two eggs (9 x 15 mm) are laid in a rock crack, where they stick firmly to the surface. Favoured cracks may be used by many individuals over many years, and accumulate 'beds' of old egg shells. **Habitat:** Prefers semi-desert regions. **Range:** This species is found from the Kuiseb River to Twyfelfontein in W. Damaraland, but is absent from the W. Namib-Naukluft Desert Park. **Subspecies:** Two races are recognized. *R.b. diporus* males have two enlarged preanal scales with pores (absent in females); it is found on Brandberg, to S. Kaokoveld. *R.b. bradfieldi* males lack preanal pores; it occurs in the region south of Brandberg.

# CROCODILIANS
## ORDER CROCODYLIA

$\mathcal{C}$rocodiles, alligators and the gharial are the last vestiges of the ruling reptiles, the archosaurs, which dominated the earth's history for over 150 million years. Crocodilians are, in fact, more closely related to birds than they are to other living reptiles. Their many unusual features include a heart that is four-chambered, with complete division of the ventricles, thus permitting more efficient blood oxygenation; an extra eyelid, the nictitating membrane, which sweeps dirt from the eyeball; an improved limb articulation that permits a better gait (the 'high walk'), so that some crocodilians can even gallop, albeit for short distances; a hard palate in the roof of the mouth; a longitudinal cloacal aperture; and a single penis. The archosaurs reached their heyday in the Jurassic era (190-130 million years ago) with the emergence of aquatic, terrestrial and even arboreal forms (the last known from Lesotho fossils). They have changed very little in the last 65 million years. All living forms are aquatic, and are distributed throughout the world's tropical regions.

Only 23 species remain, and all are endangered and now protected. Three living families are recognized: the Gavialidae, the Alligatoridae, and Crocodylidae. The latter is the only family present in Africa.

# Crocodiles
### FAMILY CROCODYLIDAE

Crocodiles can be recognized by the fourth mandibular tooth which is visible when the jaw is closed (it is hidden in a socket in alligators). The first fossils occur in the late Cretaceous period of Europe and N. America. Many living species are large, but claims of nine- to 10-metre giants are exaggerated. Of the 15 species (in three genera), only three occur in Africa

## True Crocodiles  *Crocodylus*

All true crocodiles are very similar in appearance, the species differing mainly in the shape of the snout and minor details of scalation.

The larger species (the saltwater crocodile and the Nile crocodile) both take large game, including man, while the smaller species (Johnston's crocodile and Morelet's crocodile) feed mainly on fish and small mammals.

Fossils are known from the Upper Cretaceous period. The 13 living species are distributed throughout the tropical regions of the world; they are poorly represented in Amazonia, where they are replaced by the caimans. Two species occur in Africa. The African slender-snouted croco-dile, *C. cataphractus*, is found in W. and central Africa, inhabiting the larger rivers. The Nile crocodile is the only species that enters the subcontinent.

### Nile Crocodile  *Crocodylus niloticus* (Pl. 96)
*Total length 2,5-3,5 m; max 5,9 m.*
Nile crocodiles may exceptionally exceed 1 000 kg in weight. The jaws are long, and have prominent teeth. The eyes and valved nostrils are situated on top of the head. The skin is covered with geometrically arranged, horny plates, many of which are keeled and bony. The plates on top of the head are fused to the skull. The hind feet are webbed. The tail is 40% of the total body length, rectangular in cross-section and has two raised dorsal keels. The young are greenish, with irregular black markings over

the back and sides, and the throat and belly are uniform straw-yellow. Adults are darker, being uniform olive to grey, with a yellow or cream belly.

**Biology and breeding:** Young crocodiles dig a burrow (sometimes communally) up to 3 m long in which they shelter for the first 4-5 years. They spend a lot of time out of water and eat small prey. Subadults prefer swamps and backwaters, eating fish, terrapins, birds and small mammals. Adults grasp prey with a fast, sideways swipe of the head. The tail may be used to knock over vegetation to dislodge nestling birds or to direct fish to within striking distance of the jaws. They feed on fish, particularly catfish, but also ambush game coming to drink. Antelope are usually taken, but zebra and buffalo may be overcome. Attacks on humans (and fatalities) are relatively common. Large food items are softened by biting. If too large to be swallowed whole, prey is torn to bits by the crocodile seizing a mouthful and spinning on its long axis. Carrion is readily taken. Co-operative behaviour in feeding is known, for example herding fish together into shallow water. On hot days, they come ashore to bask. At high temperatures they lie with mouth agape, losing excess heat by evaporation. The oft-quoted tale of Egyptian plovers pecking clean the teeth of crocodiles, which dates back to the Greeks, has never been confirmed. They swim effortlessly, using the broad, flattened tail. The webbed hind feet allow careful manoeuvring during mating and when preparing to ambush food. The valved nostrils and gular flap at the back of the mouth enable them to feed underwater. They live for up to 60 years in captivity, and very large wild specimens may live to 100 years. Hunting has caused a decline in crocodile numbers (SA RDB, Vulnerable).

Crocodilians are attentive parents, and nest construction and the care of the young is very advanced. Sexual maturity is reached in 12-15 years at about 2-3 m (70-100 kg). At the start of the breeding season (May), males develop a dominance hierarchy. Courtship is elaborate, and mating takes place in the water in July-August. The female selects a suitable sunny sand bank that is above floodwater level and which has good drainage and cover nearby. She will use it, unless disturbed, for the rest of her life. At night, usually in November, she digs a hole (30-45 cm deep) with her hind legs, and lays 16-80 white, hard-shelled eggs (70-78 x 50-56 mm, 85-125 g). The nest site is defended against predators and other crocodiles, and during this period the female does not eat, but may go to the water to drink. The male remains in the vicinity, but is not allowed near the nest mound. After 84-90 days the hatchlings, while still in the egg, give a high-pitched cheeping noise that is audible 20 m away. The female carefully opens the nest and takes the young into her mouth. The hatchlings (280-320 mm TL) are taken to the water, washed and released. They remain in a 'crèche area' for 6-8 weeks. The sex of hatchlings is determined by egg incubation temperature; unlike chelonians (page 24), females are produced at lower temperatures (26-30°C) and males at higher ones (31-34°C).

**Habitat:** Larger rivers, lakes and swamps, but also river mouths, estuaries and mangrove swamps. **Range:** Okavango Basin, Cunene River and major rivers draining to the east coast, south to Tugela River (and historically to East London). Viable populations now restricted mainly to game reserves. Elsewhere, on Madagascar (indicating limited marine excursions) and throughout Africa (except at high altitudes and in deserts). Now extinct on other Indian Ocean islands and in coastal Mediterranean regions. **Subspecies:** A number have been proposed, based on minor differences in scutellation; they are all of doubtful validity.

denotes species which are on record as having caused human fatalities

denotes species which can inflict serious bites, but which have not been recorded as having caused human fatalities

Great Escarpment (Valley of Desolation, Graaff-Reinet)

Kalahari hardveld with mesic acacia savannah (Lobatse, Botswana)

Succulent karroid veld (near Springbok, Little Namaqualand)

Namib Desert (Swakopmund, Namibia)

PLATE 1

Lowveld arid savannah (Mpumalanga)          Granite inselbergs with euphorbia trees (near Pietersburg, Northern Province)

Cape fold mountains with fynbos (Cedarberg, SW Cape)          Maputaland with coastal dune thicket and swamp (Kosi Bay, NE KwaZulu-Natal)

Rocky desert (near the Brandberg, Namibia)

PLATE 2

Undescribed sp. of dwarf chameleon, Swartberg *(Bradypodion* sp.) p. 220

Recently described Swartberg gecko *(Afrogecko swartbergensis)* p. 236

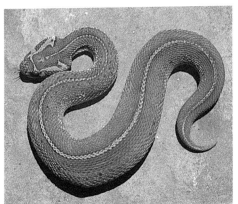

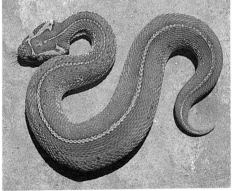

Plated lizard, blue-throated phase *(Gerrhosaurus flavigularis)* p. 178

Puff adder, unusual striped phase *(Bitis arietans)* p. 114

Brown house snake, xanthic phase *(Lamprophis fuliginosus)* p. 74

Puff adder/Gaboon adder, hybrid *(B. arietans/B. gabonica)* pp. 114/115

PLATE 3

Angulate tortoise *(Chersina angulata)* p. 30

Angulate tortoise, light phase *(Chersina angulata)* p. 30

Leopard tortoise *(Geochelone pardalis)* p. 29

Leopard tortoise, light phase *(Geochelone pardalis)* p. 29

Leopard tortoise, egg and hatchling – note egg tooth *(Geochelone pardalis)* p. 29

PLATE 4

Bell's hinged tortoise *(Kinixys belliana belliana)* p. 34

Speke's hinged tortoise *(Kinixys spekii)* p. 34

Parrot-beaked tortoise, male *(Homopus areolatus)* p. 27

Natal hinged tortoise, female *(Kinixys natalensis)* p. 35

Parrot-beaked tortoise, female *(Homopus areolatus)* p. 27

PLATE 5

Greater padloper *(Homopus femoralis)* p. 26

Greater padloper, hatchling *(Homopus femoralis)* p. 26

Nama padloper *(Homopus sp.)* p. 28

Karoo or Boulenger's padloper *(Homopus boulengeri)* p. 27

Speckled padloper *(Homopus signatus signatus)* p. 28

Speckled padloper *(Homopus signatus cafer)* p. 28

PLATE 6

Geometric tortoise *(Psammobates geometricus)* p. 32

Geometric tortoise, juvenile *(Psammobates geometricus)* p. 32

Tent tortoise *(Psammobates tentorius tentorius)* p. 32

Serrated or Kalahari tent tortoise *(Psammobates oculiferus)* p. 31

Tent tortoise *(Psammobates tentorius verroxii)* p. 32

Tent tortoise *(Psammobates tentorius trimeni)* p. 32

PLATE 7

Green turtle *(Chelonia mydas)* p. 39

Hawksbill turtle *(Eretmochelys imbricata)* p. 40

Olive ridley turtle *(Lepidochelys olivacea)* p. 41

Loggerhead turtle, adult *(Caretta caretta)* p. 41

Loggerhead turtle, hatchling *(Caretta caretta)* p. 41

PLATE 8

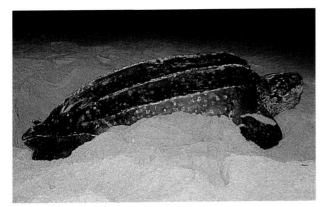
Leatherback turtle, adult *(Dermochelys coriacea)* p. 37

Leatherback turtle, hatchling *(Dermochelys coriacea)* p. 37

Zambezi soft-shelled terrapin *(Cycloderma frenatum)* p. 43

Nile soft-shelled terrapin *(Trionyx triunguis)* p. 43

Nile soft-shelled terrapin *(Trionyx triunguis)* p. 43

PLATE 9

American red-eared terrapin, juvenile *(Trachemys scripta)* p. 36

American red-eared terrapin *(Trachemys scripta)* p. 36

Marsh or Helmeted terrapin *(Pelomedusa subrufa)* p. 45

Marsh or Helmeted terrapin, juvenile *(Pelomedusa subrufa)* p. 45

Marsh or Helmeted terrapin withdrawing head sideways *(Pelomedusa subrufa)* p. 45

# PLATE 10

Yellow-bellied hinged terrapin *(Pelusios castanoides)* p. 47

Serrated hinged terrapin *(Pelusios sinuatus)* p. 46

Okavango hinged terrapin *(Pelusios bechuanicus)* p. 47

Mashona hinged terrapin *(Pelusios rhodesianus)* p. 47

Pan hinged terrapin *(Pelusios subniger subniger)* p. 46

PLATE 11

🕱 Gaboon adder *(Bitis gabonica gabonica)* p. 115

🕱 Puff adder *(Bitis arietans arietans)* p. 114

🕱 Puff adder, dark phase *(Bitis arietans arietans)* p. 114

🕱 Puff adder *(Bitis arietans arietans)* p. 114

🕱 Berg adder, Mpumalanga *(Bitis atropos)* p. 115

🕱 Berg adder, SW Cape *(Bitis atropos)* p. 115

🕱 Berg adder, E. Cape *(Bitis atropos)* p. 115

PLATE 12

Horned adder, N. Cape *(Bitis caudalis)* p. 116

Horned adder, Etosha in Namibia *(Bitis caudalis)* p. 116

Horned adder, N. Province *(Bitis caudalis)* p. 116

Many-horned adder *(Bitis cornuta)* p. 116

Desert mountain adder *(Bitis xeropaga)* p. 117

PLATE 13

🕱 Lowland swamp viper *(Proatheris superciliaris)* p. 119

🕱 Plain mountain adder, Compassberg *(Bitis inornata)* p. 117

🕱 Red adder *(Bitis rubida)* p. 117

🕱 Péringuey's adder *(Bitis peringueyi)* p. 119

🕱 Red adder, Cedarberg *(Bitis rubida)* p. 117

🕱 Namaqua dwarf adder *(Bitis schneideri)* p. 118

PLATE 14

Common/Rhombic night adder, Zimbabwe *(C. rhombeatus)* p. 113

Common/Rhombic night adder, E. Cape *(C. rhombeatus)* p. 113

Snouted night adder *(Causus defilippii)* p. 113

Common/Rhombic egg eater *(Dasypeltis scabra)* p. 95

East African egg eater *(Dasypeltis medici medici)* p. 96

Dwarf beaked snake *(Dipsina multimaculata)* p. 87

PLATE 15

Western keeled snake *(Pythonodipsas carinata)* p. 82

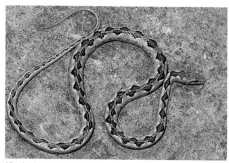

Viperine bark snake *(Hemirhagerrhis viperinus)* p. 86

Variegated or Spotted slug eater *(Duberria variegata)* p. 80

Mopane snake *(H. nototaenia)* p. 86

Mozambique shovel-snout *(Prosymna janii)* p. 84

Sundevall's shovel-snout *(Prosymna sundevallii)* p. 84

PLATE 16

Spotted house snake, Karoo *(Lamprophis guttatus)* p. 74

Spotted house snake, Mpumalanga *(Lamprophis guttatus)* p. 74

African rock python *(Python sebae natalensis)* p. 59

Anchieta's dwarf python *(Python anchietae)* p. 59

Spotted/Rhombic skaapsteker *(P.r. rhombeatus)* p. 88

Dwarf beaked snake *(Dipsina multimaculata)* p. 87

PLATE 17

Many-spotted snake *(Amplorhinus multimaculatus)* p. 82

Mole snake *(Pseudaspis cana)* p. 80

Elongate quill-snouted snake *(X.m. inornatus)* p. 69

Twig or Vine snake *(Thelotornis capensis capensis)* p. 100

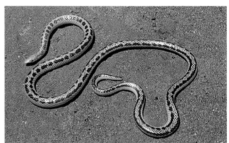

Bicoloured quill-snouted snake *(X.b. bicolor)* p. 68

Shield-nose snake *(Aspidelaps scutatus intermedius)* p. 104

PLATE 18

Two-striped shovel-snout *(Prosymna bivittata)* p. 84

Fisk's house snake *(Lamprophis fiskii)* p. 75

Spotted harlequin snake *(Homoroselaps lacteus)* p. 102

Eastern tiger snake *(Telescopus semiannulatus semiannulatus)* p. 97

Eastern tiger snake *(Telescopus semiannulatus polystictus)* p. 97

Beetz's tiger snake, Namib Desert *(Telescopus beetzii)* p. 98

PLATE 19

☠ Cape cobra, juvenile *(Naja nivea)* p. 108

☠ Cape cobra, adult in speckled phase *(Naja nivea)* p. 108

☠ Coral snake *(Aspidelaps lubricus lubricus)* p. 103

☠ Rinkhals *(Hemachatus haemachatus)* p. 109

☠ Snouted cobra, banded phase *(Naja a. annulifera)* p. 106

☠ Black-necked spitting cobra *(Naja nigricollis nigricincta)* p. 109

PLATE 20

☠ Günther's garter snake *(Elapsoidea guentheri)* p. 105

☠ Angolan garter snake *(Elapsoidea semiannulata)* p. 105

☠ Boulenger's garter snake, juvenile *(Elapsoidea boulengeri)* p. 105

☠ Sundevall's garter snake, juvenile *(E. sunderwallii media)* p. 106

☠ Sundevall's garter snake, juvenile *(E. sunderwallii decosteri)* p. 106

☠ Sundevall's garter snake, adult *(E. sunderwallii decosteri)* p. 106

PLATE 21

Grey-bellied grass snake *(Psammophylax variabilis)* p. 89

Rhombic skaapsteker, striped phase *(P.r. rhombeatus)* p. 88

Striped skaapsteker *(Psammophylax tritaeniatus)* p. 88

Dwarf sand snake *(Psammophis angolensis)* p. 91

Stripe-bellied sand snake *(Psammophis subtaeniatus subtaeniatus)* p. 91

PLATE 22

Jalla's sand snake *(Psammophis jallae)* p. 90

Cape sand snake *(Psammophis leightoni leightoni)* p. 90

Fork-marked sand snake *(Psammophis leightoni trinasalis)* p. 90

Namib sand snake *(Psammophis leightoni namibensis)* p. 90

Karoo sand snake or Whip snake *(Psammophis notostictus)* p. 90

Cross-marked or Montane grass snake *(Psammophis crucifer)* p. 92

Olive grass snake *(Psammophis mossambicus)* p. 92

PLATE 23

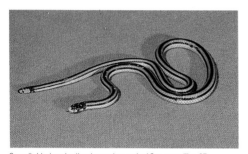

Gerard's black and yellow burrowing snake *(C.g. gerardi)* p. 67

Striped harlequin snake *(Homoroselaps dorsalis)* p. 103

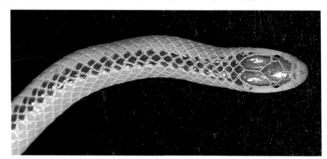

Kalahari purple-glossed snake *(Amblyodipsas ventrimaculata)* p. 66

Eastern purple-glossed snake *(A.m. microphthalma)* p. 66

Bicoloured quill-snouted snake *(Xenocalamus bicolor lineatus)* p. 68

Bicoloured quill-snouted snake *(Xenocalamus bicolor lineatus)* p. 68

PLATE 24

Cape file snake *(Mehelya capensis capensis)* p. 78

Ornate green snake *(Philothamnus ornatus)* p. 94

Eastern striped swamp snake *(Limnophis bangweolicus)* p. 82

☠ Yellow-bellied sea snake *(Pelamis platurus)* p. 111

Aurora house snake, hatchling *(Lamprophis aurora)* p. 75

Namibian wolf snake *(Lycophidion namibianum)* p. 77

PLATE 25

Semiornate snake *(Meizodon semiornatus)* p. 93

Reticulated centipede eater *(Aparallactus lunulatus)* p. 63

South-western shovel-snout *(Prosymna frontalis)* p. 84

Cape centipede eater *(Aparallactus capensis)* p. 64

Black centipede eater *(Aparallactus guentheri)* p. 64

Shield-nose snake *(Aspidelaps scutatus scutatus)* p. 104

Coral snake *(Aspidelaps lubricus infuscatus)* p. 103

PLATE 26

☠ Forest cobra *(Naja melanoleuca)* p. 107

☠ Snouted cobra, plain phase *(N. annulifera annulifera)* p. 106

☠ Snouted cobra *(Naja annulifera)* p. 106

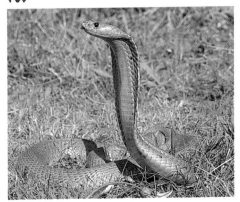

☠ Cape cobra, plain phase *(Naja nivea)* p. 108

☠ Mozambique spitting cobra or M'fezi *(Naja mossambica)* p. 108

PLATE 27

Common slug eater with new-born young *(Duberria lutrix lutrix)* p. 79

Mole snake, plain phase *(Pseudaspis cana)* p. 80

Southern brown egg eater *(Dasypeltis inornata)* p. 96

Brown house snake *(Lamprophis fuliginosus)* p. 74

Swazi rock snake *(Lamprophis swazicus)* p. 75

PLATE 28

Transvaal quill-snouted snake *(Xenocalamus transvaalensis)* p. 68

Variegated wolf snake *(Lycophidion variegatum)* p. 76

Sundevall's shovel-snout, speckled phase *(P. sundevallii lineata)* p. 84

East African shovel-snout *(P. stuhlmannii)* p. 85

Sundevall's shovel-snout, striped phase *(P. sundevallii lineata)* p. 84

PLATE 29

Eastern green snake *(Philothamnus natalensis occidentalis)* p. 95

Green water snake *(Philothamnus hoplogaster)* p. 94

Spotted bush snake *(Philothamnus semivariegatus)* p. 93

Spotted bush snake *(Philothamnus semivariegatus)* p. 93

Western green snake *(Philothamnus angolensis)* p. 94

Green mamba *(Dendroaspis angusticeps)* p. 110

PLATE 30

Boomslang, male in speckled phase *(Dispholidus t. typus)* p. 99

Boomslang, green phase *(Dispholidus t. typus)* p. 99

Boomslang, female in olive phase *(Dispholidus t. typus)* p. 99

Boomslang, juvenile *(Dispholidus t. typus)* p. 99

Twig or Vine snake *(T. capensis mossambicanus)* p. 100

Marbled tree snake *(D. aulica)* p. 98

PLATE 31

🕱 Sundevall's garter snake, adult *(E. sundevallii media)* p. 106

Aurora house snake *(Lamprophis aurora)* p. 75

Olive house snake *(Lamprophis inornatus)* p. 74

Yellow-bellied house snake *(Lamprophis fuscus)* p. 75

Common brown water snake *(Lycodonomorphus rufulus)* p. 73

Mulanje water snake *(Lycodonomorphus leleupi mlanjensis)* p. 73

PLATE 32

Dusky-bellied water snake *(L. laevissimus)* p. 72

Floodplain water snake *(Lycodonomorphus obscuriventris)* p. 73

Herald or Red-lipped snake *(Crotaphopeltis hotamboeia)* p. 97

Barotse water snake *(Crotaphopeltis barotseensis)* p. 97

Olive marsh snake *(Natriciteres olivacea)* p. 81

Forest marsh snake *(Natriciteres variegata sylvatica)* p. 81

PLATE 33

Short-snouted grass snake *(Psammophis brevirostris brevirostris)* p. 91

Cross-marked grass snake, plain phase *(Psammophis crucifer)* p. 92

Leopard grass snake *(P.b. leopardinus)* p. 91

Western sand snake *(Psammophis trigrammus)* p. 89

Rufous beaked snake *(Rhamphiophis rostratus)* p. 86

Rufous beaked snake *(Rhamphiophis rostratus)* p. 86

PLATE 34

☠ Black mamba *(Dendroaspis polylepis)* p. 110

☠ Black mamba *(Dendroaspis polylepis)* p. 110

☠ Black spitting cobra, hatchling
*(N. nigricollis woodi)* p. 109

☠ Black spitting cobra, adult *(N. nigricollis woodi)* p. 109

Mole snake, black phase *(Pseudaspis cana)* p. 80

☠ Rinkhals shamming death, plain phase *(H. haemachatus)* p. 109

PLATE 35

Angola file snake *(Mehelya vernayi)* p. 79

Black file snake *(Mehelya nyassae)* p. 79

Cape wolf snake *(Lycophidion capense capense)* p. 76

Pygmy wolf snake *(Lycophidion pygmaeum)* p. 77

Dwarf wolf snake *(Lycophidion nanum)* p. 78

PLATE 36

Olive marsh snake *(Natriciteres olivacea)* p. 81

☠ Natal black snake *(Macrelaps microlepidotus)* p. 65

Olive marsh snake *(Natriciteres olivacea)* p. 81

☠ Boulenger's garter snake, adult *(E. boulengeri)* p. 105

☠ Sundevall's garter snake *(Elapsoidea sunderwallii longicauda)* p. 106

PLATE 37

☠ Southern or Bibron's burrowing asp, dark belly phase *(Atractaspis bibronii)* p. 62

☠ Southern or Bibron's burrowing asp, light belly phase *(Atractaspis bibronii)* p. 62

☠ Burrowing asp *(A. duerdeni)* p. 63

Common purple-glossed snake *(Amblyodipsas polylepis)* p. 66

☠ Duerden's burrowing asp *(Atractaspis duerdeni)* p. 63

Natal purple-glossed snake *(Amblyodipsas concolor)* p. 65

PLATE 38

Delalande's beaked blind snake *(Rhinotyphlops lalandei)* p. 53

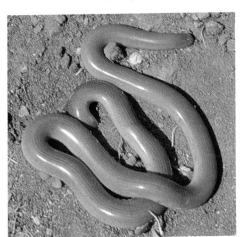
Bibron's blind snake *(Typhlops bibronii)* p. 55

Slender blind snake *(Typhlops obtusus)* p. 54

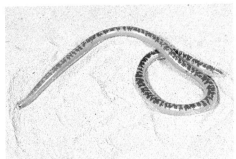
Schinz's beaked blind snake *(Rhinotyphlops schinzi)* p. 53

Schlegel's beaked blind snake, spotted phase *(R. schlegelii petersii)* p. 54

Schlegel's beaked blind snake, striped phase *(R.s schlegelii)* p. 54

PLATE 39

Fornasini's blind snake *(Typhlops fornasinii)* p. 54

Flower-pot snake *(Ramphotyphlops braminus)* p. 53

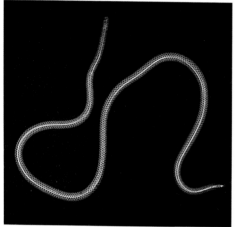

Peters' thread snake *(Leptotyphlops scutifrons scutifrons)* p. 57

Slender thread snake *(Leptotyphlops gracilior)* p. 56

Long-tailed thread snake *(Leptotyphlops longicaudus)* p. 56

Distant's thread snake *(Leptotyphlops distanti)* p. 57

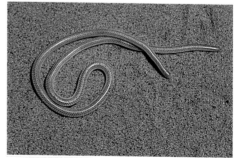

Western thread snake *(Leptotyphlops occidentalis)* p. 57

PLATE 40

Dusky spade-snouted worm lizard *(Monopeltis infuscata)* p. 126

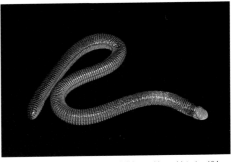

Anchieta's spade-snouted worm lizard *(Monopeltis anchietae)* p. 124

Slender spade-snouted worm lizard *(M.s. sphenorhynchus)* p. 126

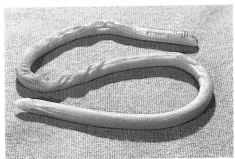

Blunt-tailed worm lizard *(Dalophia pistillum)* p. 127

Kalahari spade-snouted worm lizard *(Monopeltis leonhardi)* p. 125

Zimbabwe spade-snouted worm lizard *(M. rhodesiana)* p. 125

PLATE 41

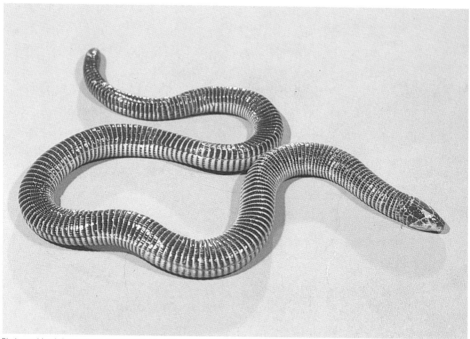

Black round-headed worm lizard *(Zygaspis nigra)* p. 124

Kalahari round-headed worm lizard *(Zygaspis quadrifrons)* p. 123

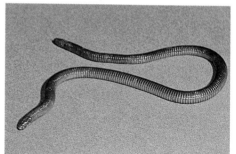

Violet round-headed worm lizard *(Zygaspis violacea)* p. 123

Lang's round-headed worm lizard *(Chirindia langi langi)* p. 122

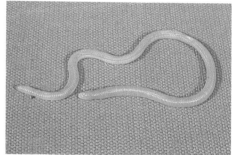

Swynnerton's round-headed worm lizard *(Chirindia swynnertoni)* p. 122

PLATE 42

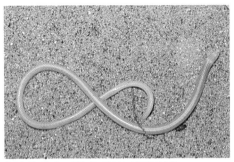

Brain's blind legless skink *(Typhlosaurus braini)* p. 136

Boulenger's blind legless skink *(Typhlosaurus vermis)* p. 138

Lomi's blind legless skink *(Typhlosaurus lomii)* p. 138

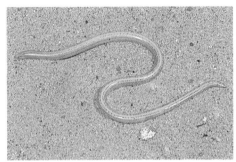

Meyer's blind legless skink *(Typhlosaurus meyeri)* p. 138

Coastal legless skink, orange phase *(Acontias litoralis)* p. 133

PLATE 43

Giant legless skink *(Acontias plumbeus)* p. 134

Thin-tailed legless skink *(Acontias gracilicauda gracilicauda)* p. 133

Percival's legless skink *(Acontias percivali occidentalis)* p. 134

Coastal legless skink, dark phase *(Acontias litoralis)* p. 133

Percival's legless skink *(Acontias percivali tasmani)* p. 134

Cuvier's blind legless skink *(Typhlosaurus caecus)* p. 136

PLATE 44

Cape legless skink *(Acontias meleagris orientalis)* p. 133

Cape legless skink *(Acontias meleagris meleagris)* p. 133

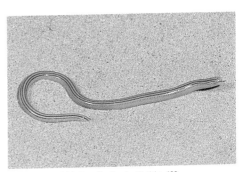

Striped legless skink *(Acontias lineatus tristis)* p. 133

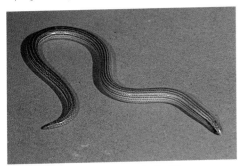

Kalahari burrowing skink *(Typhlacontias rohani)* p. 147

FitzSimons' burrowing skink *(Typhlacontias brevipes)* p. 147

PLATE 45

Woodbush legless skink *(Acontophiops lineatus)* p. 135

Cregoi's blind legless skink *(Typhlosaurus cregoi cregoi)* p. 137

Striped blind legless skink *(Typhlosaurus lineatus subtaeniatus)* p. 137

Striped blind legless skink *(Typhlosaurus lineatus lineatus)* p. 137

Golden blind legless skink *(Typhlosaurus aurantiacus fitzsimonsi)* p. 136

PLATE 46

Mozambique dwarf burrowing skink *(Scelotes mossambicus)* p. 141

Gronovi's dwarf burrowing skink *(Scelotes gronovii)* p. 142

Limpopo dwarf burrowing skink *(S.l. limpopoensis)* p. 144

Zululand dwarf burrowing skink & new-born babies *(S. arenicolus)* p. 140

Algoa dwarf burrowing skink *(Scelotes anguineus)* p. 140

Smith's dwarf burrowing skink *(Scelotes inornatus)* p. 143

PLATE 47

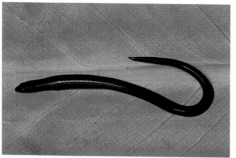

Mozambique dwarf burrowing skink *(Scelotes mossambicus)* p. 141

Lowveld dwarf burrowing skink *(Scelotes bidigittatus)* p. 140

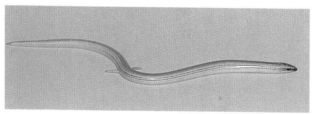

Silvery dwarf burrowing skink *(Scelotes bipes)* p. 141

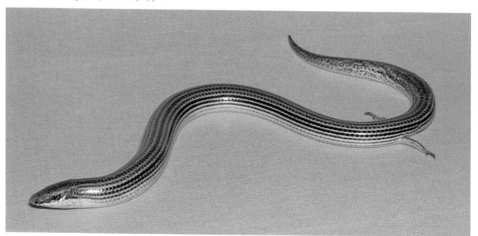

Striped dwarf burrowing skink *(Scelotes sexlineatus)* p. 141

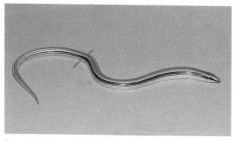

Kasner's dwarf burrowing skink *(Scelotes kasneri)* p. 144

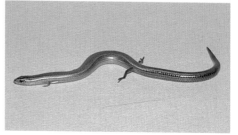

Cape dwarf burrowing skink *(Scelotes caffer)* p. 141

PLATE 48

Montane dwarf burrowing skink *(Scelotes mirus)* p. 145

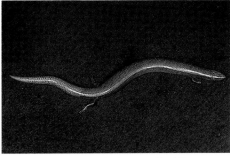

Western dwarf burrowing skink *(Scelotes capensis)* p. 142

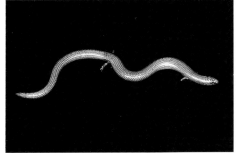

Albert's burrowing skink *(Sepsina alberti)* p. 145

Mozambique writhing skink *(Lygosoma afrum)* p. 150

Sundevall's writhing skink *(Lygosoma sundevallii sundevallii)* p. 150

PLATE 49

Cape grass lizard *(Chamaesaura anguina anguina)* p. 185

Large-scaled grass lizard *(Chamaesaura macrolepis macrolepis)* p. 185

Transvaal grass lizard *(Chamaesaura aenea)* p. 185

FitzSimons' long-tailed seps *(Tetradactylus africanus fitzsimonsi)* p. 182

African long-tailed seps *(Tetradactylus africanus africanus)* p. 182

PLATE 50

Common long-tailed seps (Tetradactylus tetradactylus) p. 183

Breyer's long-tailed seps (Tetradactylus breyeri) p. 182

Arnold's skink (Proscelotes arnoldi) p. 139

Short-legged seps (Tetradactylus seps) p. 183

Wahlberg's snake-eyed skink (Panaspis wahlbergii) p. 159

Bouton's skink (Cryptoblepharus boutonii) p. 149

PLATE 51

Red-sided skink, male *(Mabuya homalocephala)* p. 153

Eastern coastal skink *(Mabuya depressa)* p. 153

Cape skink *(Mabuya capensis)* p. 152

Hoesch's skink *(Mabuya hoeschi)* p. 153

Western three-striped skink *(Mabuya occidentalis)* p. 156

PLATE 52

Boulenger's skink *(Mabuya boulengeri)* p. 152

Variable skink *(Mabuya varia)* p. 157

Variegated skink *(Mabuya variegata variegata)* p. 158

Variegated skink *(Mabuya variegata punctulata)* p. 158

Wedge-snouted skink *(Mabuya acutilabris)* p. 151

PLATE 53

Striped skink, KwaZulu-Natal *(Mabuya striata striata)* p. 156

Kalahari tree skink *(Mabuya spilogaster)* p. 156

Striped skink, Johannesburg *(Mabuya striata punctatissima)* p. 156

Striped skink, NE Botswana *(Mabuya striata wahlbergii)* p. 156

Western rock skink, male *(Mabuya sulcata sulcata)* p. 157

Western rock skink, male and female in striped phase *(Mabuya sulcata sulcata)* p. 157

PLATE 54

Ovambo tree skink *(Mabuya binotata)* p. 151

Five-lined or Rainbow skink, male *(Mabuya quinquetaeniata margaritifer)* p. 154

Five-lined or Rainbow skink, female *(Mabuya quinquetaeniata margaritifer)* p. 154

Angolan blue-tailed skink *(Mabuya laevis)* p. 155

Angolan blue-tailed skink *(Mabuya laevis)* p. 155

PLATE 55

Shovel-snouted lizard *(Meroles anchietae)* p. 164

Wedge-snouted desert lizard *(Meroles cuneirostris)* p. 165

Smith's desert lizard *(Meroles ctenodactylus)* p. 165

Reticulated desert lizard, plain phase *(Meroles reticulatus)* p. 167

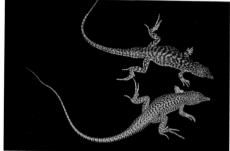

Reticulated desert lizard, reticulated phase *(Meroles reticulatus)* p. 167

Small-scaled desert lizard *(Meroles micropholidotus)* p. 166

PLATE 56

Spotted desert lizard *(Meroles suborbitalis)* p. 167

Bushveld lizard, adult *(Heliobolus lugubris)* p. 161

Knox's desert lizard *(Meroles knoxii)* p. 166

Bushveld lizard, hatchling *(Heliobolus lugubris)* p. 161

Namaqua sand lizard, Karoo *(Pedioplanis namaquensis)* p. 172

Namaqua sand lizard, Namib Desert *(Pedioplanis namaquensis)* p. 172

PLATE 57

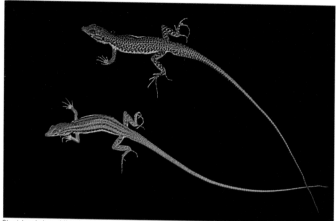

Short-headed sand lizard, male and female in colour phases *(Pedioplanis breviceps)* p. 170

Short-headed sand lizard, male *(Pedioplanis breviceps)* p. 170

Husab sand lizard *(Pedioplanis husabensis)* p. 174

Western sand lizard *(Pedioplanis undata)* p. 173

Waterberg sand lizard *(Pedioplanis rubens)* p. 173

Plain sand lizard *(Pedioplanis inornata)* p. 174

PLATE 58

Cape sand lizard *(Pedioplanis laticeps)* p. 171

Spotted sand lizard *(Pedioplanis lineoocellata pulchella)* p. 172

Spotted sand lizard *(Pedioplanis lineoocellata pulchella)* p. 172

Burchell's sand lizard, female *(Pedioplanis burchelli)* p. 171

Burchell's sand lizard, hatchling *(Pedioplanis burchelli)* p. 171

Burchell's sand lizard, male *(Pedioplanis burchelli)* p. 171

PLATE 59

Spotted sandveld lizard *(Nucras intertexta)* p. 168

Holub's sandveld lizard *(Nucras holubi)* p. 169

Western sandveld lizard *(Nucras taeniolata)* p. 169

Karoo sandveld lizard *(Nucras livida)* p. 170

Western sandveld lizard *(Nucras tessellata)* p.170

PLATE 60

Blue-tailed sandveld lizard *(Nucras caesicaudata)* p. 168

Delalande's sandveld lizard *(Nucras lalandii)* p. 168

Common rough-scaled lizard *(Ichnotropis squamulosa)* p. 163

Cape rough-scaled lizard *(Ichnotropis capensis)* p. 162

Blue-tailed tree lizard *(Holaspis guentheri laevis)* p. 161

PLATE 61

Common mountain lizard *(Tropidosaura montana montana)* p. 176

Cape mountain lizard, male *(Tropidosaura gularis)* p. 175

Cape mountain lizard, female *(Tropidosaura gularis)* p. 175

Cottrell's mountain lizard *(Tropidosaura cottrelli)* p. 175

Southern rock lizard *(Australolacerta australis)* p. 163

Soutpansberg rock lizard *(Australolacerta rupicola)* p. 164

PLATE 62

Nile monitor *(Varanus niloticus)* p. 210

Nile monitor, hatchling *(Varanus niloticus)* p. 210

Nile monitor, adults mating *(Varanus niloticus)* p. 210

Rock monitor *(Varanus albigularis albigularis)* p. 209

Rock monitor, hatchling *(Varanus albigularis albigularis)* p. 209

PLATE 63

Rough-scaled plated lizard *(Gerrhosaurus major major)* p. 179

Giant plated lizard *(Gerrhosaurus validus validus)* p. 181

Desert plated lizard *(Angolosaurus skoogi)* p. 177

Namaqua plated lizard *(Gerrhosaurus typicus)* p. 180

Kalahari plated lizard *(Gerrhosaurus multilineatus auritus)* p. 179

PLATE 64

Black-lined plated lizard *(Gerrhosaurus nigrolineatus)* p. 180

Yellow-throated plated lizard *(Gerrhosaurus flavigularis)* p. 178

Short-legged seps *(Tetradactylus seps)* p. 183

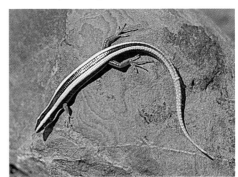

Dwarf plated lizard *(Cordylosaurus subtessellatus)* p. 178

Giant girdled lizard or Sungazer *(Cordylus giganteus)* p. 189

PLATE 65

Large-scaled girdled lizard *(Cordylus macropholis)* p. 190

Tropical girdled lizard *(Cordylus tropidosternum tropidosternum)* p. 194

Tropical girdled lizard *(Cordylus tropidosternum jonesi)* p. 194

Tasman's girdled lizard *(Cordylus tasmani)* p. 194

Cape girdled lizard, coastal form *(Cordylus cordylus)* p. 187

Cape girdled lizard, inland form *(Cordylus cordylus)* p. 187

PLATE 66

Black girdled lizard *(Cordylus niger)* p. 188

Transvaal girdled lizard *(Cordylus vittifer)* p. 195

Zimbabwe girdled lizard *(Cordylus rhodesianus)* p. 193

Herero girdled lizard *(Cordylus pustulatus)* p. 193

Dwarf Karoo girdled lizard *(Cordylus aridus)* p. 191

McLachlan's girdled lizard *(Cordylus mclachlani)* p. 190

PLATE 67

Peers' girdled lizard *(Cordylus peersi)* p. 192

Lawrence's girdled lizard *(Cordylus lawrenci)* p. 189

Namaqua girdled lizard *(Cordylus namaquensis)* p. 192

Armadillo girdled lizard *(Cordylus cataphractus)* p. 186

Armadillo girdled lizard, defence *(Cordylus cataphractus)* p. 186

PLATE 68

Jordan's girdled lizard, juvenile *(Cordylus jordani)* p. 193

Karoo girdled lizard, Central Karoo *(Cordylus polyzonus)* p. 192

Karoo girdled lizard, NW Cape *(Cordylus polyzonus)* p. 192

Karoo girdled lizard, NE Karoo *(Cordylus polyzonus)* p. 192

Karoo girdled lizard, S. Namibia *(Cordylus polyzonus)* p. 192

PLATE 69

Van Dam's girdled lizard *(Cordylus vandami)* p. 197

Warren's girdled lizard *(Cordylus warreni warreni)* p. 195

Warren's girdled lizard *(Cordylus warreni barbertonensis)* p. 195

Van Dam's girdled lizard *(Cordylus vandami)* p. 197

Warren's girdled lizard *(Cordylus warreni depressus)* p. 195

PLATE 70

Regal girdled lizard *(Cordylus regius)* p. 196

Blue-spotted girdled lizard *(Cordylus coeruleopunctatus)* p. 187

Graceful crag lizard *(Pseudocordylus capensis)* p. 205

Spiny crag lizard *(Pseudocordylus spinosus)* p. 208

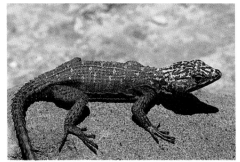

Graceful crag lizard *(Pseudocordylus capensis)* p. 205

PLATE 71

Cape crag lizard *(P.m. microlepidotus)* see C at right, p. 208

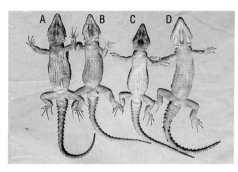

Belly colours of Cape crag lizard subsp. *(P. microlepidotus)* p. 208

Cape crag lizard *(P.m. namaquensis)* see D top right, p. 208

Cape crag lizard *(P.m. fasciatus)* see B top right, p. 208

Cape crag lizard, Transkei, see A top right, p. 208

PLATE 72

Drakensberg crag lizard *(Pseudocordylus melanotus melanotus)* p. 206

Drakensberg crag lizard, male *(P.m. subviridis)* p. 206

Drakensberg crag lizard, female *(P.m. subviridis)* p. 206

Drakensberg crag lizard, male *(Pseudocordylus melanotus subviridis)* p. 206

Northern crag lizard *(Pseudocordylus transvaalensis)* p. 207

PLATE 73

Waterberg flat lizard *(Platysaurus minor)* p. 200

Cape flat lizard *(Platysaurus capensis)* p. 198

Sekukhune flat lizard *(Platysaurus orientalis fitzsimonsi)* p. 199

Dwarf flat lizard *(Platysaurus guttatus)* p. 200

Soutpansberg flat lizard *(Platysaurus relictus)* p. 204

PLATE 74

Common flat lizard *(Platysaurus intermedius intermedius)* p. 201

Common flat lizard *(Platysaurus intermedius rhodesianus)* p. 201

Wilhelm's flat lizard *(Platysaurus intermedius wilhelmi)* p. 201

Natal flat lizard *(Platysaurus intermedius natalensis)* p. 201

Natal flat lizard, showing belly *(P.i. natalensis)* p. 201

PLATE 75

Southern tree agama *(Acanthocerus atricollis)* p. 218

Southern rock agama, breeding male *(Agama atra atra)* p. 214

Southern rock agama, male *(Agama atra atra)* p. 214

Southern rock agama, female *(Agama atra atra)* p. 214

Southern rock agama with juvenile eagle *(Agama atra atra)* p. 214

Knobel's rock agama *(Agama atra knobeli)* p. 214

PLATE 76

Namibian rock agama, male *(Agama planiceps planiceps)* p. 217

Namibian rock agama, female *(Agama planiceps planiceps)* p. 217

Kirk's rock agama *(Agama kirkii)* p. 217

Southern spiny agama *(Agama hispida)* p. 216

Southern spiny agama, female *(Agama hispida)* p. 216

PLATE **77**

Makgadikgadi spiny agama *(Agama makarikarica)* p. 216

Etosha agama *(Agama etoshae)* p. 215

Ground agama *(Agama aculeata aculeata)* p. 212

Peter's ground agama *(Agama armata)* p. 213

Ground agama *(Agama aculeata distanti)* p. 212

Anchieta's agama *(Agama anchietae)* p. 214

PLATE 78

Giant ground gecko *(Chondrodactylus angulifer angulifer)* p. 237

Koch's barking gecko *(Ptenopus kochi)* p. 266

Carp's barking gecko *(Ptenopus carpi)* p. 265

Common barking gecko *(Ptenopus garrulus maculatus)* p. 265

Web-footed gecko *(Palmatogecko rangei)* p. 263

Web-footed gecko *(Palmatogecko rangei)* p. 263

PLATE 79

Kaoko web-footed gecko *(Palmatogecko vanzyli)* p. 264

Kalahari ground gecko *(Colopus wahlbergii wahlbergii)* p. 238

Koch's thick-toed gecko *(Pachydactylus kochii)* p. 254

Marico thick-toed gecko *(P.m. mariquensis)* p. 256

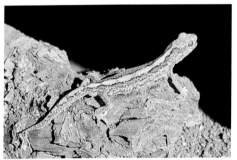

Marico thick-toed gecko, striped phase *(P.m. mariquensis)* p. 256

Marico thick-toed gecko *(P.m. latirostris)* p. 256

PLATE 80

Speckled thick-toed gecko, speckled phase *(P. punctatus)* p. 259     Speckled thick-toed gecko, grey phase *(P. punctatus)* p. 259

Ocellated thick-toed gecko, spotted phase, SW Cape *(Pachydactylus geitje)* p. 254

Spotted thick-toed gecko *(Pachydactylus maculatus)* p. 255

Ocellated thick-toed gecko, mottled phase, Beaufort West *(P. geitje)* p. 254     Golden spotted thick-toed gecko *(Pachydactylus oculatus)* p. 256

PLATE 81

Austen's thick-toed gecko *(Pachydactylus austeni)* p. 250

Western Cape thick-toed gecko *(Pachydactylus labialis)* p. 253

Tiger thick-toed gecko, hatchling *(Pachydactylus tigrinus)* p. 261

Tiger thick-toed gecko, adult *(Pachydactylus tigrinus)* p. 261

Transvaal thick-toed gecko *(Pachydactylus affinis)* p. 250

PLATE 82

Cape thick-toed gecko *(Pachydactylus capensis)* p. 252

Van Son's thick-toed gecko *(Pachydactylus vansoni)* p. 262

O'Shaughnessy's thick-toed gecko *(P.o. oshaughnessyi)* p. 252

Rough thick-toed gecko *(Pachydactylus r. formosus)* p. 259

Rough thick-toed gecko *(Pachydactylus r. rugosus)* p. 259

PLATE 83

Bibron's thick-toed gecko *(Pachydactylus bibronii)* p. 251

Turner's thick-toed gecko, sloughing *(Pachydactylus turneri)* p. 254

Bibron's thick-toed gecko, dark phase
*(Pachydactylus bibronii)* p. 251

Thin-skinned thick-toed gecko showing skin torn in defence, Central Karoo *(P. kladeroderma)* p. 257

FitzSimons' thick-toed gecko *(Pachydactylus fitzsimonsi)* p. 255

Thick-toed gecko, green phase, Little Namaqualand *(P. namaquensis)*

PLATE 84

Kaokoveld thick-toed gecko *(Pachydactylus oreophilus)* p. 258

Large-scaled thick-toed gecko *(Pachydactylus scutatus)* p. 260

Velvety thick-toed gecko, hatchling *(Pachydactylus bicolor)* p. 251

Velvety thick-toed gecko, juvenile *(Pachydactylus bicolor)* p. 251

Velvety thick-toed gecko, adult *(Pachydactylus bicolor)* p. 251

PLATE 85

Western spotted thick-toed gecko *(Pachydactylus serval purcelli)* p. 260

Western spotted thick-toed gecko *(Pachydactylus s. serval)* p. 260

Banded thick-toed gecko *(Pachydactylus fasciatus)* p. 253

Weber's thick-toed gecko, Namaqualand *(Pachydactylus weberi)* p. 263

Banded thick-toed gecko, juvenile *(Pachydactylus fasciatus)* p. 253

Weber's thick-toed gecko, Central Namibia *(Pachydactylus weberi)* p. 263

PLATE 86

Braack's dwarf leaf-toed gecko *(Goggia braacki)* p. 240

Striped dwarf leaf-toed gecko *(Goggia lineata)* p. 241

Marbled leaf-toed gecko *(Afrogecko porphyreus)* p. 237

Marbled leaf-toed gecko, striped phase *(Afrogecko porphyreus)* p. 237

Small-scaled leaf-toed gecko *(Goggia microlepidota)* p. 242

PLATE 87

Karoo flat gecko *(Afroedura karroica)* p. 233

Amatola flat gecko *(Afroedura amatolica)* p. 232

Transvaal flat gecko *(Afroedura transvaalica)* p. 236

African flat gecko *(Afroedura a. africana)* p. 231

Hawequa flat gecko *(Afroedura hawequensis)* p. 232

PLATE 88

Pondo flat gecko *(Afroedura pondolia)* p. 234

Giant Swazi flat gecko *(Afroedura major)* p. 234

Lowveld flat gecko *(Afroedura langi)* p. 235

Moreau's tropical house gecko *(Hemidactylus mabouia)* p. 243

Tasman's tropical house gecko *(Hemidactylus tasmani)* p. 243

Flat-headed tropical house gecko *(Hemidactylus platycephalus)* p. 244

PLATE 89

Muller's velvet gecko *(Homopholis mulleri)* p. 245

Wahlberg's velvet gecko, spotted phase, male *(Homopholis wahlbergii)* p. 244

Bernard's dwarf gecko *(Lygodactylus bernardi)* p. 246

Namaqua day gecko *(Phelsuma ocellata)* p. 264

Festive gecko *(Narudasia festiva)* p. 249

Wahlberg's velvet gecko, female *(Homopholis wahlbergii)* p. 244

PLATE 90

Cape dwarf gecko *(Lygodactylus capensis capensis)* p. 246

Bradfield's dwarf gecko *(Lygodactylus bradfieldi)* p. 246

Spotted dwarf gecko *(Lygodactylus o. ocellatus)* p. 248

Chobe dwarf gecko *(Lygodactylus chobiensis)* p. 247

Methuen's dwarf gecko *(Lygodactylus methueni)* p. 247

Stevenson's dwarf gecko *(Lygodactylus stevensoni)* p. 249

PLATE 91

Common Namib day gecko *(Rhoptropus afer)* p. 267

Bradfield's Namib day gecko *(Rhoptropus b. bradfieldi)* p. 268

Bradfield's Namib day gecko *(Rhoptropus bradfieldi diporus)* p. 268

Kaokoveld Namib day gecko *(Rhoptropus biporosus)* p. 267

Boulton's Namib day gecko *(Rhoptropus boultoni)* p. 268

Barnard's Namib day gecko *(Rhoptropus barnardi)* p. 267

PLATE 92

Natal Midlands dwarf chameleon *(Bradypodion thamnobates)* p. 224

Cape dwarf chameleon *(Bradypodion pumilum)* p. 223

Drakensberg dwarf chameleon *(Bradypodion dracomontanum)* p. 222

Southern dwarf chameleon *(Bradypodion ventrale)* p. 225

Namaqua dwarf chameleon *(Bradypodion occidentale)* p. 226

PLATE 93

Karoo dwarf chameleon *(Bradypodion karrooicum)* p. 226

Robertson dwarf chameleon *(Bradypodion gutturale)* p. 226

Transkei dwarf chameleon *(Bradypodion caffrum)* p. 221

Knysna dwarf chameleon, threat display *(B. damaranum)* p. 221

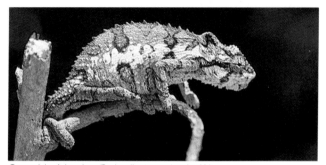

Transvaal dwarf chameleon *(Bradypodion transvaalense)* p. 224

PLATE 94

Black-headed dwarf chameleon *(Bradypodion melanocephalum)* p. 222

Setaro's dwarf chameleon *(Bradypodion setaroi)* p. 223

Smith's dwarf chameleon *(Bradypodion taeniabronchum)* p. 224

Zululand dwarf chameleon *(Bradypodion nemorale)* p. 223

Smith's dwarf chameleon, grey phase, female *(B. taeniabronchum)* p. 224

Marshall's African leaf chameleon, adult male (left), female (right) *(Rhampholeon marshalli)* p. 229

PLATE 95

Flap-neck chameleon *(Chamaeleo dilepis)* p. 227

Flap-neck chameleon, juvenile *(Chamaeleo dilepis)* p. 227

Namaqua chameleon *(Chamaeleo namaquensis)* p. 228

Nile crocodile *(Crocodylus niloticus)* p. 269

Nile crocodile in water *(Crocodylus niloticus)* p. 269

PLATE 96

Slender blind snake *(Typhlops obtusus)* p. 54

Black thread snake *(Leptotyphlops nigricans)* p. 56

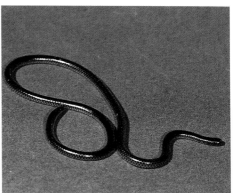

Eastern thread snake *(Leptotyphlops conjunctus incognitus)* p. 56

Damara thread snake *(Leptotyphlops labialis)* p. 58

Forest thread snake *(Leptotyphlops sylvicolus)* p. 57

PLATE 97

Stripe-bellied sand snake *(Psammophis subtaeniatus orientalis)* p. 91

Visser's shovel-snout *(Prosymna visseri)* p. 85

Pygmy wolf snake *(Lycophidion pygmaeum)* p. 77

Eastern wolf snake
*(Lycophidion semiannule)* p. 77

Cream-spotted mountain snake *(Montaspis gilvomaculata)* p. 83

PLATE 98

Cunene racer *(Coluber* sp.*)* p. 99

Spotted bush snake, Namaqualand *(Philothamnus semivariegatus)* p. 93

 Southern adder *(Bitis armata)* p. 118

 Albany adder *(Bitis albanica)* p. 118

PLATE 99

Van Dam's round-headed worm lizard *(Zygaspis vandami arenicola)* p. 123    Cape spade-snouted worm lizard (*Monopeltis capensis*) p. 125

Short-headed legless skink *(Acontias breviceps)* p. 132

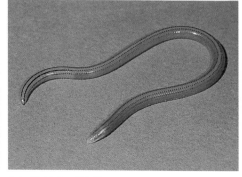

Golden blind legless skink *(Typhlosaurus aurantiacus aurantiacus)* p. 136    Gariep blind legless skink *(Typhlosaurus gariepensis)* p. 137

PLATE 100

Speckled burrowing skink *(Typhlacontias punctatissimus)* p. 146

Johnson's burrowing skink *(Typhlacontias johnsonii)* p. 146

Bourquin's dwarf burrowing skink *(Scelotes bourquini)* p. 143

Angola burrowing skink *(Sepsina angolensis)* p. 146

PLATE 101

Speckled-lipped skink *(Mabuya maculilabris maculilabris)* p. 155

Eastern coastal skink *(Mabuya depressa)* p. 153

Grass skink *(Mabuya megalura)* p. 155

Chimba skink *(Mabuya chimbana)* p. 152

PLATE 102

Ornate sandveld lizard *(Nucras ornata)* p. 169

Kaokoveld sand lizard *(Pedioplanis gaerdesi)* p. 174

Essex's mountain lizard *(Tropidosaura essexi)* p. 175

Spotted-neck snake-eyed skink *(Panaspis sp.)* p. 159

Spotted sand lizard *(Pedioplanis lineoocellata lineoocellata)* p. 172

PLATE 103

Oelofsen's girdled lizard *(Cordylus oelofseni)* p. 188

Campbell's girdled lizard *(Cordylus campbelli)* p. 186

Rooiberg girdled lizard *(Cordylus imkeae)* p. 191

Dwarf girdled lizard *(Cordylus minor)* p. 190

Cloete's girdled lizard *(Cordylus cloetei)* p. 191

Dwarf crag lizard *(Pseudocordylus nebulosus)* p. 206

Machodoe's girdled lizard *(Cordylus machadoi)* p. 195

# PLATE 104

Gorongosa girdled lizard, male (lower), female (upper) *(C. mossambicus)*

Gorongosa girdled lizard, male *(Cordylus mossambicus)* p. 196

Waterberg girdled lizard *(Cordylus breyeri)* p. 197

Waterberg flat lizard *(Platysaurus minor)* p. 200

Broadley's flat lizard *(Platysaurus broadleyi)* p. 199

Emperor flat lizard, male (lower), female (upper) *(P. imperator)* p. 200

Emperor flat lizard *(Platysaurus imperator)* p. 200

PLATE 105

Common flat lizard *(Platysaurus intermedius inopinus)* p. 201

Orange-throated flat lizard *(Platysaurus monotropis)* p. 202

Pungwe flat lizard, male (lower) & female (upper)
*(Platysaurus pungweensis blakei)* p. 203

Ocellated flat lizard, male (upper) *(Platysaurus ocellatus)* p. 203

Lebombo flat lizard *(Platysaurus lebomboensis)* p. 203

Striped flat lizard, male (right), female (left) *(Platysaurus torquatus)* p. 204

PLATE 106

Mozambique agama *(Agama mossambica)* p. 217

Hall's flat gecko *(Afroedura halli)* p. 233

Mountain flat gecko *(Afroedura nivaria)* p. 233

Marley's flat gecko with eggs *(Afroedura marleyi)* p. 234

Woodbush flat gecko *(Afroedura multiporis multiporis)* p. 235

Haacke's flat gecko *(Afroedura multiporis haackei)* p. 235

PLATE 107

Péringuey's coastal leaf-toed gecko *(Cryptactites peringueyi)* p. 239

Swartberg African leaf-toed gecko *(Afrogecko swartbergensis)* p. 236

Richtersveld dwarf leaf-toed gecko *(G. gemmula)*

Essex's dwarf leaf-toed gecko *(Goggia essexi)* p. 240

Hewitt's dwarf leaf-toed gecko *(Goggia hewitti)* p. 241

Cedarberg dwarf leaf-toed gecko *(Goggia hexapora)* p. 241

PLATE 108

Black-spotted dwarf gecko *(Lygodactylus nigropunctatus nigropunctatus)* p. 248

Granite dwarf gecko *(Lygodactylus graniticolus)* p. 247

Lawrence's dwarf gecko *(Lygodactylus lawrencei)* p. 247

Black-spotted dwarf gecko *(L.n. incognitus)* p. 248

Black-spotted dwarf gecko *(L.n. montiscaeruli)* p. 248

PLATE 109

Long-headed tropical house gecko *(H. longicephalus)* p. 243

Tasman's tropical house gecko *(H. tasmani)* p. 243

Spotted dwarf gecko *(Lygodactylus ocellatus soutpansbergensis)* p. 248

Waterberg dwarf gecko *(Lygodactylus waterbergensis)* p. 249

Namaqua thick-toed gecko *(Pachydactylus namaquensis)* p. 257

Haacke's thick-toed gecko *(Pachydactylus haackei)* p. 258

PLATE 110

Brandberg thick-toed gecko *(Pachydactylus gaiasensis)* p. 258

Schertz's thick-toed gecko *(Pachydactylus scherzi)* p. 259

Angolan banded thick-toed gecko, hatchling *(P. caraculicus)* p. 253

Angolan banded thick-toed gecko, subadult *(Pachydactylus caraculicus)* p. 253

Angolan banded thick-toed gecko, adult *(P. caraculicus)* p. 253

Barnard's thick-toed gecko *(Pachydactylus rugosus barnardi)* p. 259

PLATE 111

San Steyn's thick-toed gecko *(Pachydactylus sansteyni)* p. 261

Tsodilo thick-toed gecko *(Pachydactylus tsodiloensis)* p. 262

Western spotted thick-toed gecko, hatchling *(Pachydactylus serval)* p. 260

Lobatse hinged tortoise *(Kinixys lobatsiana)* p. 35

Namaqua dwarf leaf-toed gecko *(Goggia rupicola)* p. 242

PLATE 112

# GLOSSARY

**Abdominal:** Pertaining to the region of the abdomen; a scute on the plastron of a chelonian shell (see illustration, page 26).
**Adaptation:** A morphological, physiological or behavioural feature, evolved over time that particularly suits an organism (or group of related organisms) to its way of life.
**Anal:** Pertaining to the region of the anus; a scute on the plastron of a chelonian shell (see illustration, page 26); a scale in front of the cloacal opening in squamates (see illustration, page 51).
**Anapsid:** Descriptive of a skull in which there are no openings in the temporal region.
**Annulus (pl. annuli):** A ring on the scute of a chelonian shell, representing a period of growth; a body segment of an amphisbaenian (worm lizard).
**Anterior:** The front.
**Apical pit:** A sense organ near the tip of the body scales of some squamates.
**Aposematic:** Warning; usually bright body coloration, advertising that a species is dangerous or poisonous.
**Aquatic:** Living in water.
**Arboreal:** Living in or among trees.
**Arribada:** A simultaneous, mass emergence of sea turtles on to a small beach to lay their eggs.
**Areola (pl. areolae):** The central region of a chelonian scute, which may be raised or hollow.
**Autotomy:** The voluntary shedding of a part of the body. (Caudal autotomy: the voluntary shedding of the tail.)
**Axillary:** Pertaining to the region of the armpit; a scute on the plastron of a chelonian shell (see illustrations, pages 26 and 44).

**Bicarinate:** See Carinate.
**Bicuspid:** See Cuspid.
**Biped:** An animal that walks on two feet.
**Bridge:** The part of a chelonian shell where the carapace joins the plastron.
**Buttock tubercle:** The enlarged, conical scale found on the rear upper part of the hind leg of some tortoises.

**Carapace:** Upper section of a chelonian shell.
**Carinate:** Having ridges, as in some lizard scales. (Bicarinate: having two ridges;

tricarinate: having three ridges; quinque-carinate: having five ridges.)
**Casque:** The helmet-like structure found on the back of the head of some chameleons.
**Caudal:** Pertaining to the tail.
**Chelonian:** A shield reptile (tortoises, turtles and terrapins).
**Chin shields:** The enlarged scales found beneath the head of some lizards and snakes.
**Circumtropical:** Encircling the earth, in the area between 23°30′N and 23°30′S.
**Class:** The taxonomic category ranking below 'phylum' and above 'order'.
**Cloaca:** The common chamber into which the urinary, digestive and reproductive systems discharge their contents, and which opens to the exterior.
**Clutch:** Collective noun for all the eggs laid by a single female at one time.
**Commensal species:** Species living together, all usually benefiting from the association.
**Conical:** Descriptive of a raised scale that narrows to a pointed centre.
**Coronoid:** A bone in the lower jaw of some reptiles.
**Costal:** A scute on the carapace of a chelonian shell (see illustrations, pages 26 and 37).
**Cranial:** Pertaining to the skull. (Cranial crests are found on top of the head.)
**Crepuscular:** Active at dawn and dusk.
**Cryptic:** Hidden or camouflaged.
**Cuspid:** Having tooth-like projections. (Biscuspid: having two cusps; tricuspid: having three cusps.)
**Cycloid:** Descriptive of a scale with an evenly curved, free border, like the scales of many fish.

**Diverticulum (pl. diverticula):** An elongate sac with only one opening. (Diverticulate lungs have numerous blind branches rather than a single, large sac.)
**Distal:** Furthest from the body.
**Dorsal:** Pertaining to the upper surface of the body.
**Dorsolateral:** The upper surface of the body, bordering the backbone.

**Family:** The taxonomic category ranking below 'order' and above 'genus'.
**Fauna:** The animal life of a locality or region.

**Femoral:** Pertaining to the upper part of the hind limb (the thigh).

**Frontal:** A scale on the head of a reptile (see illustrations, pages 55, 69 and 130).

**Frontonasal:** A scale on the head of a reptile (see illustration, page 130).

**Frontoparietal:** A scale on the head of a reptile (see illustration, page 130).

**Genus (pl. genera):** The taxonomic category ranking below 'family' and above 'species'.

**Glandular:** Descriptive of the modified secretory scale found on the thigh or in front of the cloaca of some lizards.

**Girdles:** The supporting structure of the limbs, for example the hips and shoulders.

**Granular:** Descriptive of small, usually non-overlapping, scales.

**Gular:** Pertaining to the throat region; a plate on the plastron of a chelonian shell (see illustration, page 26).

**Hemipenis (pl. hemipenes; adj. hemipenial):** One of the grooved copulatory structures present in male squamate reptiles.

**Herbivorous:** Eating plant matter.

**Hinge:** A flexible joint in the shell of some chelonians that allows the front or rear of the shell to close.

**Imbricate:** Descriptive of an overlapping scale.

**Incubation:** Keeping eggs warm to ensure continuous development.

**Inframarginal:** A scute on the plastron of a sea turtle shell (see illustration, page 37).

**Intergular:** A scute on the plastron of a terrapin shell (see illustration, page 44).

**Internasal:** A scale on the head of a reptile (see illustration, page 69).

**Interparietal:** A scale on the head of a reptile (see illustrations, pages 55 and 130).

**Interspaces:** The spaces between blotches.

**Interstitial skin:** The (usually thin) skin lying between the scales.

**Introduced:** A species brought from areas where it occurs naturally to areas where it has not previously occurred; alien or 'exotic' (also known as foreign) species are always introduced.

**Invertebrate:** An animal that lacks a backbone.

**Juxtaposed:** Description of scales that touch but do not overlap.

**Keel:** A prominent ridge, occurring on the back of some turtles and on the dorsal scales of some snakes.

**Keratin (adj. keratinized):** A hard, tough, non-soluble skin protein; horns, nails and claws are made of keratin.

**Labial:** Pertaining to the lip region; a scale on the head of a reptile (see illustrations, pages 52, 55, 69 and 130).

**Lamella (pl. lamellae):** Any thin, plate-like or scale-like structure.

**Lateral:** Pertaining to the sides of the body.

**LD$_{50}$:** The lethal dose (LD) that will kill half (50%) of the animals into which it is injected; used as an indication of venom toxicity.

**Loreal:** Pertaining to the region on the side of the head, between the nostril and the eye; a scale on the head of a reptile (see illustrations, pages 69 and 130).

**Marine:** Living in the sea.

**Mandibular:** A bone in the lower jaw.

**Marginal:** A plate on the edge of the carapace of a chelonian shell (see illustrations, pages 26 and 37).

**Maxillary:** A bone in the upper jaw.

**Medial:** Pertaining to the region near the middle of the body.

**Melanistic:** Darker or blacker than 'normal'.

**Mental:** A scale on the head of a reptile (see illustration, page 130).

**Mimic:** A species that resembles a different species, usually a distasteful or inedible one.

**Mucronate:** Descriptive of body scales that are strongly overlapping and drawn into a spine.

**Nasal:** Pertaining to the region of the nose; a scale on the head of a reptile (see illustrations, pages 52, 55 and 130).

**Nasorostral:** A scale, sometimes resulting from the fusion of the nasal and the rostral, on the head of a reptile.

**Nocturnal:** Active at night.

**Nuchal:** A scute at the front of the carapace of a chelonian shell (see illustration, page 26).

**Occipital:** Pertaining to the region at the back of the skull; a scale on the head of a reptile (see illustration, page 130).

**Oceanic:** Living in the open seas.

**Ocellus (pl. ocelli):** Eye-like, ring-shaped spot.

**Ocular:** Pertaining to the region of the eye. (The subocular is the scale below the eye on the head of a reptile; see illustration, page 130.)
**Orbit:** The eye socket.
**Order:** The taxonomic category ranking below 'class' and above 'family'.
**Osteoderm:** A very small bone in the skin of some reptiles.
**Osteological:** Pertaining to the bones.
**Oviduct:** The tube which carries eggs from the ovary.
**Oviparous:** Reproduction by eggs which hatch outside the female's body.

**Palatine:** A bone in the roof of the mouth.
**Papilla (pl. papillae):** A small skin projection that may be sensitive to touch.
**Parietal:** Pertaining to the region on the crown of the head; paired bone forming part of the roof and sides of the skull; scale on the head of a reptile (see illustrations, pages 69 and 130).
**Parthenogenetic:** Pertaining to the ability of females to develop fertile eggs without mating with a male.
**Parturition:** The act or process of birth.
**Pectoral:** Pertaining to the region of the body where the forelimbs originate; a scute on the plastron of a chelonian shell (see illustration, page 26).
**Pheromone:** A substance produced and discharged by an organism which induces a response in another individual of the same species.
**Pineal eye:** A primitive, light-sensitive area on the top of the head of some lizards and also extinct reptiles. Although it is called an eye, it is not used for vision, but controls seasonal breeding.
**Plastron (adj. plastral):** The lower surface of the chelonian shell.
**Polymorphism:** The occurrence of more than one type of individual in a species.
**Pore:** A minute opening or passage.
**Posterior:** The rear or back part.
**Pre-:** In front of.
**Prefrontal:** A scale on the head of a reptile (see illustrations, pages 52, 55, 69 and 130).
**Ptosis:** Drooping of the eyelids.

**Race:** A population of a species which is distinguishable from the rest of that species; a subspecies.

**Recurved:** Descriptive of a tooth that bends backwards.
**Reticulate:** Resembling a network.
**Retractile:** A part that may be drawn inwards.
**Riverine:** Living in or near rivers.
**Rupicolous:** Living on and among rocks.
**Rostral:** Pertaining to the rostrum (nose); a scale at the front of the nose of a reptile (see illustrations, pages 52, 55, 69 and 130).

**SA RDB:** South African Red Data Book.
**Scale:** A thin, flattened, plate-like structure that forms part of the surface covering of various vertebrates, especially fishes and reptiles.
**Scansors:** Specialized pads composed of thousands of minute hairs that allow the animal to climb vertical surfaces; found on the toe-tips of many geckos.
**Scat:** Faecal pellet.
**Scute:** Any enlarged scale on the body of a reptile, or also the horny plates of a chelonian shell.
**Sedentary:** Not free-living.
**Septum (pl. septa):** A partition separating two cavities or masses of tissue.
**Sub-:** Beneath.
**Subcontinent:** The African continent south of a line joining the Cunene and Zambezi rivers.
**Sublingual:** Pertaining to the area beneath the tongue.
**Submarginal:** Pertaining to the area near the margin.
**Subspecies:** See Race.
**Sulcus:** A surface groove; a groove in the hemipenis of squamates along which sperm flows.
**Supra-:** Above.
**Supraciliary:** Pertaining to the region above the eyelid; a scale on the head of a lizard (see illustration, page 130).
**Sutures:** The junction of two parts which are immovably connected.
**Sympatric:** Living in the same region.

**Tarsal:** Pertaining to the lower part of the hind limb, above the foot.
**Taxonomy:** The science of classification; the arrangement of animals and plants into groups based on their natural relationships.
**Temporal:** Pertaining to the region to the side of the forehead; a scale on the head of a reptile (see illustrations, pages 69 and 130).

385

**Terrestrial:** Living on the ground.
**Tricuspid:** See Cuspid.
**Tubercle:** A small, rounded protuberance.
**Tympanic:** Pertaining to region of ear; a scale on head of lizard (see illustration, page 130).
**Tympanum:** The ear drum.

**µg/kg:** An abbreviation for the amount of venom which will kill an animal, related to its body mass. Sea snake venom has a toxicity of 130 µg/kg; 0,013g will kill a 100-kg animal ('µg' is the symbol for a microgram, one-millionth of a gram).
**Unicuspid:** Having one cusp. See Cuspid.

**Ventral:** Pertaining to the under surface of the body .

**Vertebral:** Pertaining to the region of the backbone; a scute on the carapace of a chelonian shell (see illustrations, pages 26 and 37).
**Vestigial:** Being smaller and of a more simple structure (a remnant) than in an evolutionary ancestor.
**Viviparous:** Reproduction that involves giving birth to live young which develop in the mother's body.

**Xanthic:** Having only red pigmentation in the skin.

**Zonary:** Descriptive of the concentric zones of pigment usually found on a scute of a chelonian shell.

# SOCIETIES AND THEIR PUBLICATIONS

The **Herpetological Association of Africa** has an international membership and is based in southern Africa. It produces the *African Journal of Herpetology*, for scientific notes and major articles, and *African Herp News*, a newsletter for announcements, short notes on life history, distribution and venoms, husbandry hints and news items. Details of membership can be obtained from the Secretary, Herpetological Association of Africa, P O. Box 20142, Durban North, 4016, Kwazulu-Natal, South Africa.

The **Society for the Study of Amphibians and Reptiles** is an international society based in North America. It produces the *Journal of Herpetology* for scientific publications and the *Herpetological Review* for more general articles, announcements and book reviews. An irregular facsimile series reprints classic works that are out of print. Details of membership can be obtained from the Society for the Study of Amphibians and Reptiles, Department of Zoology, Ohio University, Athens, Ohio 45701, United States of America.

The **Herpetologist's League** is an international society based in North America It produces a journal, *Herpetologica*, for normal scientific publications and *Herpetological Monographs* for longer, detailed studies. Details of membership can be obtained from the Secretary, Herpetologist's League, College of Arts and Sciences, Florida International University, North Miami, FL 33181, United States of America.

# SUGGESTED FURTHER READING

Books marked with an asterisk (*) are out of print but are available in libraries.

*Auerbach, R. (1987). *Reptiles and Amphibians of Botswana*. Mokwepa Consultants (privately printed), Gaborone.
Baard, E.H.W. (1994). *Cape Tortoises: Their Identification and Care*. Cape Nature Conservation, Cape Town.
*Boycott, R. C. and Bourquin, O. (1988). *The South African Tortoise Book: A Guide to Southern African Tortoises, Terrapins and Turtles*. Southern Book Publishers, Johannesburg.
*Branch, W. R. (Ed.) (1988). *South African Red Data Book - Reptiles and Amphibians*. South African Scientific Programmes Report (Report 151), CSIR, Pretoria.
Broadley, D. G. (1990). *FitzSimons' Snakes of Southern Africa*. Delta Books (Pty) Ltd, Johannesburg and Cape Town.
Halliday, T. and Adler, K. (Eds.) (1986). *The Encyclopaedia of Reptiles and Amphibians*. George Allen and Unwin, London.
*Jacobsen, N. (1985). *Ons Reptiele*. CUM-Boeke, Roodepoort.
Patterson, R. and Bannister, A. (1987). *South African Reptile Life*. C. Struik Publishers, Cape Town.
*Pienaar, U. de V., Haacke, W. D., and Jacobsen N. (1983). *The Reptiles of the Kruger National Park*. National Parks Board, Pretoria.
*Pooley, A. (1982). *Discoveries of a Crocodile Man*. William Collins Sons and Co. Ltd, London and Johannesburg.
Spawls, S. and W. R. Branch. (1995). *Dangerous Snakes of Africa*. Southern Book Publishers, Halfway House.

# LOCAL MUSEUMS AND INSTITUTIONS INVOLVED IN HERPETOLOGICAL RESEARCH

The following centres have herpetologists or other staff who can identify specimens and answer questions:

## Museums
J R Ellerman Museum, Department of Zoology, University of Stellenbosch, Stellenbosch, 7600, South Africa.
National Museum, P. O. Box 266, Bloemfontein, 9300, South Africa.
Natural History Museum of Zimbabwe, P. O. Box 240, Bulawayo, Zimbabwe.
Port Elizabeth Museum and Snake Park, P. O. Box 13147, Humewood, 6013, South Africa.
South African Museum, P. O. Box 61, Cape Town, 8000, South Africa.
State Museum, P. O. Box 1203, Windhoek, Namibia.
Transvaal Museum, P. O. Box 413, Pretoria, 0001, South Africa.

## Nature Conservation Departments
Western Cape Conservation, Jonkershoek Nature Conservation Station, Private Bag 5014, Stellenbosch, 7600, South Africa.
Eastern Cape Conservation, Natal Parks Board, P. O. Box 662, Pietermaritzburg, 3200, South Africa.
Department of Agriculture and Nature Conservation, Private Bag 13306, Windhoek, Namibia.
Transvaal Division of Nature Conservation, Private Bag X209, Pretoria, 0001, South Africa.

## Snake and Crocodile Parks
FitzSimons Snake Park, P. O. Box 10457, Marine Parade, Durban, 4056. South Africa.
Kwena Gardens Crocodile Farm, P. O. Box 234, Sun City, Bophuthatswana. Port Elizabeth.
  Museum and Snake Park, P. O. Box 13147, Humewood, 6013, South Africa.
Transvaal Snake Park, P. O. Box 97, Halfway House, 1685, South Africa.

# PHOTOGRAPHIC CREDITS

All photographs in this book are by Bill Branch except for those listed below. Numbers in brackets refer to photographs counted from left to right and top to bottom of each plate.

**J. Akester:** Pl. 16 (3); Pl. 67 (3); Pl. 82 (4); Pl. 83 (3).
**G. Alexander:** Pl. 47 (6).
**A. Bannister:** Pl. 16 (5); Pl. 19 (6); Pl. 21 (6); Pl. 23 (6); Pl. 24 (5); Pl. 74 (1).
**H. Berger-Dell'mour:** Pl. 40 (3); Pl. 41 (2); Pl. 49 (2, 3); 51 (2); 56 (4, 5, 6); Pl. 58 (1, 2, 3, 4, 5); Pl. 61 (3, 4); Pl. 67 (4); 80 (3); 90 (5); 92 (4, 5).
**R. Boycott:** Pl. 2 (1, 4); Pl. 5 (1); 9 (1); 14 (1); Pl. 18 (1); Pl. 35 (4, 6).
**D. Broadley:** Pl. 25 (2).
**M. Burger:** Pl. 108 (4).
**J. Coates-Palgrave:** Pl. 21 (2); Pl. 24 (1); Pl. 33 (5); Pl. 36 (5); Pl. 39 (3); Pl. 41 (4); Pl. 42 (1, 5); Pl. 53 (1); Pl. 61 (5); Pl. 78 (1); Pl. 89 (6); Pl. 95 (6).
**A. de Villiers:** Pl. 6 (5, 6); Pl. 7 (4, 6); Pl. 10 (1); Pl. 48 (3, 4, 5, 6).
**M. Griffin:** Pl. 16 (2); Pl. 20 (6); Pl. 24 (3); Pl. 38 (3); Pl. 43 (1, 4); Pl. 80 (1); Pl. 99 (1).
**W. Haacke:** Pl. 11 (3, 4); Pl. 15 (5); Pl. 16 (4); Pl. 17 (6); Pl. 25 (3); Pl. 29 (1, 2); Pl. 36 (1); Pl. 37 (1, 3); Pl. 41 (3); Pl. 42 (3); Pl. 45 (4, 5); Pl. 46 (2); Pl. 50 (3); Pl. 78 (2); Pl. 86 (3, 5); Pl. 97 (4, 5); Pl. 89 (2); Pl. 100 (5); Pl. 101 (1, 2, 3); Pl. 102 (4); Pl. 103 (3); Pl. 104 (2); Pl. 104 (5); Pl. 104 (7); Pl. 105 (1, 2); Pl. 105 (5, 6, 7); Pl. 106 (2, 3, 4, 6); Pl. 107 (3); Pl. 107 (5); Pl. 109 (1, 2, 3); Pl. 110 (1, 3, 4); Pl. 111 (1, 3, 4, 5); Pl. 112 (1, 2).
**L. Hoffmann:** Pl. 40 (7).
**G.R. Hughes:** Pl. 8 (3); Pl. 9 (2).

**N. Jacobsen:** Pl. 23 (1); Pl. 46 (1); Pl. 62 (6); Pl. 74 (3); Pl. 89 (3); Pl. 103 (4); Pl. 105 (3); Pl. 107 (6); Pl. 109 (4); Pl. 109 (5).
**P. le Fras Mouton:** Pl. 57 (3); Pl. 104 (1).
**Johan Marais:** Pl. 12 (5); Pl. 18 (6); Pl. 20 (4); Pl. 22 (2); Pl. 24 (6); Pl. 37 (5); Pl. 39 (4); Pl. 45 (3); Pl. 49 (4); Pl. 52 (2); Pl. 70 (1); Pl. 74 (4, 5); Pl. 82 (3); Pl. 90 (4); 98 (5).
**C. Mattison:** Pl. 40 (2).
**C. McCartney:** Pl. 60 (3).
**G. McLachlan:** Pl. 85 (1, 2).
**National Museum:** Pl. 107 (2).
**National Parks Board:** Pl. 11 (5); Pl. 23 (7); Pl. 24 (4); Pl. 26 (3); Pl. 34 (5, 6); Pl. 41 (5); Pl. 46 (5); Pl. 48 (2); Pl. 61 (1).
**G. Rasmussen:** Pl. 98 (4).
**C. Schlettwein:** Pl. 52 (4); Pl. 55 (4, 5).
**A. Schoeman:** Pl. 9 (4, 5); Pl. 56 (1); Pl. 64 (3).
**C. Stuart:** Pl. 26 (2); Pl. 42 (4); Pl. 81 (1); Pl. 83 (2).
**S. Spawls:** Pl. 18 (5); Pl. 29 (3); Pl. 33 (4); Pl. 38 (4); Pl. 54 (4); Pl. 57 (4); Pl. 60 (1, 2); Pl. 64 (4); Pl. 78 (4); Pl. 80 (2); Pl. 90 (2); Pl. 91 (4).
**C. Tilbury:** Pl. 11 (1); Pl. 22 (1); Pl. 25 (5); Pl. 28 (2); Pl. 32 (6); Pl. 37 (2); Pl. 38 (2); Pl. 44 (1); Pl. 51 (3); Pl. 53 (4, 5); Pl. 54 (1); Pl. 55 (1); Pl. 61 (2); Pl. 64 (1); Pl. 65 (1); Pl. 75 (3); Pl. 76 (3, 4); Pl. 77 (1, 3); Pl. 78 (3); Pl. 81 (2); Pl. 85 (3, 5); Pl. 86 (2); Pl. 89 (4); Pl. 90 (3, 6); Pl. 92 (6); Pl. 93 (2, 3, 5); Pl. 94 (2, 3); Pl. 95 (1, 2, 4); Pl. 96 (4).

Copyright for these photographs remains with the owners.

# INDEX TO SCIENTIFIC NAMES

Numbers refer to pages on which orders, families, genera and species accounts appear.

393

# INDEX TO COMMON NAMES AND CHECKLIST

Numbers refer to pages on which species accounts appear.

397

**Mamba**
- [ ] Black 110
- [ ] Green 110

**Python**
- [ ] Anchieta's Dwarf 59
- [ ] African Rock 59

**Racer**
- [ ] Cunene 99

**Rinkhals**
- [ ] Rinkhals 109

**Shovel-snout**
- [ ] Angola 84
- [ ] East African 85
- [ ] Mozambique 84
- [ ] South-western 84
- [ ] Sundevall's 84
- [ ] Two-striped 84
- [ ] Visser's 85

**Skaapsteker**
- [ ] Spotted or Rhombic 88
- [ ] Striped 88

**Slug Eater**
- [ ] Common 79
- [ ] Spotted 80
- [ ] Variegated 80

**Snake**
- [ ] Coral 103
- [ ] Cream-spotted Mountain 83
- [ ] Eastern Striped Swamp 82
- [ ] Flower-pot 53
- [ ] Gerard's Black and Yellow Burrowing 67
- [ ] Herald or Red-lipped 97
- [ ] Lined Olympic 87
- [ ] Many-spotted 82
- [ ] Mole 80
- [ ] Mopane 86
- [ ] Spotted Bush 93
- [ ] Swazi Rock 75
- [ ] Semiornate 93
- [ ] Shield-nose 104
- [ ] Twig or Vine 100
- [ ] Western Keeled 82
- [ ] Whip 90
- [ ] White-lipped 66
- [ ] Yellow-bellied Sea 111

**Bark Snake**
- [ ] Eastern 86
- [ ] Viperine 86

**Beaked Snake**
- [ ] Dwarf 87
- [ ] Rufous 86

**Beaked Blind Snake**
- [ ] Schinz's 53

- [ ] Boyle's 53
- [ ] Delalande's 53
- [ ] Schlegel's 54

**Black Snake**
- [ ] Natal 65

**Blind Snake**
- [ ] Bibron's 55
- [ ] Fornasini's 54
- [ ] Slender 54

**File Snake**
- [ ] Angola 79
- [ ] Black 79
- [ ] Cape 78

**Garter Snake**
- [ ] Angolan 105
- [ ] Boulenger's 105
- [ ] Günther's 105
- [ ] Sundevall's 106

**Grass Snake**
- [ ] Cross-marked or Montane 92
- [ ] Grey-bellied 89
- [ ] Olive 92

**Green Snake**
- [ ] Eastern 95
- [ ] Ornate 94
- [ ] Water 94
- [ ] Western 94

**Harlequin Snake**
- [ ] Spotted 102
- [ ] Striped 103

**House Snake**
- [ ] Aurora 75
- [ ] Brown 74
- [ ] Fisk's 75
- [ ] Olive 74
- [ ] Spotted 74
- [ ] Yellow-bellied 75

**Marsh Snake**
- [ ] Forest 81
- [ ] Olive 81

**Purple-glossed Snake**
- [ ] Common 66
- [ ] Eastern 66
- [ ] Kalahari 66
- [ ] Natal 65

**Quill-snouted Snake**
- [ ] Bicoloured 68
- [ ] Elongate 69
- [ ] Sabi 68
- [ ] Transvaal 68

**Sand Snake**
- [ ] Dwarf, 91
- [ ] Jalla's 90

399